KB087572

적중 100

영어 기출 문제집

중 3

능률 | 김성곤

Best Collection

구성과 특징

교과서의 주요 학습 내용을 중심으로 학습 영역별 특성에 맞춰 단계별로 다양한 학습 기회를 제공하여
단원별 학습능력 평가는 물론 중간 및 기말고사 시험 등에 완벽하게 대비할 수 있도록 내용을 구성

Words & Expressions

Step1 Key Words 단원별 핵심 단어 설명 및 풀이
Key Expression 단원별 핵심 숙어 및 관용어 설명
Word Power 반대 또는 비슷한 뜻 단어 배우기
English Dictionary 영어로 배우는 영어 단어

Step2 실력평가 단원별 수시평가 대비 주관식, 객관식 문제풀이

Step3 서술형 대비 학업성취도 및 수행능력평가 대비 서술형 문제풀이

Conversation

Step1 핵심 의사소통 소통에 필요한 주요 표현 방법 요약
핵심 Check 기본적인 표현 방법 및 활용능력 확인

Step2 대화문 익히기 교과서 대화문 심층 분석 및 확인

Step3 교과서 확인학습 빈칸 채우기를 통한 문장 완성 능력 확인

Step4 기본평가 시험대비 기초 학습 능력 평가

Step5 실력평가 단원별 수시평가 대비 주관식, 객관식 문제풀이

Step6 서술형 대비 학업성취도 및 수행능력평가 대비 서술형 문제풀이

Grammar

Step1 주요 문법 단원별 주요 문법 사항과 예문을 알기 쉽게 설명
핵심 Check 기본 문법사항에 대한 이해 여부 확인

Step2 기본평가 시험대비 기초 학습 능력 평가

Step3 실력평가 단원별 수시평가 대비 주관식, 객관식 문제풀이

Step4 서술형 대비 학업성취도 및 수행능력평가 대비 서술형 문제풀이

Reading

Step1 구문 분석 단원별로 제시된 문장에 대한 구문별 분석과 내용 설명
확인문제 문장에 대한 기본적인 이해와 인지능력 확인

Step2 확인학습A 빈칸 채우기를 통한 문장 완성 능력 확인

Step3 확인학습B 제시된 우리말을 영어로 완성하여 작문 능력 키우기

Step4 실력평가 단원별 수시평가 대비 주관식, 객관식 문제풀이

Step5 서술형 대비 학업성취도 및 수행능력평가 대비 서술형 문제풀이
교과서 구석구석 교과서에 나오는 기타 문장까지 완벽 학습

Composition

|영역별 핵심문제|

단어 및 어휘, 대화문, 문법, 독해 등 각 영역별 기출문제의 출제 유형을 분석하여 실전에 대비하고 연습할 수 있도록 문제를 배열

|단원별 예상문제|

기출문제를 분석한 후 새로운 시험 출제 경향을 더하여 새롭게 출제될 수 있는 문제를 포함하여 시험에 완벽하게 대비할 수 있도록 준비

|서술형 실전 및 창의사고력 문제|

학교 시험에서 점차 늘어나는 서술형 시험에 집중 대비하고 고득점을 취득하는데 만전을 기하기 위한 학습 코너

|단원별 모의고사|

영역별, 단계별 학습을 모두 마친 후 실전 연습을 위한 모의고사

교과서 파헤치기

- **단어Test1~3** 영어 단어 우리말 쓰기, 우리말을 영어 단어로 쓰기, 영영풀이에 해당하는 단어와 우리말 쓰기
- **대화문Test1~2** 대화문 빈칸 완성 및 전체 대화문 쓰기
- **본문Test1~5** 빈칸 완성, 우리말 쓰기, 문장 배열연습, 영어 작문하기 복습 등 단계별 반복 학습을 통해 교과서 지문에 대한 완벽한 습득
- **구석구석지문Test1~2** 지문 빈칸 완성 및 전문 영어로 쓰기

Contents

Lesson

6

Take Part in the Economy

 의사소통 기능

- 선호에 대해 묻고 답하기
  A: Which do you prefer?
  B: I prefer the white shoes to the black ones.

- 상기시키기
  Don't forget to talk about their bad points too.

 언어 형식

- The+비교급 ~, the+비교급 …
  The fewer products we buy, **the more** resources we save.

- 분사구문
  Seeing a lot of positive reviews, I decided to borrow a bike helmet.

Words & Expressions

교과서

Key Words

- **app** [æp] 명 애플리케이션, 응용 프로그램
- **allow** [əláu] 동 허가하다, 허용하다
- **allowance** [əláuəns] 명 용돈
- **balanced** [bǽlənst] 형 균형 잡힌
- **borrow** [bárou] 동 빌리다
- **broken** [bróukən] 형 망가진, 고장 난
- **camping** [kǽmpiŋ] 명 캠핑
- **choose** [tʃuːz] 동 선택하다, 고르다
- **communicate** [kəmjúːnəkèit] 동 의사소통하다
- **concern** [kənsɔ́ːrn] 명 우려, 근심
- **condition** [kəndíʃən] 명 상태, 조건
- **discount** [dískaunt] 명 할인
- **download** [dáunlòud] 동 다운로드하다
- **economy** [ikánəmi] 명 경제
- **exact** [igzǽkt] 형 정확한, 정밀한
- **experience** [ikspíəriəns] 동 경험하다
- **fee** [fiː] 명 요금, 수수료
- **fix** [fiks] 동 고치다
- **freely** [fríːli] 부 자유롭게
- **improve** [imprúːv] 동 향상하다, 개선하다
- **issue** [íʃuː] 명 문제(점), 쟁점
- **lender** [léndər] 명 빌려주는 사람

- **negative** [néɡətiv] 형 부정식인, 나쁜
- **owner** [óunər] 명 주인, 소유주
- **personal** [pɔ́rsənl] 형 개인의, 개인적인
- **policy** [páləsi] 명 정책
- **positive** [pázətiv] 형 긍정적인
- **prefer** [prifɔ́ːr] 동 ~을 더 좋아하다, 선호하다
- **product** [prádʌkt] 명 상품
- **provide** [prəváid] 동 제공하다
- **purpose** [pɔ́ːrpəs] 명 목적
- **reasonable** [ríːzənəbl] 형 타당한, 합리적인, (값이) 적당한
- **refund** [rifʌ́nd] 명 환불
- **regularly** [réɡjulərli] 부 정기적으로
- **reliable** [riláiəbl] 형 믿을 수 있는
- **resource** [ríːsɔːrs] 명 자원
- **return** [ritɔ́ːrn] 동 돌려주다, 반납하다
- **share** [ʃɛər] 동 함께 쓰다, 공유하다
- **spend** [spend] 동 (돈을) 쓰다
- **upload** [ʌ́plòud] 동 업로드하다, 전송하다
- **upset** [ʌ́pset] 형 화난, 속상한
- **user** [júːzər] 명 사용자
- **weakness** [wíːknis] 명 약점
- **wherever** [hwɛərévər] 부 어디든지

Key Expressions

- **ask for** ~을 요청하다, 필요로 하다
- **be aware of** ~을 알고 있다
- **by -ing** ~함으로써
- **environmentally friendly** 친환경적인
- **focus on** 초점을 맞추다
- **for free** 무료로
- **help+목적어+동사원형** (목적어)가 ~하는 것을 도와주다
- **less than** ~보다 적은, ~ 미만의
- **look after** ~을 돌보다
- **look for** ~을 찾다

- **on sale** 할인 중인
- **out of town** 도시를 떠나, 다른 곳으로 떠나
- **pick up** ~을 찾아오다
- **prefer A to B** A를 B보다 더 좋아하다
- **search for** ~을 찾다
- **send messages to** ~에게 메시지를 보내다
- **take care of** ~을 돌보다
- **What if ~?** ~하면 어쩌지?, ~라면 어떻게 될까?
- **without -ing** ~하지 않고

Word Power

※ 서로 비슷한 뜻을 가진 어휘

☐ **broken** 망가진, 고장 난 : **out of order** 고장 난

☐ **concern** 우려, 근심 : **worry** 걱정, 근심

☐ **fix** 고치다 : **repair** 고치다, 수선하다

☐ **provide** 제공하다 : **furnish** 제공하다

☐ **reliable** 믿을 수 있는 : **trustworthy** 신뢰할 수 있는, 믿을 수 있는

☐ **upset** 화난, 속상한 : **troubled** 걱정스러운, 곤란한

☐ **choose** 선택하다, 고르다 : **select** 고르다, 선택하다

☐ **exact** 정확한, 정밀한 : **accurate** 정확한, 한 치의 오차 없는

☐ **improve** 향상하다, 개선하다 : **enhance** 향상시키다

☐ **purpose** 목적 : **goal** 목적, 목표

☐ **take care of** ~을 돌보다 : **look after** ~을 돌보다

☐ **weakness** 약점 : **fault** 결점, 단점

※ 서로 반대의 뜻을 가진 어휘

☐ **be aware of** ~을 알다 ↔ **be unaware of** ~을 모르다

☐ **less than** ~보다 적은, ~ 미만의 ↔ **more than** ~보다 많이, ~ 이상의

☐ **positive** 긍정적인 ↔ **negative** 부정적인

☐ **reasonable** 타당한, 합리적인, (값이) 적당한 ↔ **unreasonable** 불합리한, 부당한

☐ **regularly** 정기적으로 ↔ **irregularly** 불규칙적으로

☐ **upload** 업로드하다, 전송하다 ↔ **download** 다운로드하다

☐ **lender** 빌려주는 사람 ↔ **borrower** 빌리는 사람

☐ **reliable** 믿을 수 있는 ↔ **unreliable** 믿을 수 없는

☐ **weakness** 약점 ↔ **strength** 장점

English Dictionary

☐ **choose** 선택하다, 고르다
→ to decide which person or thing you want to have
원하는 사람이나 사물을 결정하다

☐ **concern** 우려, 근심
→ a fact or situation that worries you
걱정시키는 사실이나 상황

☐ **economy** 경제
→ the system according to which the money, industry and trade of a country or region are organized
한 나라나 지역의 화폐, 산업 및 무역이 구조화되는 체제

☐ **freely** 자유롭게
→ many times or in large quantities
많은 횟수로 혹은 많은 양으로

☐ **improve** 향상하다, 개선하다
→ to achieve or produce something of a better standard or quality than before
이전보다 더 나은 기준이나 품질로 어떤 것을 생산하거나 성취하다

☐ **negative** 부정적인, 나쁜
→ unpleasant, depressing, or harmful
불쾌한, 암울한, 혹은 해를 입히는

☐ **provide** 제공하다
→ to give something that someone needs or wants to them, or make it available
누군가가 필요로 하거나 원하는 무언가를 주거나 이용할 수 있게 하다

☐ **reliable** 믿을 수 있는
→ able to be trusted, or consistently good in quality or performance
신뢰할 수 있는, 혹은 품질이나 성과가 지속적으로 좋은

☐ **reasonable** 타당한, 합리적인, (값이) 적당한
→ based on or using good judgment and therefore fair, practical and sensible
좋은 판단에 기반하거나 좋은 판단을 사용하여서 공정하며, 실질적이고, 분별 있는

☐ **weakness** 약점
→ the state or condition of lacking strength
장점이 부족한 상태나 조건

서답형

01 다음 짝지어진 단어의 관계가 같도록 빈칸에 알맞은 말을 쓰시오.

> reasonable : unreasonable
> = reliable : _____

02 다음 영영풀이가 가리키는 것을 고르시오.

> the state or condition of lacking strength

① weakness ② purpose
③ concern ④ resource
⑤ owner

03 다음 중 밑줄 친 부분의 뜻풀이가 바르지 <u>않은</u> 것은?

① This hotel is quite good, and the price is <u>reasonable</u>. (이유 있는)
② She is <u>positive</u> about her future. (긍정적인)
③ We need to discuss this <u>issue</u> right now. (문제, 쟁점)
④ There are many skin <u>treatment</u> programs offered by this clinic. (치료)
⑤ The doctor was worried about the patient's <u>condition</u>. (상태)

서답형

04 다음 우리말에 맞게 빈칸에 알맞은 말을 쓰시오.

(1) 정부는 새로운 교육 정책을 주의 깊게 고려해야 한다.
➡ The government should consider the new educational _____ carefully.

(2) 그 회사는 내년에 새로운 상품을 출시할 것이다.
➡ The company will release a new _____ next year.

(3) 그녀의 부모님은 그녀에게 적은 용돈을 주신다.
➡ Her parents give her a small _____.

서답형

05 다음 문장의 빈칸에 들어갈 말을 〈보기〉에서 골라 쓰시오.

> ┤ 보기 ├
> environmentally friendly / looked for
> / looked after / less than / asked for

(1) I _____ my cat carefully.
(2) Before my mom went out, she _____ the key on her desk.
(3) This product is _____ made.
(4) Preparing our project, I _____ help to my English teacher.
(5) The whole show is performed in _____ one hour.

06 다음 주어진 문장의 밑줄 친 <u>fix</u>와 같은 의미로 쓰인 것은?

> They are sending an engineer to <u>fix</u> the car.

① We need to <u>fix</u> a date for the next meeting.
② Would you <u>fix</u> a post to the wall?
③ Do you know how to <u>fix</u> a mosquito net?
④ I need to <u>fix</u> this machine to make it work again.
⑤ My kid tried to <u>fix</u> a feather in his hat.

01 다음 짝지어진 단어의 관계가 같도록 빈칸에 알맞은 말을 쓰시오.

> wide : narrow = positive : _____

02 다음 우리말에 맞게 빈칸에 알맞은 말을 쓰시오.

(1) 5세 이하의 어린이들은 무료로 버스를 탈 수 있다.

➡ Kids under five years old can ride the bus _____ _____.

(2) 회의는 환경적 주제들에 초점이 맞추어졌다.

➡ The meeting was _____ _____ environmental issues.

(3) 지수는 속보를 알고 있었다.

➡ Jisu was _____ _____ the breaking news.

03 다음 문장의 빈칸에 들어갈 말을 〈보기〉에서 골라 쓰시오.

> ┤ 보기 ├
> weaknesses / spend / improve / discount / fee

(1) Your first monthly bill includes an installation _____.

(2) Our soccer team didn't win because of a few different _____.

(3) I'm going to _____ my English and go to the US.

(4) How much money do you _____ on food?

(5) Children get a _____ of two dollars on tickets.

04 다음 우리말과 일치하도록 주어진 어구를 배열하여 완성하시오.

(1) 그는 가능한 한 빨리 그의 아들의 출생을 등록해야 한다.

(as / register / he / the birth / possible / soon / as / should / of / his son)

➡ _____

_____

(2) 그녀는 아무에게도 그녀의 약점에 대해 터놓고 싶어 하지 않는다.

(to / weakness / doesn't / she / her / anyone / about / open up / want / to)

➡ _____

_____

(3) 현명한 소비자들은 항상 돈을 절약하려고 노력한다.

(to / money / wise / always / save / try / consumers)

➡ _____

_____

05 다음 우리말과 일치하도록 주어진 단어를 이용하여 완성하시오.

(1) 내 여동생은 팝 음악(pop music)보다 록 음악(rock music)을 더 좋아한다. (prefer)

➡ _____

(2) 그 계산대 직원(cashier)은 그 학생에게 할인을 해 주었다. (give)

➡ _____

(3) 그 판매원은 나에게 환불해 주지 않았다. (salesperson)

➡ _____

Conversation

1 선호에 대해 묻고 답하기

A Which sandwich do you prefer, the special one or the classic one?
스페셜 샌드위치와 클래식 샌드위치 중 어떤 샌드위치가 더 좋으니?

B Well, I prefer the special sandwich to the classic one. It's the healthier choice. 음. 나는 클래식 샌드위치보다 스페셜 샌드위치가 더 좋아. 그게 더 건강한 선택이야.

■ A와 B 두 가지 중에서 어떤 것을 선호하는지 물을 때 'Which (one) do you prefer, A or B?'로 표현한다. 같은 표현으로 'Which (one) do you like better, A or B?', 'Which (one) do you like more, A or B?', 'Which (one) do you want to ~ more?' 등을 쓸 수 있다.

■ 대답할 때는 'I prefer ~.' 또는 'I like 목적어 better.', 'I like 목적어 more.'라고 말한다. 'B보다 A를 더 선호한다'라고 대답할 때는 'I prefer A to B.', 'I like A better than B.' 또는 'I like A more than B.'라고 말한다.

선호 묻고 대답하기

- Which (one) do you prefer, A or B?
- Which (one) do you like better, A or B?
- Which (one) do you like more, A or B?
- Which (one) do you want to ~ more?
- I prefer ~. / I prefer A to B.
- I like 목적어 better. / I like A better than B.
- I like 목적어 more. / I like A more than B.
- I want/would like 목적어 better.
- I want/would like 목적어 more.

핵심 Check

1. 다음 대화에서 빈칸에 들어갈 말로 적절하지 <u>않은</u> 것은?

A: These two pairs of shoes are on sale! _____

B: Well, I prefer the white shoes to the black ones.

A: Why is that? The black ones are cheaper.

B: Yes, but I like the design of the white ones better.

① Which do you prefer?   ② Which do you like more?

③ Which do you like better?   ④ Which do you want to give?

⑤ Which do you want more?

② 상기시키기

A Don't forget to feed your puppy before you leave for work.
출근하기 전에 강아지에게 밥 주는 것을 잊지 마.

B Right. Thanks for reminding me. 맞아. 상기시켜 줘서 고마워.

■ 상대방에게 어떤 일에 대해 상기시키는 표현으로 'Don't forget to부정사 ~.'라는 말을 쓸 수 있다. 이 때, forget 뒤에는 to부정사가 쓰이므로 to 뒤에는 동사원형을 써야 한다. 이에 대한 대답으로 'Thanks for reminding me.'라고 말할 수 있다.

   • Don't forget to lock up at night. 밤에 문단속하는 것을 잊지 마.

■ 같은 표현으로 'remember to부정사'나 'Be sure to부정사'를 쓸 수 있다.

   • Remember to call me when you arrive! 도착하면 잊지 말고 전화해!

      = Be sure to call me when you arrive!

■ 'forget to부정사'와 'forget -ing'

'forget+to부정사'는 '(미래에) ~할/하는 것을 잊다'라는 의미이다. 반면에 'forget+동명사'는 '(과거에) ~한 것을 잊다'라는 의미이다. 따라서 대화 상대에게 무엇을 상기시킬 때는 미래의 의미를 내포한 to부정사를 쓰는 것이 맞다. 이외에도 to부정사와 동명사에 따라 의미가 변하는 동사로는 remember, stop, try, regret 등이 있다.

   • Don't forget to take out the garbage tomorrow. 내일 쓰레기를 내놓는 것을 잊지 마라.

   • I forgot taking out the garbage last night. 난 어젯밤에 쓰레기를 내놓았다는 사실을 잊었다.

핵심 Check

2. 다음 대화에서 밑줄 친 우리말을 영작하시오.

   A: I'm going to get a refund for these clothes this evening. I found I have similar ones.

   B: Okay, 영수증 갖고 가는 것을 잊지 마렴. Last time you couldn't get a refund because you didn't bring it.

   A: Okay, Mom. I won't forget this time.

   ➡ _____

Listen & Talk 1 B

G: ❶Which do you prefer, the Special Sandwich or the Classic Sandwich?

B: Well, the Special Sandwich is the healthier choice. ❷It's made with lots of fresh vegetables and other healthy ❸ingredients.

G: But it's much more expensive than the Classic Sandwich.

B: I know, but I prefer the Special Sandwich to the Classic Sandwich. ❹Eating healthy is important to me.

G: I prefer the cheaper one. I'll spend my money on books instead.

B: I guess our spending habits are different.

여: 스페셜 샌드위치와 클래식 샌드위치 중 어떤 것이 더 좋으니?

남: 음. 스페셜 샌드위치가 더 건강한 선택이야. 그것은 신선한 야채들과 다른 건강한 재료들로 만들어졌어.

여: 하지만 그건 클래식 샌드위치보다 훨씬 더 비싸잖아.

남: 맞아. 하지만 나는 클래식 샌드위치보다 스페셜 샌드위치가 더 좋아. 나에게는 건강하게 먹는 것이 중요하거든.

여: 나는 더 저렴한 것이 더 좋아. 대신 나는 내 돈을 책 사는 데 쓸래.

남: 우리는 소비 습관이 다른 것 같구나.

❶ A와 B 두 가지 중 어떤 것을 선호하는지 묻는 표현이다.　❷ It은 Special Sandwich를 가리킨다.
❸ ingredient: 재료　❹ 동명사가 주어로 동사로는 단수 동사(is)가 이어진다.

Check(√) True or False

(1) The girl likes the Classic Sandwich more than the Special Sandwich.　T ☐ F ☐

(2) The boy has the same spending habit as the girl.　T ☐ F ☐

 Listen & Talk 2 B

G: What should we sell at the ❶flea market next month?

B: Before we choose anything ❷to sell, I think we need to do some market research.

G: Market research? Why do we need ❸that?

B: Because it helps us ❹find out what items are popular these days.

G: I see. Then we can decide what to sell at the market.

B: That's right. It will also help us set ❺reasonable prices for our items.

G: Cool. Is there anything else we should do?

B: Oh, ❻don't forget to register our names by this Friday.

G: Right. Thanks for reminding me.

여: 우리 다음 달에 벼룩시장에서 무엇을 판매해야 할까?

남: 우리가 판매할 물건을 선택하기 전에 시장 조사부터 좀 해야 할 것 같아.

여: 시장 조사? 우리가 그게 왜 필요한데?

남: 왜냐하면 우리가 시장 조사를 통해 요즘 어떤 물건이 인기 있는지 알아내는 데 도움이 되기 때문이지.

여: 그렇구나. 그럼 벼룩시장에서 무엇을 판매할지 정할 수 있겠다.

남: 맞아. 그리고 시장 조사를 통해 우리는 판매할 물건에 합리적인 가격을 정하는 데 도움이 될 거야.

여: 좋아. 그 외에 우리가 해야 할 다른 게 있을까?

남: 오, 우리 이름을 이번 주 금요일까지 등록하는 것을 잊지 마.

여: 맞아. 알려 줘서 고마워.

❶ flea market: 벼룩시장　❷ anything을 꾸며주는 to부정사의 형용사적 용법이다.
❸ that은 market research를 가리킨다.　❹ help의 목적격보어로 원형부정사 find out이 이어진다.
❺ resonable: 합리적인　❻ 상대방에게 어떤 일에 대해 상기시키는 표현으로 'remember to ~'로 바꾸어 표현할 수 있다.

Check(√) True or False

(3) They are preparing something for the flea market.　T ☐ F ☐

(4) The girl forgot registering their names last Friday.　T ☐ F ☐

Listen & Talk 1 A

G: These two pairs of shoes are ❶on sale! Which do you prefer?

B: Well, I ❷prefer the white shoes to the black ones.

G: ❸Why is that? The black ones are cheaper.

B: Yes, but I like the design of the white ones better.

❶ on sale: 할인 중인

❷ prefer A to B: B보다 A를 더 선호하다

❸ 선호하는 이유를 묻는 질문으로 'Why do you think so?' 등으로 바꾸어 표현할 수 있다.

Listen & Talk 1 C

G1: I think my hair is too ❶curly. I want to ❷straighten my hair. Can you ❸recommend a good place?

G2: Sure. I know two places, Styles Studio and Hair Castle.

G1: Is there any difference between the two?

G2: Well, Styles Studio provides free treatment to keep your hair healthy.

G1: That's great. What about Hair Castle?

G2: Hair Castle doesn't provide treatment ❹for free, but they give student ❺discounts.

G1: Okay. Which do you prefer?

G2: I prefer Styles Studio to Hair Castle. It's important for me to get hair treatment regularly.

❶ curly: 곱슬거리는   ❷ straighten: 곧게 펴다

❸ recommend: 추천하다   ❹ for free: 무료로

❺ discount: 할인

Listen & Talk 2 A

B: I'm going to ❶get a refund for these clothes this evening. I found I have similar ones.

W: Okay. Don't forget to bring your ❷receipt. Last time you couldn't get a refund because you didn't bring ❸it.

B: Okay, Mom. I won't forget ❸it this time.

❶ get a refund: 환불받다

❷ receipt: 영수증

❸ it은 receipt를 가리킨다.

Listen & Talk 2 C

G: I tried Spring Chips recently, and now I want to review ❶them.

B: That sounds fun. How will you do your review?

G: I'll make a video. I want to ❷focus on their delicious taste!

B: Okay, but don't forget to talk about their bad points too.

G: I won't. I want to give a ❸balanced review.

B: Good. Your video will make it easier for people to choose better products.

G: That's exactly ❹what I want. ❺I'd like to give people more useful information about the product.

❶ them은 Spring Chips를 가리킨다.

❷ focus on: ～에 초점을 맞추다

❸ balanced: 균형 잡힌

❹ 선행사를 포함하는 관계대명사로 '～하는 것'으로 해석한다.

❺ would you like to: ～하고 싶다

Do It Yourself

G: Jinho, look! These two speakers look pretty cool.

B: Yeah, ❶they do. Which do you prefer, the red one or the black one?

G: I prefer the red one to the black one. ❷It's only 20 dollars, and ❷it comes with a discount coupon for music downloads.

B: Although the black one is 40 dollars, I think ❸it's the right one for me. I heard ❸it has better ❹sound quality.

❶ they는 two speakers를 가리킨다.

❷ it은 모두 'the red one'을 가리킨다.

❸ it은 모두 'the black one'을 가리킨다.

❹ sound quality: 음질

● 다음 우리말과 일치하도록 빈칸에 알맞은 말을 쓰시오.

Listen & Talk 1 A

G: These two _____ of shoes are on sale! _____ _____ _____ _____?

B: Well, I _____ the white shoes _____ the black ones.

G: Why is that? The black ones are _____.

B: Yes, but I like the _____ of the white ones _____.

Listen & Talk 1 B

G: Which do you _____, the Special Sandwich or the Classic Sandwich?

B: Well, the Special Sandwich is the _____ _____. It's made with lots of fresh vegetables and _____ healthy _____.

G: But it's _____ more _____ than the Classic Sandwich.

B: I know, but I prefer the Special Sandwich to the Classic Sandwich. _____ _____ is important _____ me.

G: I prefer the _____ one. I'll spend my money _____ books _____.

B: I guess _____ _____ _____ are different

Listen & Talk 1 C

G1: I think my hair is too _____. I want to _____ my hair. Can you _____ a good place?

G2: Sure. I know two places, Styles Studio and Hair Castle.

G1: Is there any _____ between the _____?

G2: Well, Styles Studio provides _____ _____ to keep your hair _____.

G1: That's great. What about Hair Castle?

G2: Hair Castle doesn't provide treatment for _____, but they give _____ _____.

G1: Okay. Which do you _____?

G2: I prefer Styles Studio to Hair Castle. It's important _____ me _____ get hair treatment _____.

 해석

여: 이 두 켤레의 신발이 세일 중이네! 어떤 것이 너 좋으니?

남: 음, 나는 검은색 신발보다 흰색 신발이 더 좋아.

여: 왜? 검은색 신발이 더 저렴하잖아.

남: 맞아, 하지만 나는 흰색 신발의 디자인이 더 좋아.

여: 스페셜 샌드위치와 클래식 샌드위치 중 어떤 것이 더 좋으니?

남: 음, 스페셜 샌드위치가 더 건강한 선택이야. 그것은 신선한 야채들과 다른 건강한 재료들로 만들어졌어.

여: 하지만 그건 클래식 샌드위치보다 훨씬 더 비싸잖아.

남: 맞아, 하지만 나는 클래식 샌드위치보다 스페셜 샌드위치가 더 좋아. 나에게는 건강하게 먹는 것이 중요하거든.

여: 나는 더 저렴한 것이 더 좋아. 대신 나는 내 돈을 책 사는 데 써.

남: 우리는 소비 습관이 다른 것 같구나.

여1: 내 머리가 너무 곱슬곱슬한 것 같아. 머리카락을 곧게 펴고 싶어. 좋은 곳을 추천해 줄 수 있니?

여2: 물론이지. 난 스타일 스튜디오와 헤어 캐슬, 두 군데를 알고 있어.

여1: 두 군데의 차이점이 있니?

여2: 음, 스타일 스튜디오는 머리카락을 건강하게 유지해 주는 트리트먼트를 무료로 제공해 줘.

여1: 그것 좋으네. 헤어 캐슬은 어때?

여2: 헤어 캐슬은 트리트먼트를 무료로 제공해 주지는 않지만, 학생 할인을 해줘.

여1: 그렇구나. 넌 어느 곳을 선호하니?

여2: 나는 헤어 캐슬보다 스타일 스튜디오를 선호해 나한테 헤어 트리트먼트를 규칙적으로 받는 것이 중요해.

Listen & Talk 2 A

B: I'm going to _____ _____ _____ for these clothes this evening. I found I have _____ ones.

W: Okay. _____ _____ to bring your _____. Last time you couldn't _____ _____ _____ because you didn't bring it.

B: Okay, Mom. I _____ _____ it this time.

Listen & Talk 2 B

G: What should we sell at the _____ _____ next month?

B: Before we choose anything to sell, I think we need to do some _____ _____.

G: _____ _____? Why do we need _____?

B: Because it helps us _____ out _____ _____ _____ these days.

G: I see. Then we can _____ _____ _____ _____ at the market.

B: That's right. It will also help us _____ _____ prices for our items.

G: Cool. Is there _____ _____ we should do?

B: Oh, don't forget to _____ our names _____ this Friday.

G: Right. Thanks for _____ me.

Listen & Talk 2 C

G: I tried Spring Chips recently, and now I want to _____ them.

B: That sounds fun. _____ will you do your _____?

G: I'll make a video. I want to _____ _____ their delicious taste!

B: Okay, but don't forget _____ _____ about their _____ _____ too.

G: I won't. I want to give a _____ _____.

B: Good. Your video will make _____ _____ _____ people _____ _____ _____ _____ _____.

G: That's exactly what I want. I'd like to give people more _____ _____ about the product.

Do It Yourself

G: Jinho, look! These two _____ look pretty cool.

B: Yeah, they do. _____ _____ _____ _____ _____ _____ _____, the red one or the black one?

G: I prefer the red one _____ the black one. It's only 20 dollars, and it comes with a _____ _____ for music downloads.

B: Although the black one is 40 dollars, I think it's the right one for me. I heard it has _____ _____ _____ _____.

남: 저 오늘 저녁에 이 옷들을 환불하려고 해요. 제가 비슷한 옷들을 갖고 있다는 것을 발견했거든요.

여: 그래. 영수증 갖고 가는 것 잊지 마렴. 저번에 네가 영수증을 가지고 가지 않는 바람에 환불을 못 받았잖니.

남: 알겠어요, 엄마. 이번에는 잊지 않을게요.

여: 우리 다음 달에 벼룩시장에서 무엇을 판매해야 할까?

남: 우리가 판매할 물건을 선택하기 전에 시장 조사부터 좀 해야 할 것 같아.

여: 시장 조사? 우리가 그게 왜 필요한데?

남: 왜냐하면 우리가 시장 조사를 통해 요즘 어떤 물건이 인기 있는지 알아내는 데 도움이 되기 때문이지.

여: 그렇구나. 그럼 벼룩시장에서 무엇을 판매할지 정할 수 있겠다.

남: 맞아. 그리고 시장 조사를 통해 우리는 판매할 물건에 합리적인 가격을 정하는 데 도움이 될 거야.

여: 좋아. 그 외에 우리가 해야 할 다른 게 있을까?

남: 오, 우리 이름을 이번 주 금요일까지 등록하는 것을 잊지 마.

여: 맞아. 알려 줘서 고마워.

여: 내가 요새 스프링 칩스를 먹어봤는데, 이제 그것을 비평해 보고 싶어.

남: 그거 재밌겠다. 어떻게 비평할 거니?

여: 나는 동영상을 만들려고 해. 스프링 칩스의 맛있는 맛에 초점을 맞추고 싶어!

남: 그래, 하지만 그것의 단점에 대해서도 이야기하는 것을 잊지 마.

여: 잊지 않을 거야. 나는 균형 잡힌 비평을 보여주고 싶어.

남: 좋아. 네 동영상 덕분에 사람들이 더 나은 제품을 선택하는 것이 쉬워지겠구나.

여: 그것이 바로 내가 원하는 거야. 나는 사람들에게 제품에 대한 더 유용한 정보를 주고 싶어.

여: 진호, 이것 봐! 이 스피커 두 개 꽤 멋져 보이는데.

남: 응, 정말 그러네. 빨간색 스피커와 검은색 스피커 중에서 어떤 것이 더 좋니?

여: 나는 검은색 스피커보다 빨간색 스피커가 더 좋아. 그것은 20달러밖에 안 하고, 음악 다운로드를 할인해 주는 쿠폰도 같이 있잖아.

남: 검은색 스피커가 40달러이지만, 그것이 나한테 맞는 것 같아. 그게 더 나은 음질을 갖고 있다고 들었거든.

[01~02] 다음 대화를 읽고 물음에 답하시오.

Suji: Which do you prefer, the Special Sandwich or the Classic Sandwich?

Brian: (A) It's made with lots of fresh vegetables and other healthy ingredients.

Suji: (B) But it's much more expensive than the Classic Sandwich.

Brian: (C) I know, but I prefer the Special Sandwich _____ⓐ_____ the Classic Sandwich. Eating healthy is important ___ⓑ___ me.

Suji: (D) I prefer the cheaper one. I'll spend my money on books instead.

Brian: (E) I guess our spending habits are different.

01 위 대화의 (A)~(E) 중 다음 문장이 들어가기에 적절한 곳은?

> Well, the Special Sandwich is the healthier choice.

① (A) ② (B) ③ (C) ④ (D) ⑤ (E)

02 위 대화의 빈칸 ⓐ와 ⓑ에 공통으로 들어갈 전치사를 쓰시오.

➡ _____

[03~04] 다음 대화를 읽고 물음에 답하시오.

Jack: I'm going to get a refund for these clothes this evening. I found I have similar (A)[it / ones / that].

Mom: Okay. Don't forget (B)[bring / bringing / to bring] your receipt. Last time you couldn't get a refund because you didn't bring ⓐit.

Jack: Okay, Mom. I won't forget ⓑit this time.

03 위 대화의 밑줄 친 ⓐ와 ⓑ가 공통으로 가리키는 것을 영어로 쓰시오.

➡ _____

04 위 대화의 괄호 (A)와 (B)에 알맞은 말이 바르게 짝지어진 것은?

① it – bringing ② it – to bring
③ ones – to bring ④ that – to bring
⑤ ones – bringing

01 다음 대화가 자연스럽게 이어지도록 순서대로 배열하시오.

A: I think my hair is too curly. I want to straighten my hair. Can you recommend a good place?

(A) That's great. What about Hair Castle?

(B) Is there any difference between the two?

(C) Sure. I know two places, Styles Studio and Hair Castle.

(D) Well, Styles Studio provides free treatment to keep your hair healthy.

(E) Hair Castle doesn't provide treatment for free, but they give student discounts.

➡ _____

[02~04] 다음 대화를 읽고 물음에 답하시오.

Sujin: What should we sell at the flea market next month?

Tom: Before we choose anything ⓐto sell, I think we need to do some market research.

Sujin: Market research? Why do we need ⓑ that?

Tom: Because it helps us find out ⓒwhat items are popular these days.

Sujin: I see. Then we can decide what ⓓto sell at the market.

Tom: That's right. It will also help us set reasonable prices for our items.

Sujin: Cool. Is there anything else we should do?

Tom: Oh, don't forget ⓔregistering our names by this Friday.

Sujin: Right. Thanks for reminding me.

서답형

02 위 대화의 밑줄 친 ⓐ~ⓔ 중 어색한 것을 찾아 바르게 고치시오.

➡ _____

03 위 대화를 읽고 대답할 수 없는 것은?

① What are they going to prepare for?

② Why do they need the market research?

③ What should Sujin remember to do?

④ What items are popular these days?

⑤ Until when should Sujin finish registering their names?

04 위 대화의 내용과 일치하지 않는 것은?

① Tom은 벼룩시장에서 판매할 물건을 선택하기 전에 시장 조사부터 해야 한다고 생각한다.

② 시장 조사를 통해 요즘 어떤 물건이 인기 있는지 알 수 있기 때문에 Tom은 시장 조사를 할 것을 원한다.

③ Tom은 시장 조사를 통해 판매할 물건의 합리적인 가격을 정할 수 있을 것이라고 생각한다.

④ Sujin은 Tom과 그녀의 이름을 이번 주 금요일까지 등록해야 한다.

⑤ Sujin은 시장 조사하기 전에 벼룩시장에서 무엇을 판매할지 정할 수 있다고 생각한다.

05 다음 대화의 (A)~(C)에 알맞은 말이 바르게 짝지어진 것은?

Jane: I tried Spring Chips recently, and now I want to review them.

Chris: That sounds fun. How will you do your review?

Jane: I'll make a video. I want to focus on their delicious taste!

Chris: Okay, but don't forget to talk about their bad points too.

Jane: I (A)[will / won't]. I want to give a (B)[balanced / balancing] review.

Chris: Good. Your video will make it easier for people to choose better products.

Jane: That's exactly (C)[that / what] I want. I'd like to give people more useful information about the product.

(A)	(B)	(C)
① will	balanced	that
② will	balancing	what
③ won't	balanced	what
④ won't	balancing	that
⑤ won't	balanced	that

[06~08] 다음 대화를 읽고 물음에 답하시오.

Jack: I'm going to get a refund for these clothes this evening. I found I have similar ones.

Mom: Okay. Don't forget to bring your receipt. Last time you couldn't get a refund because you didn't bring it.

Jack: Okay, Mom. I won't forget it this time.

서답형

06 What is Mom asking Jack to remember?

➡ _____

서답형

07 Why does Jack want to get a refund for the clothes?

➡ _____

서답형

08 Why couldn't Jack get a refund last time?

➡ _____

[09~10] 다음 대화를 읽고 물음에 답하시오.

Judy: I think my hair is too curly. I want to (A) [straight / straighten] my hair. Can you recommend a good place?

Gina: Sure. I know two places, Styles Studio and Hair Castle.

Judy: Is there any difference between the two?

Gina: Well, Styles Studio provides free treatment to keep your hair (B)[health / healthy].

Judy: That's great. What about Hair Castle?

Gina: Hair Castle doesn't provide treatment (C)[for / in] free, but they give student discounts.

Judy: Okay. Which do you prefer?

Gina: I prefer Styles Studio to Hair Castle. It's important for me to get hair treatment regularly.

서답형

09 위 대화의 괄호 (A)~(C)에서 알맞은 단어를 골라 쓰시오.

➡ (A) _____ (B) _____ (C) _____

10 위 대화의 내용과 일치하지 않는 것은?

① Judy는 머리가 곱슬곱슬해서 곧게 펴고 싶어 한다.

② 스타일 스튜디오는 머리카락을 건강하게 유지해 주는 트리트먼트를 무료로 제공해 준다.

③ 헤어 캐슬은 트리트먼트를 무료로 제공해 주지는 않는다.

④ 헤어 캐슬은 학생 할인을 해 준다.

⑤ Gina는 헤어 트리트먼트를 정기적으로 받는 게 중요해서 헤어 캐슬을 선호한다.

01 다음 대화가 자연스럽게 이어지도록 순서대로 배열하시오.

> (A) Why is that? The black ones are cheaper.
> (B) Yes, but I like the design of the white ones better.
> (C) Well, I prefer the white shoes to the black ones.
> (D) These two pairs of shoes are on sale! Which do you prefer?

➡ _____

[02~04] 다음 대화를 읽고 물음에 답하시오.

Suji: Which do you prefer, the Special Sandwich or the Classic Sandwich?

Brian: Well, the Special Sandwich is the healthier choice. It's made with lots of fresh vegetables and other healthy ingredients.

Suji: But it's much more expensive than the Classic Sandwich.

Brian: I know, but I prefer the Special Sandwich to the Classic Sandwich. Eating healthy is important to me.

Suji: I prefer the cheaper one. I'll spend my money on books instead.

Brian: I guess our spending habits are different.

02 What is the Special Sandwich made with?

➡ _____
_____

03 Why does Brian prefer the Special Sandwich to the Classic Sandwich?

➡ _____

04 Why does Suji like the cheaper sandwich more?

➡ _____
_____

[05~06] 다음 대화를 읽고 물음에 답하시오.

Sujin: What should we sell at the flea market next month?

Tom: Before we choose anything to sell, I think we need to do some market research.

Sujin: Market research? Why do we need that?

Tom: Because it helps us find out what items are popular these days.

Sujin: I see. Then we can decide what to sell at the market.

Tom: That's right. It will also help us set reasonable prices for our items.

Sujin: Cool. Is there anything else we should do?

Tom: Oh, don't forget to register our names by this Friday.

Sujin: Right. Thanks for reminding me.

05 위 대화에서 다음 영영풀이가 나타내는 말을 찾아 쓰시오.

> to record your/somebody's/something's name on an official list

➡ _____

06 위 대화의 내용과 일치하도록 빈칸을 완성하시오.

> Through the market research, Tom and Sujin can find out (A)_____ these days. In addition, they are able to (B)_____ for their items.

Grammar

1 The+비교급 ~, the+비교급 … 구문

- **The fewer** products we buy, **the more** resources we save.
  우리가 제품들을 더 적게 구매할수록, 우리는 더 많은 자원들을 절약한다.

- **The more** you smile, **the happier** you feel.
  당신이 더 많이 웃을수록, 당신은 더 행복하게 느낀다.

■ 'The+비교급+주어+동사 ~, the+비교급+주어+동사 …'는 '~하면 할수록 더 …하다'의 의미로, 상응하는 두 절의 형용사나 부사, 형용사를 포함한 명사절의 비교급 형태를 'the'와 함께 주어 앞으로 이동하여 만든다.

(1) 형용사, 부사

- You are **familiar** with doing something. + You have to do it **sincerely**.
  → **The more familiar** you are with doing something, **the more sincerely** you have to do it.
  당신이 어떤 일에 더 익숙해질수록, 그것을 더욱 진지하게 해야 한다.

- We get up **early**. + We will get there **soon**.
  → **The earlier** we get up, **the sooner** we will get there. 우리가 더 일찍 일어날수록, 그곳에 더 빨리 도착할 것이다.

(2) 형용사를 포함한 명사

- They read good books. + They can enjoy a rich life.
  → **The better books** they read, **the richer life** they can enjoy. 그들이 더 좋은 책들을 읽을수록, 더욱 풍성한 삶을 즐길 수 있다.

(3) 의미가 통할 경우에 '동사' 또는 '주어+동사'의 생략이 가능하다.

- **The more** the money, **the bigger** the car. 돈이 더 많을수록, 차가 더 커진다.
- **The more, the better.** 많으면 많을수록 더 좋다.

■ 'The+비교급 ~, the+비교급 …' 구문은 접속사 If 또는 As를 사용해서 전환할 수 있다.

- **The harder** you study in college, **the better job** you will get.
  = If you study harder in college, you will get a better job.
  = As you study harder in college, you will get a better job.

 핵심 Check

1. 다음 우리말에 맞게 괄호 안의 어구를 바르게 배열하시오.

   당신이 더 많이 줄수록, 더 적게 잃게 될 것이다. (the more, the less, give, lose, will, you, you)

   ➡ _____

② 분사구문

- **Seeing** a lot of positive reviews, I decided to borrow a bike helmet.
  많은 긍정적인 후기들을 보고 나서, 나는 자전거 헬멧을 빌리기로 결심했다.

- **Feeling** cold, I put on thick clothes. 추위를 느껴서, 나는 두꺼운 옷을 입었다.

■ 종속접속사가 이끄는 부사절을 분사를 이용하여 간략한 부사구로 바꾼 것이다.

- **While I was playing** basketball, I hurt my leg.
  = **Playing** basketball, I hurt my leg. 농구를 하다가, 나는 다리를 다쳤다.

■ 부사구와 주절의 관계에 따라 양보, 동시동작, 이유, 시간, 조건 등의 의미로 쓰인다.

(1) 양보: **Though I live** next door, I seldom see him.

= **Living** next door, I seldom see him. 비록 나는 이웃에 살지만, 그를 별로 보지 못한다.

(2) 동시동작(부대상황): **While she ate** ice cream, Amy listened to music.

= **Eating** ice cream, Amy listened to music. 아이스크림을 먹으며, Amy는 음악을 들었다.

(3) 이유: **As I had** no money, I gave up buying it.

= **Having** no money, I gave up buying it. 돈이 없어서 나는 그것을 사는 것을 포기했다.

(4) 시간: **When she leaves** home, she always smiles.

= **Leaving** home, she always smiles. 집을 나설 때, 그녀는 항상 미소를 짓는다.

(5) 조건: **If he turns** right, he'll see the shopping mall.

= **Turning** right, he'll see the shopping mall. 우회전하면, 그는 쇼핑몰을 보게 될 것이다.

■ 주절과 종속절의 주어가 다를 경우, 분사구문의 주어를 남겨 두는 것을 독립분사구문이라고 하며, 일반 인이 주어일 경우에는 생략 가능하다. (비인칭 독립분사구문)

(1) 독립분사구문: **As it was** stormy, the ships couldn't go out to sea.

= **It being** stormy, the ships couldn't go out to sea. 폭풍우가 불어닥쳐서, 배들이 바다로 나갈 수 없었다.

(2) 비인칭 독립분사구문: **frankly speaking**(솔직히 말해서), **considering** ~ (~를 고려하면)

(3) with+목적어+분사: Daddy fell asleep **with the light turned on**. (불이 켜진 채로)

핵심 Check

2. 다음 괄호 안에서 알맞은 것을 고르시오.

(1) Mary opened the wine, (poured / pouring) it into my glass.

(2) (Leaving / Left) alone, the baby started to cry.

01 다음 빈칸에 들어갈 말로 알맞은 것은?

> The longer the rabbit ran, the _____ it felt.

① tiring   ② most tired   ③ less tiring
④ more tired   ⑤ more tireder

02 다음 부사절을 분사구문으로 바꿔 쓸 때, 빈칸에 들어갈 말로 가장 적절한 것은?

> As she saw a lot of negative reviews, she decided not to buy the dress.
> → _____ a lot of negative reviews, she decided not to buy the dress.

① She seeing   ② As she seeing   ③ Seeing
④ Having been seen   ⑤ Being seen

03 다음 〈보기〉에서 필요한 단어를 골라, 어법에 알맞은 형태로 빈칸에 써 넣으시오.

> ┤ 보기 ├
> focus, familiar, wise, loud, high, old, big, much

(1) _____ the size is, the _____ the price will get.

(2) The _____ your surroundings are, the harder it is _____ on work.

(3) The _____ the girl got, the _____ she became.

(4) The _____ time we spend together, the _____ we will become.

04 다음 분사구문을 접속사가 이끄는 부사절로 만들 때, 빈칸에 알맞은 말을 써 넣으시오.

(1) Taking a shower, Smith sang a song.
  ➡ While _____ _____ _____ _____, Smith sang a song.

(2) Being hungry, she dropped by the restaurant.
  ➡ As _____ _____ _____, she dropped by the restaurant.

(3) Feeling scared, the little boy took a step forward.
  ➡ _____ _____ _____ _____, the little boy took a step forward.

다음 두 문장의 의미가 같도록 할 때 빈칸에 들어갈 말로 가장 적절한 것은?

> As she felt cold, Sally put on more clothes.
> → _____ cold, Sally put on more clothes.

① She felt
② Having feeling cold
③ To feel
④ Feeling
⑤ Being felt

[02~03] 다음 빈칸에 들어갈 말이 알맞게 짝지어진 것을 고르시오.

02
> The _____ you work, the _____ the results will be.

① hard – well
② more hard – more well
③ more – most
④ harder – better
⑤ hardest – best

03
> _____ her illness gets, _____ pain she will feel.

① So bad – as much painful
② The more bad – worse
③ The worse – the more
④ Worse – the more worse
⑤ The worse – the most

[04~05] 다음 우리말을 어법상 알맞게 영작한 것을 고르시오.

04
> 피아노를 연주하다가, 그녀는 숙제를 해야 할 것을 잊었다.

① While played the piano, she forgot to do her homework.

② As she was played the piano, she forgot to do her homework.
③ Playing the piano, she forgot to do her homework.
④ Having been played the piano, she forgot to do her homework.
⑤ While being played the piano, she forgot to do her homework.

05
> 공유 경제 앱을 이용해서, Sean은 돈을 아낄 수 있었다.

① Sean using the sharing economy apps, he could save some money.
② Using the sharing economy apps, Sean being able to save some money.
③ Being used the sharing economy apps, Sean could save some money.
④ Using the sharing economy apps, Sean could save some money.
⑤ Though using the sharing economy apps, Sean could save some money.

[06~07] 다음 주어진 문장의 의미가 자연스럽게 되도록 빈칸에 들어갈 말로 가장 적절한 것은?

06
> The less we buy various kinds of products, _____.

① the more money we can spend
② the worse the environment gets
③ the better the sellers will be
④ the more resources we can save
⑤ the more likely we are to ruin the nature

07

The more products you borrow instead of buying, _____.

① the more active the sharing economy will become

② the more actively the sharing economy will become

③ the more active the sharing economy will do

④ the more active the sharing economy will work

⑤ the better active the sharing economy will become

[08~10] 다음 중 밑줄 친 분사구문의 용법이 〈보기〉와 같은 것은?

08

┤ 보기 ├

<u>Seeing</u> a lot of good reviews by the users, Cassy decided to borrow the bike.

① <u>Being sick</u> all night, she went to school as if nothing happened.

② <u>Feeling tired</u> from the endless documents, he never lost his smile.

③ <u>Meeting</u> the handsome guy today, Jasmine will fall in love with him.

④ <u>Surrounded</u> by a lot of birds, the woman was feeding them.

⑤ <u>Surprised</u> by his daughter's cry, Roberto rushed in immediately.

09

┤ 보기 ├

<u>Using</u> Pet Sitter Find App, you could experience the joy of walking a dog.

① <u>Arriving</u> at the station, I learned that the train had already left for Busan.

② <u>Being tired</u> from the work, Alice can't help falling asleep.

③ <u>Producing</u> fresh air, plant-covered buildings are good for your health.

④ <u>Listening</u> to the song she composed, they will say they will sing it.

⑤ <u>Running</u> along the street, I saw a traffic accident between the buses.

10

┤ 보기 ├

<u>Born</u> in Seoul, William isn't good at speaking Korean.

① <u>Turning</u> right at the second corner, you won't miss the cafe.

② <u>Not knowing</u> how much she missed me, I was embarrassed with her tears.

③ <u>Having</u> nothing to do this afternoon, Jasmine was going to sleep in her room.

④ <u>Living</u> in Paris for over 20 years, I still can't understand the conversation between French women.

⑤ <u>Finishing</u> his assignment, Albert went outside to play basketball with friends.

11 다음 밑줄 친 부분 중 어법상 어색한 것을 고르시오.

① <u>It being rainy</u>, all the players in the ground couldn't play.

② <u>Wanting to stop him from using her car</u>, Ms. Lee told her son to wait.

③ <u>Being sensitive to the negative reviews</u>, the staff were carefully checking the state of their products.

④ <u>Being no seats available in the bus</u>, the pregnant woman decided to get off.

⑤ <u>Written in the ancient language</u>, the letters on the stone has not been completely interpreted.

12 다음 주어진 문장을 분사구문으로 만들 때 가장 적절한 것은?

> Animals aren't allowed in my apartment, so I don't have any pets.

① Not being allowed in my apartment, I don't have any pets.

② Animals not being allowed in my apartment, I don't have any pets.

③ Animals not allowing in my apartment, I don't have any pets.

④ Not animals being allowed in my apartment, I don't have any pets.

⑤ No animals allowed being in my apartment, I don't have any pets.

13 다음 〈보기〉의 문장과 가장 가까운 뜻을 가진 문장을 고르시오.

> ┤ 보기 ├
>
> As more people use the sharing economy services, they will improve more.

① Even if more people use the sharing economy services, the more will they improve.

② The people use the sharing economy services more, they will improve the more.

③ The more people use the sharing economy services, the more they will improve.

④ When more people use the sharing economy services, the better they will improve.

⑤ Most people use the sharing economy services, the more they will improve.

서답형

[14~15] 우리말과 일치하도록 괄호 안에 주어진 단어들을 바르게 배열하시오.

14 당신이 공유 경제 서비스를 더 자주 이용할수록, 지구의 자원은 더 적게 사용된다.

→ (the less, use, the sharing economy services, often, resources, the more, you) are used on Earth.

➡ _____

_____

15 어떤 제품들은 가격이 올라갈수록 더 많은 사람들이 사려고 한다.

→ (some products, buy, people, the more, the higher, gets, them, to, the price, want, of).

➡ _____

_____

16 다음 밑줄 친 분사구문을 같은 의미의 부사절로 바꿔 쓸 때 적절하지 <u>않은</u> 것은?

① <u>Using various services</u>, we have increased the sharing economy.

→ As we use various services,

② <u>Waving their hands</u>, the players walked out of the ground.

→ While they were waving their hands,

③ <u>Eating some baked potatoes</u>, Marco waited for his mom to come home.

→ As he was eating some baked potatoes,

④ The sharing economy expands rapidly, <u>making a lot of resources saved.</u>

→ though it makes a lot of resources saved.

⑤ <u>Walking along the street</u>, he saw a man walking six puppies.

→ When he walked along the street,

01 다음 우리말과 일치하도록 괄호 안에 주어진 어구들을 바르게 배열하여 문장을 완성하시오.

(1) 그녀가 더 큰 돈을 벌수록, 그녀의 가족들은 더 많이 원한다. (the more, she, want, makes, money, her family, the bigger)

➡ _____

_____

_____

(2) 그 서비스를 더 자주 이용할수록, 우리는 공유 경제를 더 빨리 촉진하게 될 것이다. (we, we, the sharing economy, the service, often, the more, the faster, use, promote, will)

➡ _____

_____

_____

(3) 그녀가 열심히 일할수록, 그녀의 미래는 더욱 밝아질 것이다. (her future, works, the brighter, she, be, the harder, will)

➡ _____

_____

_____

(4) 그 시스템을 더 자세하게 알수록, 공유 경제에 대한 우리의 신뢰는 더 강해진다. (the system, the stronger, in, closely, we, know, the sharing economy, the more, our trust, becomes)

➡ _____

_____

_____

(5) 그 앱이 더 자주 사용될수록, 개인정보에 대한 우려는 더 커진다. (the greater, the app, is, the personal information, frequently, the concern, about, used, gets, the more)

➡ _____

_____

_____

02 다음 〈보기〉에 있는 접속사를 한 번씩만 사용하여, 각 문장의 밑줄 친 분사구문을 부사절로 바꾸시오. (단, 진행형 불가, 주어는 가능한 대명사로 표현할 것.)

┌─ 보기 ─┐
though / and / while / because / when /
if
└────────┘

(1) Looking through the window of the restaurant, Mike suddenly found the woman who had lied to him passing by.

➡ _____

_____

(2) The sharing economy improves the world, making resources less used.

➡ _____

_____

(3) Having trouble that you cannot talk to your loved ones, try sharing it with one that you have never met before.

➡ _____

_____

(4) Not wanting to disturb his daughter, Mr. Brown was quietly waiting for her to finish her practice.

➡ _____

_____

(5) Using various kinds of apps, we can borrow the things that we don't have to buy at a small fee or for free.

➡ _____

_____

(6) There being some weaknesses with the services, you can see a lot of positive reviews on their websites.

➡ _____

_____

03 다음 그림을 보고, 우리말에 맞게 괄호 안의 단어를 활용하여 빈칸을 채우시오.

쓰레기를 덜 버릴수록, 교실이 더 깨끗해진다.
→ _____, _____
the classroom becomes. (the, we, little, clean, throw away) 어법상 알맞게 어형 변화할 것, 7 단어)

04 다음 우리말과 일치하도록 괄호 안에 주어진 단어들을 바르게 배열하시오.

(1)

자주 필요하지 않은 물건들을 빌려 쓰기 때문에, Jasmine은 돈을 많이 저축해 왔다.
→ (that, doesn't often, borrowing, she, need, things), Jasmine has saved a lot of money.

➡ _____

(2)

불과 2년 전에 건설되었음에도 불구하고, 그 아파트는 비가 올 때마다 물이 샌다.
→ (built, ago, having, only, though, been, two years), the apartment leaks whenever it rains.

➡ _____

(3)

텐트가 없었기 때문에, 우리는 애플리케이션을 이용하여 하나를 빌렸다.
→ (we, having, not, any, one, borrowed, tents) using the application.

➡ _____

(4)

주변에 이용 가능한 공유 경제 서비스 앱들이 있음에도 불구하고, 사람들은 새 제품을 구매하는 경향이 있다.
→ (being, available, service apps, though, sharing economy, there) around them, people tend to buy new products.

➡ _____

05 다음 괄호 안에 주어진 단어를 이용하여 어법에 맞게 빈칸을 완성하시오.

(1) _____ _____ (many) books the students read, _____ _____ (wise) they will become.

(2) _____ _____ (far) the old lady walks every day, _____ _____ (healthy) she will become.

(3) _____ _____ (old) the girl grew, _____ _____ (much) she looked like her grandmother.

(4) _____ _____ (loud) the boy practices speaking, _____ _____ (confident) he feels.

Reading

Life in the Sharing Economy

Son: What should we do this weekend, Dad?

Dad: Why don't we go camping?

Son: But we don't have a tent. Should we buy one? Also, who will
= a tent
take care of our dog?

Dad: Don't worry. I know some apps that can help us.
주격 관계대명사

Borrow from your neighbors!

Ask Your Neighbors helps people easily find items that they can
목적격 관계대명사
borrow from others. First, users download the app and search for
= other people
another user that has the item they need. Then they pick up the item
주격 관계대명사   the item과 they need 사이에 목적격 관계대명사 that[which] 생략
and return it later.
the item

Jasmine: December 12, 2019

I asked for a board game and got one in less than 30 minutes. I love
= a board game
saving money by borrowing things that I don't often need. Also, I think
목적격 관계대명사
it's environmentally friendly. The fewer products we buy, the more
the+비교급 …, the+비교급 ~: …하면 할수록, 더 ~하다
resources we save.

---

share 함께 쓰다, 공유하다

economy 경제

take care of ~을 돌보다

app 애플리케이션(= application), 응용 프로그램

neighbor 이웃

search for ~을 찾다

resource 자원, 재료

 확인문제

- 다음 문장이 본문의 내용과 일치하면 T, 일치하지 않으면 F를 쓰시오.

1 Ask Your Neighbors helps people easily find items that they can borrow from others. □

2 First, lenders download the app and search for another user that has the item they need. □

3 Users of Ask Your Neighbors pick up the item and return it later. □

4 Jasmine asked for a board game and got one in more than 30 minutes. □

5 Jasmine loves saving money by borrowing things that she doesn't often need. □

6 Jasmine thinks that buying things is environmentally friendly. □

Cassandra: March 7, 2020

Seeing a lot of positive reviews, I decided to borrow a bike helmet.
분사구문(때). = After I saw a lot of positive reviews.
When I got it, however, it was broken. I was so upset!

Ask Your Neighbors: March 9, 2020

We're sorry that you had such a negative experience. To fix this issue,
such+a+형용사+명사
we are asking lenders to update the pictures of their items regularly.
ask+목적어+to부정사
This will let other users know the exact condition of the product.
let+목적어+원형부정사

I can look after your pet!

Pet Sitter Finder is the perfect app for pet lovers and pet owners. It
helps pet owners find reliable people to look after their pets. When a
help+목적어+원형부정사[to부정사]
pet owner is looking for pet sitters, he or she uploads a post. Pet sitters
or dog walkers can then send messages to the owner. The owner checks
V1
their reviews and chooses the best person.
V2

George: November 12, 2019

I use this app whenever I'm going out of town. I have some concerns
복합관계부사: ~할 때는 언제나
about my personal information though. What if people use my phone
하지만(부사)   ~라면 어쩌지?
number for other purposes?

positive 긍정적인

negative 부정적인

issue 쟁점, 사안

exact 정확한, 정밀한

condition 상태, 조건

look after ~을 살피다[돌보다]

owner 주인, 소유주

reliable 믿을 수 있는

pet sitter 반려동물 돌보는 사람

upload 올리다, 업로드하다

concern 우려, 근심

personal 개인의, 개인적인

what if ~라면 어쩌지?

확인문제

- 다음 문장이 본문의 내용과 일치하면 T, 일치하지 않으면 F를 쓰시오.

1 After she saw a lot of positive reviews, Cassandra decided to borrow a bike
   helmet. ☐

2 When Cassandra got a bike helmet, it was in good condition. ☐

3 Ask Your Neighbors is sorry that Cassandra had such a negative experience. ☐

4 Ask Your Neighbors is the perfect app for pet lovers and pet owners. ☐

5 George doesn't have any concerns in using this app. ☐

Pet Sitter Finder: November 14, 2019

We're aware of this issue. We're now developing a system that
_{주격 관계대명사}
allows users to communicate freely without showing their personal
_{allow+목적어+to–V(목적격보어)} _{동명사}
information.

Samantha: February 22, 2020

Animals aren't allowed in my apartment, so I don't have any pets.
_{수동태(be+p.p.): 행위자가 불분명하거나 중요하지 않을 때 'by+행위자' 생략 가능}
However, by using Pet Sitter Finder, I can experience the joy of
walking a dog.
_{동명사(전치사 of의 목적어)}

Son: What great apps! We can borrow a tent and find someone to take
_{What+(a)+형용사+명사!}
care of our dog.

Dad: That's right. These kinds of services are part of the "sharing
economy." People can share their items with others and provide
_{share A with B: A를 B와 공유하다}
services to them at a small fee or for free.
_{무료로}

Son: But these services do have some weaknesses. Some people left
_{강조의 조동사}
negative reviews about the services.

Dad: Well, I think the more people use the services, the more they will
_{the+비교급 …, the+비교급 ~: …하면 할수록 더 ~하다}
improve.

be aware of ~을 인지하다[알다]

develop 발달시키다, 개발하다

kind 종류, 유형; 친절한

provide 제공하다

fee 요금, 수수료

weakness 약점

improve 개선하다

확인문제

● 다음 문장이 본문의 내용과 일치하면 T, 일치하지 않으면 F를 쓰시오.

1 Pet Sitter Finder is aware of the personal information issue. ☐

2 Pet Sitter Finder is now developing a system that allows users to communicate freely after showing their personal information. ☐

3 Animals aren't allowed in Samantha's apartment. ☐

4 Samantha doesn't have any pets, so she can't experience the joy of walking a dog. ☐

5 The son says that they can borrow a tent and find someone to take care of their dog. ☐

• 우리말을 참고하여 빈칸에 알맞은 말을 쓰시오.

1 Life in the _____ _____

2 Son: _____ _____ _____ _____ this weekend, Dad?

3 Dad: _____ _____ _____ go camping?

4 Son: But we _____ _____ a tent.

5 Should we buy _____?

6 Also, who will _____ _____ _____ our dog?

7 Dad: _____ _____. I know some apps that can help us.

8 _____ **from your neighbors!**

9 Ask Your Neighbors _____ _____ _____ _____ items that they can borrow from others.

10 First, users download the app and search for another user that has _____ _____ _____ _____.

11 Then they pick up the item and _____ _____ later.

12 Jasmine: _____ _____, 2019

13 I _____ _____ a board game and got _____ in less than 30 minutes.

14 I love saving money _____ _____ things that I don't often need.

15 Also, I think it's _____ _____.

16 _____ _____ _____ we buy, _____ _____ _____ we save.

1 공유 경제 속 삶

2 아들: 아빠, 우리 이번 주말에 뭐 할 거예요?

3 아빠: 캠핑 가는 건 어떠니?

4 아들: 그런데 우리 텐트가 없잖아요.

5 하나 사야 할까요?

6 게다가 우리 개는 누가 돌봐요?

7 아빠: 걱정하지 마. 내가 우리를 도와줄 수 있는 몇 개의 앱들을 알고 있지.

8 당신의 이웃들로부터 빌려라!

9 Ask Your Neighbors는 사람들이 다른 사람들로부터 빌릴 수 있는 물건을 쉽게 찾도록 돕는다.

10 우선, 사용자들은 그 앱을 내려받고 그들이 필요한 물건을 가지고 있는 또 다른 사용자를 찾는다.

11 그러고 나서 그들은 그 물건을 받아서 나중에 반납한다.

12 Jasmine / 2019년 12월 12일

13 저는 보드게임을 요청했고 30분도 안 되어 하나를 구했어요.

14 저는 제가 자주 필요하지 않은 것들을 빌림으로써 돈을 아낄 수 있다는 것이 마음에 들어요.

15 게다가 이것이 환경친화적이라고 생각해요.

16 우리가 제품들을 더 적게 구매할수록, 우리는 더 많은 자원들을 아끼는 거예요.

17 Cassandra: _____ 7, 2020

18 _____ a lot of positive reviews, I decided _____ _____ a bike helmet.

19 When I got it, however, it _____ _____.

20 I was _____ _____!

21 Ask Your Neighbors: _____ _____, 2020

22 We're sorry that you had _____ _____ _____ _____.

23 _____ _____ this issue, we are asking lenders _____ _____ _____ _____ of their items regularly.

24 This will _____ other users _____ the exact condition of the product.

25 **I can _____ _____ your pet!**

26 Pet Sitter Finder is _____ _____ _____ for pet lovers and pet owners.

27 It helps pet owners find _____ _____ to look after their pets.

28 When a pet owner is looking for pet sitters, he or she uploads _____ _____.

29 Pet sitters or dog walkers can then _____ _____ _____ the owner.

30 The owner _____ their reviews and _____ the best person.

31 George: _____ 12, 2019

32 I use this app _____ I'm going out of town.

17	Cassandra / 2020년 3월 7일
18	많은 긍정적인 후기들을 보고 나서, 저는 자전거 헬멧을 빌리 기로 결심했어요.
19	그러나 제가 그것을 얻었을 때, 그것은 망가져 있었어요.
20	저는 몹시 기분이 상했어요!
21	Ask Your Neighbors / 2020년 3월 9일
22	고객님이 그런 부정적인 경험을 겪게 해 드려 죄송합니다.
23	이 문제를 바로잡기 위해서, 저 희는 빌려주는 사람들에게 그들 의 물건 사진을 정기적으로 업 데이트해 줄 것을 요구하고 있 습니다.
24	이것이 다른 사용자들에게 그 제품의 정확한 상태를 알 수 있 도록 해 줄 것입니다.
25	제가 당신의 반려동물을 돌볼 수 있어요!
26	Pet Sitter Finder는 반려동물을 좋아하는 사람들과 반려동물 주 인들을 위한 완벽한 앱이다.
27	그것은 반려동물 주인들이 그들 의 반려동물을 돌보는 데 신뢰할 만한 사람들을 찾도록 돕는다.
28	반려동물 주인이 반려동물을 돌 보는 사람들을 찾을 때, 그 또는 그녀는 게시물을 올린다.
29	그러고 나서 반려동물을 돌보는 사람들이나 개를 산책시키는 사 람들이 주인에게 메시지를 보낼 수 있다.
30	주인은 그들의 후기들을 확인하 고 최고의 사람을 선택한다.
31	George / 2019년 11월 12일
32	저는 교외로 나갈 때마다 이 앱 을 사용해요.

33 I have some concerns about my _____ _____ though.

34 What if people use my phone number _____ _____ _____?

35 Pet Sitter Finder: _____ _____, _____

36 We're _____ _____ this issue.

37 We're now developing a system that _____ users to communicate freely _____ _____ their personal information.

38 Samantha: _____ 22, 2020

39 Animals _____ _____ in my apartment, so I don't have any pets.

40 However, _____ _____ Pet Sitter Finder, I can experience the joy of _____ a dog.

41 Son: _____ great apps!

42 We can borrow a tent and find someone _____ _____ _____ _____ our dog.

43 Dad: That's _____.

44 These kinds of services are part of the "_____ _____."

45 People can _____ their items _____ others and provide services to them _____ _____ _____ _____ _____ or _____ _____.

46 Son: But these services _____ have some _____.

47 Some people _____ _____ about the services.

48 Dad: Well, I think _____ people use _____ _____, the more they will improve.

---

33 하지만 저의 개인 정보에 대한 몇 가지 걱정이 있어요.

34 만약 다른 사람들이 제 전화번호를 다른 목적으로 사용하면 어쩌죠?

35 Pet Sitter Finder / 2019년 11월 14일

36 저희는 이 문제를 알고 있습니다.

37 저희는 현재 사용자들이 자신의 개인 정보를 보여주지 않으면서 자유롭게 소통할 수 있는 시스템을 개발하는 중입니다.

38 Samantha / 2020년 2월 22일

39 동물들이 제 아파트에서는 허락되지 않아서, 저는 반려동물을 키울 수 없어요.

40 그런데 Pet Sitter Finder를 이용하면서, 저는 개를 산책시키는 즐거움을 경험할 수 있어요.

41 아들: 정말 좋은 앱들이네요!

42 우리는 텐트를 빌리고 우리 개를 돌볼 누군가를 찾을 수 있어요.

43 아빠: 그렇지.

44 이런 종류의 서비스가 '공유 경제'의 일부란다.

45 사람들은 자신의 물건을 다른 사람들과 공유할 수 있고 적은 비용이나 무료로 그들에게 서비스를 제공할 수 있어.

46 아들: 하지만 사실 이런 서비스들은 몇 가지 약점들을 가지고 있어요.

47 몇몇 사람들이 서비스에 대해 부정적인 후기들을 남겼잖아요.

48 아빠: 글쎄, 나는 사람들이 그 서비스들을 더 많이 사용할수록, 그것들이 더 개선될 것이라고 생각해.

• 우리말을 참고하여 본문을 영작하시오.

1 공유 경제 속 삶
➡ _____

2 아들: 아빠, 우리 이번 주말에 뭐 할 거예요?
➡ _____

3 아빠: 캠핑 가는 건 어떠니?
➡ _____

4 아들: 그런데 우리 텐트가 없잖아요.
➡ _____

5 하나 사야 할까요?
➡ _____

6 게다가 우리 개는 누가 돌봐요?
➡ _____

7 아빠: 걱정하지 마. 내가 우리를 도와줄 수 있는 몇 개의 앱들을 알고 있지.
➡ _____

8 당신의 이웃들로부터 빌려라!
➡ _____

9 Ask Your Neighbors는 사람들이 다른 사람들로부터 빌릴 수 있는 물건을 쉽게 찾도록 돕는다.
➡ _____

10 우선, 사용자들은 그 앱을 내려받고 그들이 필요한 물건을 가지고 있는 또 다른 사용자를 찾는다.
➡ _____

11 그리고 나서 그들은 그 물건을 받아서 나중에 반납한다.
➡ _____

12 Jasmine / 2019년 12월 12일
➡ _____

13 저는 보드게임을 요청했고 30분도 안 되어 하나를 구했어요.
➡ _____

14 저는 제가 자주 필요하지 않은 것들을 빌림으로써 돈을 아낄 수 있다는 것이 마음에 들어요.
➡ _____

15 게다가 이것이 환경친화적이라고 생각해요.
➡ _____

16 우리가 제품들을 더 적게 구매할수록, 우리는 더 많은 자원들을 아끼는 거예요.
➡ _____

17 Cassandra / 2020년 3월 7일

➡ _____

18 많은 긍정적인 후기들을 보고 나서, 저는 자전거 헬멧을 빌리기로 결심했어요.

➡ _____

19 그러나 제가 그것을 얻었을 때, 그것은 망가져 있었어요.

➡ _____

20 저는 몹시 기분이 상했어요!

➡ _____

21 Ask Your Neighbors / 2020년 3월 9일

➡ _____

22 고객님이 그런 부정적인 경험을 겪게 해 드려 죄송합니다.

➡ _____

23 이 문제를 바로잡기 위해서, 저희는 빌려주는 사람들에게 그들의 물건 사진을 정기적으로
업데이트해 줄 것을 요구하고 있습니다.

➡ _____

24 이것이 다른 사용자들에게 그 제품의 정확한 상태를 알 수 있도록 해 줄 것입니다.

➡ _____

25 제가 당신의 반려동물을 돌볼 수 있어요!

➡ _____

26 Pet Sitter Finder는 반려동물을 좋아하는 사람들과 반려동물 주인들을 위한 완벽한 앱이다.

➡ _____

27 그것은 반려동물 주인들이 그들의 반려동물을 돌보는 데 신뢰할 만한 사람들을 찾도록 돕는다.

➡ _____

28 반려동물 주인이 반려동물을 돌보는 사람들을 찾을 때, 그 또는 그녀는 게시물을 올린다.

➡ _____

29 그러고 나서 반려동물을 돌보는 사람들이나 개를 산책시키는 사람들이 주인에게 메시지를
보낼 수 있다.

➡ _____

30 주인은 그들의 후기들을 확인하고 최고의 사람을 선택한다.

➡ _____

31 George / 2019년 11월 12일

➡ _____

32 저는 교외로 나갈 때마다 이 앱을 사용해요.

➡ _____

33 하지만 저의 개인 정보에 대한 몇 가지 걱정이 있어요.

➡ _____

34 만약 다른 사람들이 제 전화번호를 다른 목적으로 사용하면 어쩌죠?

➡ _____

35 Pet Sitter Finder / 2019년 11월 14일

➡ _____

36 저희는 이 문제를 알고 있습니다.

➡ _____

37 저희는 현재 사용자들이 자신의 개인 정보를 보여주지 않으면서 자유롭게 소통할 수 있는 시스템을 개발하는 중입니다.

➡ _____

_____

38 Samantha / 2020년 2월 22일

➡ _____

39 동물들이 제 아파트에서는 허락되지 않아서, 저는 반려동물을 키울 수 없어요.

➡ _____

40 그런데 Pet Sitter Finder를 이용하면서, 저는 개를 산책시키는 즐거움을 경험할 수 있어요.

➡ _____

41 아들: 정말 좋은 앱들이네요!

➡ _____

42 우리는 텐트를 빌리고 우리 개를 돌볼 누군가를 찾을 수 있어요.

➡ _____

43 아빠: 그렇지.

➡ _____

44 이런 종류의 서비스가 '공유 경제'의 일부란다.

➡ _____

45 사람들은 자신의 물건을 다른 사람들과 공유할 수 있고 적은 비용이나 무료로 그들에게 서비스를 제공할 수 있어."

➡ _____

46 아들: 하지만 사실 이런 서비스들은 몇 가지 약점들을 가지고 있어요.

➡ _____

47 몇몇 사람들이 서비스에 대해 부정적인 후기들을 남겼잖아요.

➡ _____

48 아빠: 글쎄, 나는 사람들이 그 서비스들을 더 많이 사용할수록, 그것들이 더 개선될 것이라고 생각해.

➡ _____

[01~03] 다음 글을 읽고 물음에 답하시오.

Son: What should we do this weekend, Dad?

Dad: ⓐWhy don't we go camping?

Son: But we don't have a tent. Should we buy ⓑone? Also, who will take care of our dog?

Dad: Don't worry. I know some apps that can help us.

01 위 글의 밑줄 친 ⓐ와 바꿔 쓸 수 없는 말을 고르시오.

① How about going camping?
② What about going camping?
③ Go camping, will you?
④ Let's go camping, shall we?
⑤ Shall we go camping?

서답형

02 위 글의 밑줄 친 ⓑone이 가리키는 것을 본문에서 찾아 쓰시오.

➡ _____

03 위 글의 뒤에 올 내용으로 가장 알맞은 것을 고르시오.

① what to do during the weekend
② the best place to go camping
③ the price of the tent for camping
④ the introduction to some apps to solve the son's worry
⑤ the clinics to take care of pets during their owners' vacation

[04~06] 다음 글을 읽고 물음에 답하시오.

Cassandra: March 7, 2020

Seeing a lot of positive reviews, I decided to borrow a bike helmet. When I got it, however, it was broken. I was so ___ⓐ___ !

Ask Your Neighbors: March 9, 2020

We're sorry that you had such a negative experience. To fix ⓑthis issue, we are asking lenders to update the pictures of their items regularly. This will let other users know the exact condition of the product.

04 위 글의 빈칸 ⓐ에 들어갈 알맞은 말을 고르시오.

① excited   ② upset
③ nervous   ④ pleased
⑤ ashamed

서답형

05 다음 빈칸 (A)와 (B)에 알맞은 단어를 넣어, 위 글의 밑줄 친 ⓑthis issue가 가리키는 내용을 완성하시오.

> When the users get the things they decided to borrow after they saw a lot of (A)_____ _____, they come to find the (B)_____ of the things is not good.

서답형

06 다음 문장에서 위 글의 내용과 다른 부분을 찾아서 고치시오.

> Ask Your Neighbors is asking lenders to download the pictures of their items regularly.

_____ ➡ _____

[07~09] 다음 글을 읽고 물음에 답하시오.

_____ⓐ_____

Ask Your Neighbors helps people easily find items that they can borrow from others. (①) First, users download the app and search for another user that has the item they need. (②)

Jasmine: December 12, 2019

I asked for a board game and got ⓑone in less than 30 minutes. (③) I love saving money by borrowing things that I don't often need. (④) Also, I think it's environmentally friendly. (⑤) The fewer products we buy, the more resources we save.

07 위 글의 빈칸 ⓐ에 들어갈 제목으로 알맞은 것을 고르시오.

① Various Apps That Make Our Lives More Convenient
② Borrow from Your Neighbors!
③ What Is Effective to Search for the Users?
④ Which Is Nicer, Buying an Item or Borrowing It?
⑤ Let's Live Environmentally Friendly Lives

08 위 글의 흐름으로 보아, 주어진 문장이 들어가기에 가장 적절한 곳은?

> Then they pick up the item and return it later.

①   ②   ③   ④   ⑤

09 위 글의 밑줄 친 ⓑone이 가리키는 것을 본문에서 찾아 쓰시오.

➡ _____

[10~12] 다음 글을 읽고 물음에 답하시오.

I can look after your pet!

Pet Sitter Finder is the perfect app for pet lovers and pet owners. It helps pet owners find reliable people to (A)look after their pets. When a pet owner is looking for pet sitters, he or she uploads a post. Pet sitters or dog walkers can then send messages to the owner. The owner checks their reviews and ____ⓐ____ the best person.

10 위 글의 빈칸 ⓐ에 choose를 알맞은 형태로 쓰시오.

➡ _____

11 위 글의 밑줄 친 (A)look after와 바꿔 쓸 수 있는 말을 모두 고르시오.

① take notice of   ② care for
③ make use of   ④ take after
⑤ take care of

12 다음 빈칸 (A)와 (B)에 알맞은 단어를 넣어, Pet Sitter Finder를 이용하여 반려동물 주인이 반려동물을 돌보는 사람들을 찾는 방법을 완성하시오.

> First a pet owner uploads a post and checks the (A)_____ about the pet sitters or dog walkers who (B)_____ _____ to him or her. Then, the owner can choose the best person among them.

[13~14] 다음 글을 읽고 물음에 답하시오.

Samantha: February 22, 2020

Animals aren't allowed in my apartment, so I don't have any pets. However, by (A)using Pet Sitter Finder, I can experience the joy of
_____ⓐ_____.

13 위 글의 빈칸 ⓐ에 들어갈 알맞은 말을 고르시오.

① developing apps
② walking a dog
③ finding reliable people
④ uploading a post
⑤ becoming a baby sitter

14 위 글의 밑줄 친 (A)using과 문법적 쓰임이 <u>다른</u> 것을 <u>모두</u> 고르시오.

① I'm <u>planning</u> to visit his house.
② She is worried about <u>taking</u> an exam.
③ Did you practice <u>playing</u> the cello?
④ I saw him <u>entering</u> the room.
⑤ <u>Playing</u> soccer is fun

[15~17] 다음 글을 읽고 물음에 답하시오.

Borrow from your neighbors!

 Ask Your Neighbors helps people easily find items that they can borrow from others. First, users download the app and search ___ⓐ___ another user that has the item they need. Then they pick up the item and return it later.

Jasmine: December 12, 2019

 I asked for a board game and got one ___ⓑ___ less than 30 minutes. I love saving money by ©<u>borrowing</u> things that I don't often need. Also, I think it's environmentally friendly. The fewer products we buy, the more resources we save.

15 위 글의 빈칸 ⓐ와 ⓑ에 들어갈 전치사가 바르게 짝지어진 것은?

	ⓐ	ⓑ		ⓐ	ⓑ
①	for	at	②	on	for
③	to	for	④	for	in
⑤	on	in			

16 위 글의 밑줄 친 ©borrowing과 문법적 쓰임이 같은 것을 <u>모두</u> 고르시오.

① My hobby is <u>playing</u> soccer.
② Look at the <u>sleeping</u> baby.
③ Do you mind <u>turning</u> down the volume?
④ He is good at <u>playing</u> the violin.
⑤ She is <u>watching</u> TV now.

17 According to the passage, which is NOT true?

① People can easily find items that they can borrow from others through the app, Ask Your Neighbors.
② First, users need to download the app and search for another user who will borrow their item.
③ Jasmine asked for a board game and got one in less than 30 minutes.
④ Jasmine loves to save money by borrowing things that she doesn't often need.
⑤ Jasmine thinks borrowing things is environmentally friendly.

[18~19] 다음 글을 읽고 물음에 답하시오.

Pet Sitter Finder: November 14, 2019

 We're aware of this issue. We're now developing a system that allows users to communicate freely without showing their personal information.

Samantha: February 22, 2020

 Animals aren't allowed in my apartment, so I don't have any pets. ___ⓐ___, by using Pet Sitter Finder, I can experience the joy of walking a dog.

18 위 글의 빈칸 ⓐ에 들어갈 알맞은 말을 고르시오.

① In other words   ② Moreover
③ However   ④ Likewise
⑤ As a result

19 위 글의 앞에 올 내용으로 가장 알맞은 것을 고르시오.

① the difficulty of developing a system
② a system that allows users to communicate freely
③ the apartment in which animals aren't allowed
④ the way to keep pets
⑤ the issue of showing the personal information

[20~21] 다음 글을 읽고 물음에 답하시오.

I can look after your pet!

Pet Sitter Finder is the perfect app for pet lovers and pet owners. It helps pet owners find reliable people to look after their pets. When a pet owner is looking for pet sitters, he or she uploads a post. Pet sitters or dog walkers can then send messages to the owner. The owner checks their reviews and chooses the best person.

George: November 12, 2019

I use this app whenever I'm going out of town. I have some concerns about my personal information ⓐthough. What if people use my phone number for other purposes?

20 위 글의 밑줄 친 ⓐthough와 같은 의미로 쓰인 것을 고르시오.

① Though he was young, he supported his family.

② Our team lost. It was a good game though.
③ Though he tried very hard, he failed the course.
④ Young though he was, he was very wise.
⑤ The wind was still blowing though it stopped raining.

21 Which question CANNOT be answered after reading the passage?

① What is Pet Sitter Finder?
② How do pet sitters or dog walkers contact a pet owner?
③ How long does it take for a pet owner to find a reliable person to look after the pet?
④ When does George use the app, Pet Sitter Finder?
⑤ What is George worried about?

[22~23] 다음 글을 읽고 물음에 답하시오.

Son: What great apps! We can borrow a tent and find someone to take care of our dog.

Dad: That's right. These kinds of services are part of the " ⓐ economy." People can share their items with others and provide services to them at a small fee or for free.

Son: But these services do have some weaknesses. Some people left negative reviews about the services.

Dad: Well, I think the more people use the services, the more they will improve.

서답형

22 본문의 한 단어를 변형하여 위 글의 빈칸 ⓐ에 들어갈 알맞은 단어를 쓰시오.

➡ _____

23 위 글의 주제로 알맞은 것을 고르시오.

① the great apps that make our lives comfortable
② the way to borrow an item
③ the benefits and weaknesses of "sharing economy"
④ how to provide services to people
⑤ the way to improve the weaknesses of "sharing economy"

24 주어진 문장 다음에 이어질 글의 순서로 가장 적절한 것은?

Pet Sitter Finder is the perfect app for pet lovers and pet owners.
(A) When a pet owner is looking for pet sitters, he or she uploads a post. Pet sitters or dog walkers can then send messages to the owner.
(B) The owner checks their reviews and chooses the best person.
(C) It helps pet owners find reliable people to look after their pets.

① (A) – (C) – (B)   ② (B) – (A) – (C)
③ (B) – (C) – (A)   ④ (C) – (A) – (B)
⑤ (C) – (B) – (A)

[25~27] 다음 글을 읽고 물음에 답하시오.

Cassandra: March 7, 2020
Seeing a lot of positive reviews, I decided to borrow a bike helmet. When I got it, however, it was broken. I was so upset!

Ask Your Neighbors: March 9, 2020
We're sorry that you had ⓐ그런 부정적인 경험. To ⓑfix this issue, we are asking lenders to update the pictures of their items regularly. This will let other users know the exact condition of the product.

25 위 글에서 알 수 있는 Cassandra의 심경 변화로 가장 알맞은 것을 고르시오.

① hopeful   → bored
② puzzled   → upset
③ bored   → amazed
④ expectant   → disappointed
⑤ nervous   → satisfied

서답형

26 위 글의 밑줄 친 ⓐ의 우리말에 맞게 such를 사용하여 4 단어로 영작하시오.

➡ _____

27 위 글의 밑줄 친 ⓑfix와 같은 의미로 쓰인 것을 고르시오.

① The car won't start. Can you fix it?
② He tried to fix a shelf to the wall.
③ I want to fix the rent at forty dollars a month.
④ She likes to fix a feather in her hat.
⑤ Why did he fix his eyes on the ground?

[01~02] 다음 글을 읽고 물음에 답하시오.

> Son: What should we do this weekend, Dad?
>
> Dad: Why don't we go ___ⓐ___ ?
>
> Son: But we don't have a tent. Should we buy one? Also, who will take care of our dog?
>
> Dad: Don't worry. I know some apps that can help us.

01 위 글의 빈칸 ⓐ에 camp를 알맞은 형태로 쓰시오.

➡ _____

02 캠핑 가자는 아빠의 제안을 듣고 아들이 걱정하는 내용 두 가지를 우리말로 쓰시오.

➡ (1) _____
(2) _____

[03~04] 다음 글을 읽고 물음에 답하시오.

> Son: What great apps! We can borrow a tent and find someone to take care of our dog.
>
> Dad: That's right. These kinds of services are part of the "sharing economy." People can share their items with others and provide services to them at a small fee or ⓐfor free.
>
> Son: But these services do have some weaknesses. Some people left negative reviews about the services.
>
> Dad: Well, I think ⓑ사람들이 그 서비스들을 더 많이 사용할수록, 그것들이 더 개선될 것이라고.

03 위 글의 밑줄 친 ⓐfor free와 바꿔 쓸 수 있는 말을 쓰시오.

➡ _____ 또는 _____ 또는

04 위 글의 밑줄 친 ⓑ의 우리말에 맞게 주어진 어휘를 알맞게 배열하시오.

> will / use / they / the more / the services / people / improve / the more / , /

➡ _____
_____

[05~07] 다음 글을 읽고 물음에 답하시오.

> Cassandra: March 7, 2020
>
> Seeing a lot of (A)[positive / negative] reviews, I decided to borrow a bike helmet. When I got it, however, it was broken. I was so upset!
>
> Ask Your Neighbors: March 9, 2020
>
> We're sorry that you had such a negative experience. To fix this issue, we are asking (B)[lenders / users] to update the pictures of their items regularly. ⓐThis will let other (C)[lenders / users] know the exact condition of the product.

05 위 글의 괄호 (A)~(C)에서 문맥상 알맞은 낱말을 골라 쓰시오.

➡ (A) _____ (B) _____ (C) _____

06 위 글의 밑줄 친 ⓐThis가 가리키는 것을 우리말로 쓰시오.

➡ _____
_____

07 본문의 내용과 일치하도록 다음 빈칸 (A)와 (B)에 알맞은 단어를 쓰시오.

> Ask Your Neighbors apologizes to (A)_____ for having given her a very (B)_____ experience.

[08~09] 다음 글을 읽고 물음에 답하시오.

Cassandra: March 7, 2020

ⓐSeeing a lot of positive reviews, I decided to borrow a bike helmet. When I got it, however, it was broken. I was so upset!

Ask Your Neighbors: March 9, 2020

We're sorry that you had such a negative experience. To fix this issue, we are asking lenders to update the pictures of their items regularly. This will let other users know the exact condition of the product.

08 위 글의 밑줄 친 ⓐ를 부사절로 고칠 때, 빈칸에 들어갈 알맞은 두 단어를 쓰시오.

➡ After _____ a lot of positive reviews

09 How can other users know the exact condition of the product that they want to borrow? Fill in the blanks (A) and (B) with suitable words.

> If (A)_____ _____ of the items are updated regularly by (B)_____, other users will be able to know the exact condition of the product.

[10~12] 다음 글을 읽고 물음에 답하시오.

George: November 12, 2019

I use this app whenever I'm going out of town. I have some concerns about my personal information though. What if people use my phone number for other purposes?

Pet Sitter Finder: November 14, 2019

We're aware of ⓐthis issue. ⓑWe're now developing a system that allows users to communicate freely without showing their personal information.

Samantha: February 22, 2020

Animals aren't allowed in my apartment, so I don't have any pets. However, by using Pet Sitter Finder, I can experience the joy of walking a dog.

10 위 글의 밑줄 친 ⓐthis issue가 가리키는 것을 우리말로 쓰시오.

➡ _____ 또는

_____

11 위 글의 밑줄 친 ⓑ를 다음과 같이 바꿔 쓸 때 빈칸에 들어갈 알맞은 단어를 쓰시오.

> We're now developing a system which lets users _____ freely without showing their personal information.

12 본문의 내용과 일치하도록 다음 빈칸 (A)와 (B)에 알맞은 단어를 쓰시오.

> Though Samantha has no (A)_____, she can experience the joy of walking a dog (B)_____ _____ _____ _____.

해석

Do It Yourself

Last Sunday, my family went to see a baseball game. Cheering for our team,
　　　　　　　　　　　　　　　　　　분사구문(= While[As] we cheered for our team. ~)
we had a really nice time together. Happily, our team won the game. Feeling
　　　　　　　　　　　　　　　　　　　　　　　　　　　　　　　분사구문(= As[Since/Because] we felt
happy about the win, we decided to celebrate. Eating fried chicken together,
happy about the win. ~)　　　　　　　to부정사의 명사적 용법　　　분사구문(= While[As] we ate
we talked about the game.　　　　　　　　　　　　　　　　　fried chicken together. ~)

구문해설 ·cheer: 응원하다　·win: 승리하다; 승리　·celebrate: 축하하다

지난 일요일, 우리 가족은 야구 경기를 보러 갔다. 우리 팀을 응원하면서, 우리는 함께 정말 좋은 시간을 가졌다. 행복하게도 우리 팀이 그 경기에서 이겼다. 승리에 대해 기쁨을 느껴서, 우리는 축하하기로 결정했다. 함께 프라이드치킨을 먹으면서, 우리는 그 경기에 대해 얘기했다.

After You Read C Get the BIG Picture

Sharing Economy

where people can share their items with or provide services to others
　　　　　　　　share A with B: A를 B와 공유하다　　　provide A to B: B에게 A를 제공하다

Ask Your Neighbors

⊕ helps people find items to borrow from others
help+목적어+원형부정사(to부정사)
⊕ helps people save money and resources
help+목적어+원형부정사(to부정사)
⊖ needs regular updates on each item's condition
　　　　　　　　　　　　　　each + 단수명사
<⊕ benefit, ⊖ weakness>

구문해설 ·share: 공유하다　·neighbor: 이웃　·provide: 제공하다　·condition: 상태, 조건
·benefit: 혜택　·weakness: 약점

공유 경제

사람들이 자신의 물건을 다른 사람들과 공유하거나 그들에게 서비스를 제공할 수 있는 곳

Ask Your Neighbors

⊕ 사람들이 다른 사람들로부터 빌릴 수 있는 물건을 찾도록 돕는다
⊕ 사람들이 돈과 자원들을 아끼도록 돕는다
⊖ 각 제품의 상태에 관해 정기적인 업데이트가 필요하다
〈⊕ 이점, ⊖ 약점〉

Culture Link

Sharing Economies Around the World

I sometimes give other people a ride on my way to work. They can get to their
　　　　　　give A B : A에게 B를 주다(4형식)　　　　　　　　　　　　　　= reach. arrive at
destinations for a small fee, and I can make some money. Ride sharing also
fee는 small/large. low/high 등과 함께 쓴다　　　　　　　　　　동명사(단수 취급)
reduces the number of cars on the road, which is environmentally friendly.
　　~의 수 a number of (×)　　　계속적 용법의 관계대명사 (앞 문장 전체가 선행사)

구문해설 ·destination: 목적지　·fee: 요금　·environmentally: 환경적으로

세계의 공유 경제

나는 때때로 출근길에 다른 사람들을 태워준다. 그들은 적은 요금을 내고 목적지에 도착할 수 있고, 나는 약간의 돈을 벌 수 있다. 출근 공유는 또한 도로 위의 차들의 수를 줄여 주는데, 그것은 환경친화적이다.

Words & Expressions

01 다음 짝지어진 단어의 관계가 같도록 빈칸에 알맞은 말을 쓰시오.

> borrow : lend = download : _____

02 다음 영영풀이가 가리키는 것을 고르시오.

> to give something that someone needs or wants to them, or make it available

① allow ② borrow ③ fix
④ improve ⑤ provide

03 다음 중 밑줄 친 부분의 뜻풀이가 바르지 않은 것은?

① Wherever you visit, you should follow the safety rules. (언제든지)
② My father takes part in the volunteer activity regularly. (규칙적으로)
③ If you don't mind, would you fix this machine for me? (고치다)
④ You can express your ideas freely during the meeting. (자유롭게)
⑤ My sister looked disappointed because of her broken toys. (망가진)

04 다음 문장의 빈칸 (A)~(C)에 들어갈 말이 바르게 짝지어진 것은?

> • The shoes are ___(A)___ sale.
> • My father is going to be ___(B)___ of town for two weeks.
> • Birds search ___(C)___ a good place to raise their young in summer.

① to – for – on ② for – in – out
③ for – on – in ④ on – for – out
⑤ on – out – for

Conversation

05 다음 대화가 자연스럽게 이어지도록 순서대로 배열하시오.

> (A) Okay, Mom. I won't forget it this time.
> (B) I'm going to get a refund for these clothes this evening. I found I have similar ones.
> (C) Okay. Don't forget to bring your receipt. Last time you couldn't get a refund because you didn't bring it.

➡ _____

[06~08] 다음 대화를 읽고 물음에 답하시오.

Judy: I think my hair is too curly. I want to straighten my hair. Can you recommend a good place?

Gina: Sure. I know two places, Styles Studio and Hair Castle.

Judy: Is there any difference between the two?

Gina: Well, Styles Studio provides free treatment to keep your hair healthy.

Judy: That's great. What about Hair Castle?

Gina: Hair Castle doesn't provide treatment for free, but they give student discounts.

Judy: Okay. Which do you prefer?

Gina: I prefer Styles Studio to Hair Castle. It's important for me to get hair treatment regularly.

06 What benefit does Styles Studio provide to the customers?

➡ _____
_____

07 Who can get discounts from Hair Castle?

➡ _____

08 Why does Gina like Styles Studio more?

➡ _____

_____

[09~10] 다음 대화를 읽고 물음에 답하시오.

Jane: I tried Spring Chips recently, and now I want to review them.

Chris: That sounds fun. How will you do your review?

Jane: I'll make a video. I want to focus on their delicious taste!

Chris: Okay, but _____(A)_____.

Jane: I won't. I want to give a balanced review.

Chris: Good. Your video will make it easier for people to choose better products.

Jane: That's exactly what I want. I'd like to give people more useful information about the product.

09 위 대화의 빈칸 (A)에 들어갈 말을 〈보기〉에 주어진 어구들을 모두 배열하여 완성하시오.

┌─── 보기 ───┐

talk / too / their / to / forget / bad points / don't / about

➡ _____

10 위 대화의 내용과 일치하지 <u>않는</u> 것은?

① Jane은 최근에 스프링 칩스를 먹어 보았다.

② Jane은 스프링 칩스의 맛있는 맛을 논평하고 싶어 한다.

③ Chris는 Jane에게 스프링 칩스의 단점도 언급할 것을 상기시켰다.

④ Jane은 균형 잡힌 비평을 내고 싶어 한다.

⑤ Jane은 더 맛있는 음식을 만들어 사람들의 선택을 받고자 한다.

11 다음 대화가 자연스럽게 이어지도록 순서대로 배열하시오.

Which do you prefer, the Special Sandwich or the Classic Sandwich?

(A) I guess our spending habits are different.

(B) But it's much more expensive than the Classic Sandwich.

(C) I prefer the cheaper one. I'll spend my money on books instead.

(D) Well, the Special Sandwich is the healthier choice. It's made with lots of fresh vegetables and other healthy ingredients.

(E) I know, but I prefer the Special Sandwich to the Classic Sandwich. Eating healthy is important to me.

➡ _____

[12~13] 다음 문장의 밑줄 친 분사구문을 부사절로 바르게 바꾼 것은?

12

Seeing a lot of negative reviews online, the researcher decided not to buy the products.

① Though she saw a lot of negative reviews online,

② Once she saw a lot of negative reviews online,

③ If she saw a lot of negative reviews online,

④ As she saw a lot of negative reviews online,

⑤ Should she see a lot of negative reviews online,

13

> There being a Pet Sitter Finder app made by her friends, she didn't use the service.

① As an app existed there where she could find a pet sitter by her friends,
② If there was a Pet Sitter Finder app made by her friends,
③ Unless there was a Pet Sitter Finder app made by her friends,
④ Even though there was a Pet Sitter Finder app made by her friends,
⑤ Because there was a Pet Sitter Finder app made by her friends,

14 다음 중 어법상 어색한 문장을 고르시오.

① The more they earn, the more they have to save for their future.
② The cooler the cold noodle is, the better it tastes.
③ The more promises you make, the harder it becomes to keep them.
④ The less we have, the more we want to receive.
⑤ The higher you go up, the more it is difficult for you to breathe.

15 다음 문장의 밑줄 친 부사절을 분사구문으로 알맞게 바꾼 것을 고르시오.

> As he wasn't aware of the personal information issues, George often forgot to secure his details.

① As he being not aware of the personal information issues,

② There being not aware of the personal information issues,
③ Being not aware of that the personal information issues,
④ As he not being aware of the personal information issues,
⑤ Not being aware of the personal information issues,

[16~17] 다음 밑줄 친 부분 중 어법상 옳은 것을 고르시오.

16 ① The sooner they start to work, the more faster they will achieve the goal.
② More the men eat, more weight they will gain.
③ The shorter the break time is, the less relaxed the employees do.
④ The heavier the tables are, the more expensive they become.
⑤ The more they think, the more they will be careful.

17 ① Caught a severe cold, Catherine was absent from school yesterday.
② Turned to the right, you'll find the shopping mall on your right.
③ Having been raised on a farm, William knows well how to feed pigs and cows.
④ Interesting in the Korean history, Chris reserved the related books at the library.
⑤ Educating in New Zealand, she speaks and writes English well.

18 다음 중 주어진 문장과 의미가 가장 가까운 문장을 고르시오.

> Everytime he spends some time with Anne, he feels better than before.

① The more he knows Anne, the happier she will be.

② The more Anne spends time with him, the happier she feels.

③ The more things he does with Anne, the happier they look.

④ The more time he spends with Anne, the happier he is.

⑤ The more time he spends with Anne, the happier he does.

Reading

[19~21] 다음 글을 읽고 물음에 답하시오.

Borrow from your neighbors!

Ask Your Neighbors helps people easily find items that they can ___ⓐ___ from others. First, users download the app and search for ⓑ그들이 필요한 물건을 가지고 있는 또 다른 사용자. Then they pick up the item and return it later.

Jasmine: December 12, 2019

I asked for a board game and got one in less than 30 minutes. I love saving money by borrowing things that I don't often need. Also, I think it's environmentally friendly. ⓒThe fewer products we buy, the more resources we save.

19 위 글의 빈칸 ⓐ에 들어갈 알맞은 말을 고르시오.

① lend ② use ③ buy
④ borrow ⑤ provide

20 위 글의 밑줄 친 ⓑ의 우리말에 맞게 주어진 어휘를 이용하여 8 단어로 영작하시오.

> another, that, the item

➡ _____

21 위 글의 밑줄 친 ⓒ를 접속사 As를 사용하여 고칠 때, 빈칸에 들어갈 알맞은 말을 쓰시오.

➡ As we buy _____ _____, we save _____ _____.

[22~24] 다음 글을 읽고 물음에 답하시오.

Cassandra: March 7, 2020

Seeing a lot of positive reviews, I decided to borrow a bike helmet. (①) When I got it, however, it was broken. (②) I was so upset! (③)

Ask Your Neighbors: March 9, 2020

We're sorry that you had such a negative experience. (④) ⓐThis will let other users to know the exact condition of the product. (⑤)

22 위 글의 흐름으로 보아, 주어진 문장이 들어가기에 가장 적절한 곳은?

> To fix this issue, we are asking lenders to update the pictures of their items regularly.

① ② ③ ④ ⑤

23 위 글의 밑줄 친 ⓐ에서 어법상 틀린 부분을 찾아 고치시오.

_____ ➡ _____ 또는

_____ ➡ _____

24 위 글의 주제로 알맞은 것을 고르시오.

① the other side of a lot of positive reviews
② the problem and its solution when borrowing things using an app
③ the unreliable "sharing services"
④ how to change the negative experience of the users
⑤ the way to update the pictures of the items regularly

[25~26] 다음 글을 읽고 물음에 답하시오.

Son: What great apps! We can borrow a tent and find someone to take care of our dog.

Dad: That's right. These kinds of services are part of the "sharing economy." People can share their items with others and provide services to them at a small fee or for free.

Son: But these services ⓐdo have some weaknesses. Some people left negative reviews about the services.

Dad: Well, I think the more people use the services, the more they will improve.

25 위 글의 밑줄 친 ⓐdo와 문법적 쓰임이 같은 것을 고르시오.

① Do you like it?
② We will do what we can to help.
③ You do look tired.
④ They do not want to go there.
⑤ She works harder than you do.

26 According to the passage, which is NOT true?

① The son says that the apps are very great.
② Dad says these kinds of services are part of the "sharing economy."
③ People can share their items with others and provide services to them at a small fee or for free.
④ These kinds of services don't have any weaknesses.
⑤ Dad thinks the more people use the services, the more they will improve.

[27~28] 다음 글을 읽고 물음에 답하시오.

I Can Share My Jump Rope with You!

Here is a jump rope that I can share. It's not new, but it's in good condition. You can borrow it for up to two days.

There are two rules:
❶ You can borrow it once a week.
❷ You must pay for the item if you lose or break it.

If you are willing to follow the rules above, feel free to contact me! I will happily share it with you.

27 위 글의 종류로 알맞은 것을 고르시오.

① essay   ② article   ③ manual
④ review   ⑤ notice

28 다음 문장에서 위 글의 내용과 다른 부분을 찾아서 고치시오.

> The users can borrow the jump rope for a week.

_____ ➡ _____

출제율 90%

01 다음 영영풀이가 가리키는 것을 고르시오.

the system according to which the money, industry and trade of a country or region are organized

① refund　　② economy　　③ issue
④ fee　　⑤ camping

출제율 95%

02 다음 주어진 문장의 밑줄 친 condition(s)과 같은 의미로 쓰인 것은?

She is in no condition to walk alone.

① You should check your conditions of employment.
② My grandfather's condition is getting better now.
③ What is a necessary condition for economic growth?
④ A good training programme is one of the conditions for successful industry.
⑤ Does she not like the conditions?

출제율 100%

03 다음 우리말을 주어진 단어를 이용하여 영작하시오.

(1) 지난주에 그 코트는 할인 중이었다. (sale, coat)

　➡ _____

(2) 그녀는 방학 동안 친구의 애완동물을 돌보았다. (take, during)

　➡ _____

(3) 이 팬케이크들은 유기농 계란으로 만들어졌다. (with, pancakes, organic)

　➡ _____

[04~05] 다음 대화를 읽고 물음에 답하시오.

Sue: Jinho, look! These two speakers look pretty cool. (A)
Jinho: (B) Yeah, they do. Which do you prefer, the red one or the black one?
Sue: (C) It's only 20 dollars, and it comes with a discount coupon for music downloads.
Jinho: (D) Although the black one is 40 dollars, I think it's the right one for me. I heard it has better sound quality. (E)

출제율 90%

04 위 대화의 (A)~(E) 중에서 주어진 문장이 들어가기에 적절한 곳은?

I prefer the red one to the black one.

① (A)　② (B)　③ (C)　④ (D)　⑤ (E)

출제율 100%

05 위 대화의 내용과 일치하지 않는 것은?

① Sue와 진호는 두 개의 스피커를 보고 있다.
② 빨간색 스피커는 20달러이다.
③ 빨간색 스피커는 음악 다운로드 할인 쿠폰도 같이 준다.
④ 진호는 빨간색 스피커가 자신에게 맞는 것 같다.
⑤ 진호는 검은색 스피커가 더 나은 음질을 갖고 있다고 들었다.

[06~07] 다음 대화를 읽고 물음에 답하시오.

Judy: I think my hair is too curly. I want to straighten my hair. Can you recommend a good place?
Gina: Sure. I know two places, Styles Studio and Hair Castle.
Judy: Is there any difference between the two?
Gina: Well, Styles Studio provides free treatment to keep your hair healthy.
Judy: That's great. What about Hair Castle?

Gina: Hair Castle doesn't provide treatment for free, but they give student discounts.

Judy: Okay. (A)Which do you prefer?

Gina: I prefer Styles Studio to Hair Castle. It's important for me to get hair treatment regularly.

출제율 90%

6 위 대화의 밑줄 친 (A)와 바꾸어 쓸 수 있는 것을 모두 고르시오.

① What are you planning to do?
② Which do you like more?
③ Which do you like better?
④ Which one do you want to visit?
⑤ What do you want have?

출제율 95%

7 위 대화의 내용과 일치하도록 빈칸을 완성하시오.

> **Gina:** Which hair shop do you want to go to straighten your hair?
>
> **Judy:** I need to save my money because my father's birthday is coming. I need to buy some present for him. I'll choose (A)_____ because I can get (B)_____.

[08~10] 다음 대화를 읽고 물음에 답하시오.

G: These two pairs of shoes are ⓐon sale! ⓑ Which do you prefer?

B: Well, I prefer the white shoes ⓒthan the black ones.

G: Why is that? The black ones ⓓare cheaper.

B: Yes, but I like the design ⓔof the white ones better.

출제율 95%

8 위 대화의 내용과 일치하도록 빈칸을 완성하시오.

> Even though the black shoes are (A)_____, the boy prefers the white shoes because of their (B)_____.

출제율 90%

9 위 대화의 밑줄 친 ⓐ~ⓔ에서 어법상 어색한 것을 골라 바르게 고치시오.

_____ ➡ _____

출제율 100%

10 위 대화의 내용과 일치하지 <u>않는</u> 것은?

① 두 켤레의 신발이 할인 중이다.
② 소년은 검은색 신발보다 흰색 신발을 더 좋아한다.
③ 검은색 신발이 더 저렴하다.
④ 소년은 흰색 신발의 디자인을 더 좋아한다.
⑤ 소녀는 검은색 신발을 구매할 것이다.

[11~12] 다음 주어진 문장의 부사절을 분사구문으로 적절히 전환한 것을 고르시오.

출제율 95%

11

> As they had not been invited to the party, the couple left the city for a quiet temple.

① Having not invited to the party, the couple left the city for a quiet temple.
② As they not having been invited to the party, the couple left the city for a quiet temple.
③ As they being not invited to the party, the couple left the city for a quiet temple.
④ Not having been invited to the party, the couple left the city for a quiet temple.
⑤ Not having invited to the party, the couple left the city for a quiet temple.

12 출제율 90%

As we expand the sharing economy around the world, we can decrease the amount of resources in making a lot of products.

① Expanding the sharing economy around the world, we can decrease the amount of resources in making a lot of products.

② When the sharing economy expanding around the world, we can decrease the amount of resources in making a lot of products.

③ As the sharing economy being expanded around the world, we can decrease the amount of resources in making a lot of products.

④ As the sharing economy expanding around the world, we can decrease the amount of resources in making a lot of products.

⑤ Expanded the sharing economy around the world, we can decrease the amount of resources in making a lot of products.

[13~14] 다음 주어진 우리말을 바르게 영작한 것을 고르면?

13 출제율 90%

당신이 더 많은 물건들을 공유한다면, 지구의 자원은 더 적게 사용될 수 있다.

① As the more you share the things, the more resources on earth are less likely to be used.

② When you share the more things, you are likely to use the global resources as little as you imagine.

③ The more you share things with others, the more less resources on earth can be used.

④ The more things you share with other people, the amount of resources used on earth will decrease.

⑤ The more things you share, the less resources on earth can be used.

14 출제율 95%

날씨가 더워질수록, 우리는 더 많은 전기 에너지가 필요하다.

① The more hotter the weather, so much more electrical energy we need.

② The hotter the weather is, the more electrical energy we need.

③ The hotter the weather will be, the more electrical energy we are needed.

④ The more hot the weather, we need the more electrical energy.

⑤ The hotter the weather is, the better electrical energy we will need.

15 출제율 100%

다음 우리말에 맞도록 괄호 안에 주어진 어휘를 알맞게 배열하여 빈칸을 채우시오.

(1) 우리가 살아가는 환경을 보호하고 싶었기 때문에, 나는 공유 경제 서비스 앱을 개발하기로 결심했다. (protect, wanting, in, to, we, the environment, live)

➡ _____

_____, I decided to develop a sharing economy service app.

(2) 비록 나는 학생들이 무엇을 원하는지 알지 못했지만, 그들이 요청한 대로 하려고 최선을 다해 노력했다. (what, not, wanted, though, the students, knowing)

➡ _____

_____, I tried my best to do what they asked.

[16~18] 다음 글을 읽고 물음에 답하시오.

Borrow from your neighbors!

Ask Your Neighbors helps people easily find items that they can borrow from others. First, users download the app and search for another user that has the item they need. Then they pick up the item and return ⓐit later.

Jasmine: December 12, 2019

I asked for a board game and got one in less than 30 minutes. I love saving money by borrowing things that I don't often need. Also, I think it's environmentally friendly. ⓑThe less products we buy, the less resources we save.

출제율 90%

16 위 글의 밑줄 친 ⓐit이 가리키는 것을 본문에서 찾아 쓰시오.

➡ _____

출제율 95%

17 위 글의 밑줄 친 ⓑ에서 어법이나 흐름상 어색한 부분을 찾아 고치시오. (두 군데)

_____ ➡ _____

_____ ➡ _____

출제율 95%

18 Ask Your Neighbors를 사용하는 방법을 우리말로 설명하시오.

➡ (1) _____

(2) _____

_____

[19~21] 다음 글을 읽고 물음에 답하시오.

_____ⓐ_____

Pet Sitter Finder is the perfect app for pet lovers and pet owners. It helps pet owners find reliable people to look after their pets. When a pet owner is looking for pet sitters, he or she uploads a post. Pet sitters or dog walkers can then send messages to the owner. The owner checks their reviews and chooses the best person.

George: November 12, 2019

I use this app ⓑwhenever I'm going out of town. I have some concerns about my personal information though. What if people use my phone number for other purposes?

출제율 95%

19 위 글의 빈칸 ⓐ에 들어갈 제목으로 알맞은 것을 고르시오.

① How about Using an App If Possible?
② How to Find Reliable People
③ I Can Look After Your Pet!
④ The Best Time to Use Pet Sitter Finder
⑤ How to Check the Reviews about Pet Sitters

출제율 95%

20 위 글의 밑줄 친 ⓑwhenever와 바꿔 쓸 수 있는 말을 고르시오.

① while ② every time
③ before long ④ the moment
⑤ as soon as

출제율 100%

21 According to the passage, which is NOT true?

① Pet Sitter Finder is the perfect app for pet lovers and pet owners.
② Pet Sitter Finder helps pet owners find reliable people to look after their pets.
③ The pet owner tests the pet sitters or dog walkers and chooses the best person.
④ George uses this app whenever he's going out of town.
⑤ George has some concerns about his personal information.

서술형 실전문제

[01~03] 다음 대화를 읽고 물음에 답하시오.

Sujin: What should we sell at the flea market next month?

Tom: Before we choose anything to sell, I think we need to do some market research.

Sujin: Market research? Why do we need that?

Tom: Because it helps us find out what items are popular these days.

Sujin: I see. Then we can decide what to sell at the market.

Tom: That's right. It will also help us set reasonable prices for our items.

Sujin: Cool. Is there anything else we should do?

Tom: Oh, don't forget to register our names by this Friday.

Sujin: Right. Thanks for reminding me.

01 What does Tom want to do to find out popular items these days?

➡ _____

02 What should Sujin remember to do?

➡ _____

_____

03 When is the flea market going to be held?

➡ _____

04 다음 〈보기〉에 주어진 단어의 조합들을 한 번씩만 사용해서 글의 흐름에 알맞게 빈칸을 채워 넣으시오. (필요시 변형할 것)

보기
soon good, hard good, small short, old–wise, few–happy

(1) The _____ the young man grew, the _____ he became.

(2) The _____ the size of the video is, the _____ it will take to post it.

(3) The _____ she finishes the final report, the _____ position she can hold in the negotiation.

(4) The _____ you study, the _____ grade you will get.

(5) The _____ classes there are right after mid term exam, the _____ the students feel.

05 다음 밑줄 친 부분에서 어법상 어색한 것을 고쳐 다시 쓰시오.

(1) <u>Having not a car</u>, Ms. Ivy couldn't take her grandson to the hospital.

➡ _____

(2) <u>We frankly speaking</u>, the prime minister of Japan doesn't look good.

➡ _____

(3) <u>Having snowed the day before</u>, the road were icy.

➡ _____

(4) <u>A little being tired</u>, Susie came down the stairs and took some rest.

➡ _____

(5) <u>Found the purse Jenny had lost</u>, he called her to come back quickly.

➡ _____

[06~08] 다음 글을 읽고 물음에 답하시오.

I can look after your pet!

Pet Sitter Finder is the perfect app for pet lovers and pet owners. It helps pet owners find reliable people to look after their pets. When a pet owner is looking for pet sitters, he or she uploads a post. Pet sitters or dog walkers can then send messages to the owner. The owner checks ⓐtheir reviews and chooses the best person.

George: November 12, 2019

I use this app whenever I'm going out of town. I have some concerns about my personal information though. ⓑ만약 다른 사람들이 제 전화번호를 다른 목적으로 사용하면 어쩌죠?

06 위 글의 밑줄 친 ⓐtheir가 가리키는 것을 본문에서 찾아 쓰시오.

➡ _____

07 위 글의 밑줄 친 ⓑ의 우리말에 맞게 한 단어를 보충하여, 주어진 어휘를 알맞게 배열하시오.

> other / use / what / phone number / purposes / people / for / my

➡ _____

08 (1) What's the advantage of 'Pet Sitter Finder'? (2) What's the disadvantage of 'Pet Sitter Finder'? Fill in the blanks (A) and (B) with suitable words.

> The advantage of 'Pet Sitter Finder' is that it helps pet owners find reliable people to (A)_____ _____ _____ _____ and the disadvantage of 'Pet Sitter Finder' is that there can be some concerns about the (B)_____ _____.

[09~10] 다음 글을 읽고 물음에 답하시오.

Borrow from your neighbors!

Ask Your Neighbors helps people easily (A)[find / finding] items that they can borrow from others. First, users (B)[download / upload] the app and search for another user that has the item they need. Then they pick up the item and return it later.

Jasmine: December 12, 2019

I asked for a board game and got one in less than 30 minutes. I love saving money by borrowing things that I don't often need. Also, I think it's environmentally friendly. The fewer products we buy, the more resources we (C)[save / waste].

09 위 글의 괄호 (A)~(C)에서 문맥이나 어법상 알맞은 낱말을 골라 쓰시오.

➡ (A) _____ (B) _____ (C) _____

10 본문의 내용과 일치하도록 다음 빈칸 (A)와 (B)에 알맞은 단어를 쓰시오.

> People can easily find what they can (A)_____ from others thanks to the (B)_____, Ask Your Neighbors.

01 다음 대화를 읽고 대화의 내용과 일치하도록 빈칸을 완성하시오.

> Suji: Which do you prefer, the Special Sandwich or the Classic Sandwich?
>
> Brian: Well, the Special Sandwich is the healthier choice. It's made with lots of fresh vegetables and other healthy ingredients.
>
> Suji: But it's much more expensive than the Classic Sandwich.
>
> Brian: I know, but I prefer the Special Sandwich to the Classic Sandwich. Eating healthy is important to me.
>
> Suji: I prefer the cheaper one. I'll spend my money on books instead.
>
> Brian: I guess our spending habits are different.

> Brian and Suji talked about their preferred sandwiches. Brian liked (A)_____ more than (B)_____, because (C)_____ is important to him. On the other hand, Suji chose the (D)_____ one, the Classic Sandwich. She wanted to spend her money on (E)_____ instead. Thus, they found that they had different (F)_____ habits.

02 다음 표의 동사, 형용사/부사, 명사 등에 나온 단어들을 각각 1개 이상 조합하여, 〈보기〉와 같이 'The+비교급 ~, the+비교급 …'을 이용한 문장을 3개 이상 만드시오. (비교급 어형 변화 가능)

Verb	Adjective/Adverb	Noun
• get • smile • study • go • have • save • see • walk • become	• many / much • good / bad / well / ill • happy / angry • often / frequent • fast / slow • few / little • cold / hot • old / young / new • rich / healthy	• people / they / we • I / you / she / he / it • student / teacher • baby / boy / girl • car / train / boat • money / body • radio / TV / movie

> 보기
>
> The fewer people want, the happier they will get.
>
> The faster the girl walks, the harder it is for her to breathe.

(1) _____

(2) _____

(3) _____

단원별 모의고사

01 다음 우리말에 맞게 빈칸에 알맞은 말을 쓰시오.

(1) 이 앱을 다운로드하는 방법을 아세요?

➡ Do you know how to _____ this app?

(2) 물은 우리의 가장 중요한 천연자원 중 하나이다.

➡ Water is one of our most important _____ _____.

(3) 나는 그 책에 대한 부정적인 서평을 읽었다.

➡ I read some _____ _____ of that book.

(4) 너는 그 단어의 정확한 의미를 알아야 한다.

➡ You need to know the _____ _____ of the word.

02 다음 문장의 빈칸에 들어갈 말을 〈보기〉에서 골라 쓰시오.

┌─ 보기 ┤
personal / provide / owner / reliable / concerns
└─

(1) We think she is the _____ of that car.

(2) Billy's car repair shop is _____.

(3) You seem to have some _____.

(4) I try not to give out my _____ information.

(5) The company will _____ some snacks at the meeting.

03 다음 주어진 우리말과 일치하도록 주어진 어구를 <u>모두</u> 배열하여 영작하시오.

(1) 내일 비가 오면 어쩌지? (tomorrow / if / it / rains / what)

➡ _____

(2) 내가 인터넷에서 요리법을 찾아볼게. (search / I'll / the Internet / the recipe / on / for)

➡ _____

(3) 어떻게 다른 아이들에게 메시지를 보낼 수 있나요? (we / how / can / to / children / other / send / messages)

➡ _____

[04~05] 다음 대화를 읽고 물음에 답하시오.

Judy: I think my hair is too curly. I want to straighten my hair. (A)

Gina: Sure. I know two places, Styles Studio and Hair Castle. (B)

Judy: Is there any difference between the two? (C)

Gina: Well, Styles Studio provides free treatment to keep your hair healthy. (D)

Judy: That's great. What about Hair Castle?

Gina: Hair Castle doesn't provide treatment for free, but they give student discounts. (E)

Judy: Okay. Which do you prefer?

Gina: I prefer Styles Studio to Hair Castle. It's important for me to get hair treatment regularly.

04 위 대화의 (A)~(E) 중에서 주어진 문장이 들어가기에 적절한 곳은?

┌────────────────────────────┐
│ Can you recommend a good place? │
└────────────────────────────┘

① (A) ② (B) ③ (C) ④ (D) ⑤ (E)

05 위 대화를 읽고 대답할 수 <u>없는</u> 것은?

① Why does Judy want to straighten her hair?

② Where does Gina recommend to Judy?

③ Which place does Judy prefer, Styles Studio or Hair Castle?

④ Where can Judy get student discounts?

⑤ Where does Gina can get treatment for free?

[06~07] 다음 대화를 읽고 물음에 답하시오.

Jack: I'm going to get a refund for these clothes this evening. I found I have similar ones.

Mom: Okay. (A)<u>Don't forget to bring your receipt.</u> Last time you couldn't get a refund because you didn't bring it.

Jack: Okay, Mom. I won't forget it this time.

06 위 대화의 밑줄 친 (A)와 바꾸어 쓸 수 있는 것을 <u>모두</u> 고르시오.

① Be sure to bring your receipt.
② Be careful not to bring your receipt.
③ Remember to bring your receipt.
④ You don't have to bring your receipt.
⑤ I'm not sure if you bring your receipt.

07 위 대화의 내용과 일치하지 <u>않는</u> 것은?

① Jack은 오늘 저녁에 옷을 환불하려고 한다.
② Jack은 환불하려는 옷들과 비슷한 옷들을 갖고 있다.
③ 엄마는 영수증 갖고 갈 것을 Jack에게 상기시키고 있다.
④ 지난번에 Jack은 영수증을 가지고 가지 않아 환불을 못 받았다.
⑤ Jack은 환불하는 것을 잊지 않을 것이다.

[08~10] 다음 대화를 읽고 물음에 답하시오.

Suji: Which do you prefer, the Special Sandwich or the Classic Sandwich?

Brian: Well, the Special Sandwich is the healthier choice. It's made with lots of fresh vegetable and other healthy ingredients.

Suji: But it's much more expensive than the Classic Sandwich.

Brian: I know, but I prefer the Special Sandwich (A)[to / than] the Classic Sandwich. (B)[Eat / Eating] healthy is important to me.

Suji: I prefer the cheaper one. I'll spend my money on books instead.

Brian: I guess our spending habits (C)[is / are] different.

08 위 대화에서 다음 영영풀이가 나타내는 말을 찾아 쓰시오.

> one of the things from which something is made, especially one of the foods that are used together to make a particular dish

➡ _____

09 위 대화의 (A)~(C)에 들어갈 말이 바르게 짝지어진 것은?

	(A)	(B)	(C)
①	to	Eat	is
②	to	Eating	are
③	to	Eating	is
④	than	Eating	are
⑤	than	Eat	is

10 위 대화를 읽고 대답할 수 <u>없는</u> 것은?

① Which sandwich does Brian prefer?
② What is the Special Sandwich made with?
③ Which sandwich is cheaper, the Special Sandwich or the Classic Sandwich?
④ What does Suji want to spend more money on?
⑤ Why is eating healthy important to Brian?

11 다음 중 어법상 옳지 <u>않은</u> 문장을 <u>모두</u> 고르면?

① Born in America, he can speak fluently.

② Weather permitting, I'll start tomorrow.

③ There being no public transportation service that night, the people had to walk their way home.

④ Worked hard to hand in the paper in time, Thomas fell asleep.

⑤ Being looked much prettier than before, the flowers are in bloom.

12 다음 주어진 문장을 분사구문으로 만들 때 가장 적절한 것은?

> When a pet owner is looking for pet sitters, he or she should upload a post.

① A pet owner looking for pet sitters, he or she should upload a post.

② Looking for pet sitters, a pet owner should upload a post.

③ When a pet owner looking for pet sitters, he or she should upload a post.

④ Looking a pet owner for pet sitters, he or she should upload a post.

⑤ Having looked for pet sitters, a pet owner should upload a post.

13 다음 중 주어진 문장과 같은 의미로 쓰인 것을 고르시오.

> The deeper we go down into the earth, the hotter it becomes.

① If we keep going down into the earth, it becomes hotter.

② As we go down into the earth, we should feel hotter.

③ Since we go down into the earth, the climate becomes hotter.

④ Though we go down into the earth, it becomes hotter.

⑤ While the air goes down into the earth, we become hotter.

14 다음 각 문장의 밑줄 친 분사구문을 부사절로 바꿀 때 어법상 어색한 것은?

① <u>Borrowing a tent,</u> we can find someone to take care of our dog through the mobile sharing service.
→ While we're borrowing a tent,

② <u>It being so cold,</u> Jordan couldn't go out to swim and play on the beach.
→ Although it was so cold,

③ <u>There being nothing to eat,</u> the young couple moved to another restaurant.
→ Since there was nothing to eat,

④ <u>Finishing the final line of the paper,</u> the professor went out for a walk.
→ After she finished the final line of the paper,

⑤ <u>Carefully checked by our service staff,</u> the condition of the product you are borrowing must be the best.
→ As it is carefully checked by our service staff,

15 다음 각 문장의 밑줄 친 부사절을 분사구문으로 바꾼 것 중 옳은 것은?

① <u>While Samantha was eating a beef sandwich,</u> her little sisters fell asleep.
→ Eating a beef sandwich,

② <u>As Ann went to bed earlier yesterday,</u> she woke up at 4 this morning.
→ Ann going to bed earlier yesterday,

③ When the towers are seen from outer space, they will look like monsters.

→ Seen from outer space,

④ If we put a coin next to its hand, the toy cat will take it away.

→ Putting a coin next to its hand,

⑤ When you borrow things more often, you can save not only some money but also some resources.

→ You borrowing things more often,

16 다음 우리말을 주어진 〈조건〉에 맞게 영작하시오.

┤ 조건 ├

1. 'the 비교급 ~, the 비교급 …' 구문을 사용할 것.
2. 주어와 시제에 유의하고, 괄호 안의 어구를 활용할 것. (내용과 어법에 맞게 변형 가능함.)
3. 글자 수 조건에 맞게 영작할 것.

(1) 더 많은 사람들이 공유 경제를 이해할수록, 더 적은 자원이 지구에서 사용될 것이다. (many, few, will, the sharing economy, understand, use, on Earth, 15 단어)

➡ _____

_____

(2) 비가 더 많이 내릴수록, 그녀는 기분이 더 즐거워졌다. (please, much, it, feel, 9 단어)

➡ _____

_____

(3) 그 가수의 인기가 더 많아질수록, 콘서트는 관객들로 더 붐비게 될 것이다. (the singer, popular, become, crowd, the concert, be, 13 단어)

➡ _____

_____

[17~18] 다음 글을 읽고 물음에 답하시오.

Jasmine: December 12, 2019

I asked for a board game and got one in less than 30 minutes. I love saving money by borrowing things that I don't often need. Also, I think ⓐit's environmentally friendly. ⓑ우리가 제품들을 더 적게 구매할수록, 우리는 더 많은 자원들을 아끼는 거예요.

17 위 글의 밑줄 친 ⓐit이 가리키는 것을 본문에서 찾아 쓰시오.

➡ _____

18 위 글의 밑줄 친 ⓑ의 우리말에 맞게 주어진 어휘를 알맞게 배열하시오.

we / more / products / the / save / we / fewer / resources / buy / the / , /

➡ _____

_____

[19~20] 다음 글을 읽고 물음에 답하시오.

Cassandra: March 7, 2020

Seeing a lot of positive reviews, I decided to borrow a bike helmet. When I got it, _____ⓐ_____, it was broken. I was so upset!

Ask Your Neighbors: March 9, 2020

We're sorry that you had such a negative experience. ⓑTo fix this issue, we are asking lenders to update the pictures of their items regularly. This will let other users know the exact condition of the product.

19 위 글의 빈칸 ⓐ에 들어갈 알맞은 말을 고르시오.

① for example   ② therefore
③ that is   ④ however
⑤ in addition

20 아래 〈보기〉에서 위 글의 밑줄 친 ⓑTo fix와 to부정사의 용법이 같은 것의 개수를 고르시오.

보기
① Do you have something interesting to read?
② Everybody was surprised to see him.
③ I got up early to get ready for the game.
④ It is important to read a lot of books.
⑤ He grew up to be a pianist.

① 1개   ② 2개   ③ 3개   ④ 4개   ⑤ 5개

[21~22] 다음 글을 읽고 물음에 답하시오.

I can look after your pet!

(①) Pet Sitter Finder is the perfect app for pet lovers and pet owners. (②) It helps pet owners find reliable people to look after their pets. (③) When a pet owner is looking for pet sitters, he or she ___ⓐ___ s a post. (④) The owner checks their reviews and chooses the best person. (⑤)

21 주어진 영영풀이를 참고하여 빈칸 ⓐ에 철자 u로 시작하는 단어를 쓰시오.

to transfer data to your computer or from your computer to another computer

➡ _____

22 위 글의 흐름으로 보아, 주어진 문장이 들어가기에 가장 적절한 곳은?

Pet sitters or dog walkers can then send messages to the owner.

①   ②   ③   ④   ⑤

[23~24] 다음 글을 읽고 물음에 답하시오.

Pet Sitter Finder: November 14, 2019
 We're aware of this issue. We're now developing a system that allows users to communicate freely without showing their personal information.

Samantha: February 22, 2020
 Animals aren't allowed in my apartment, so I don't have any pets. However, by using Pet Sitter Finder, I can experience the joy of walking a dog.

23 Why does Samantha have no pets? Answer in English beginning with "Because".

➡ _____

24 According to the passage, which is NOT true?

① Pet Sitter Finder is aware of this issue.
② Pet Sitter Finder is now developing a system that allows users to communicate freely without showing their personal information.
③ Animals aren't allowed in Samantha's apartment.
④ Samantha uses Pet Sitter Finder.
⑤ It's impossible for Samantha to walk a dog.

[25~27] 다음 글을 읽고 물음에 답하시오.

> Son: What great apps! We can borrow a tent and find someone to take care of our dog.
>
> Dad: That's right. (①) These kinds of services are part of the "sharing economy." (②) People can share their items ⓐ others and provide services to them ⓑ a small fee or for free.
>
> Son: (③) Some people left negative reviews about the services.
>
> Dad: (④) Well, I think ⓒthe more people use the services, the more they will improve. (⑤)

25 위 글의 빈칸 ⓐ와 ⓑ에 들어갈 전치사가 바르게 짝지어진 것은?

	ⓐ	ⓑ			ⓐ	ⓑ
①	for	– at		②	with	– to
③	in	– for		④	for	– to
⑤	with	– at				

26 위 글의 흐름으로 보아, 주어진 문장이 들어가기에 가장 적절한 곳은?

> But these services do have some weaknesses.

①   ②   ③   ④   ⑤

27 위 글의 밑줄 친 ⓒ를 접속사 as를 사용하여 고칠 때, 빈칸에 들어갈 알맞은 말을 쓰시오.

➡ as people use the services _____, they will improve _____.

[28~30] 다음 글을 읽고 물음에 답하시오.

> **I Can Share My Jump Rope with You!**
>
> Here is a jump rope that I can share. It's not new, but it's in good condition. You can borrow it for ⓐup to two days.
>
> There are two rules:
>
> ❶ You can borrow it once a week.
>
> ❷ You must pay for the item if you lose or break it.
>
> If you are willing to follow the rules above, feel free ⓑ contact me! I will happily share it with you.

28 위 글의 밑줄 친 ⓐup to와 같은 의미로 쓰인 것을 고르시오.

① He is up to the job.
② It's up to you.
③ What are you up to?
④ I can take up to four people in my car.
⑤ Her latest book isn't up to her usual standard.

29 위 글의 빈칸 ⓑ에 알맞은 말을 쓰시오.

➡ _____

30 위 글의 줄넘기를 빌릴 때의 두 가지 규칙을 우리말로 쓰시오.

➡ (1) _____
   (2) _____

Lesson 7

Future Changes through Technology

 의사소통 기능

- 설명 요청하기
  Could you explain how it works?

- 가능성 정도 표현하기
  It is likely that we will have to change how we get our food.

 언어 형식

- 가정법 과거
  Cooking and cleaning **would be** easier **if** you **had** one.

- '목적'을 나타내는 so that 구문
  It can navigate roads for you **so that** you can relax and enjoy the ride.

Words & Expressions

Key Words

- **artificial**[ɑ̀ːrtəfíʃəl] 형 인공적인, 인위적인
- **awesome**[ɔ́ːsəm] 형 굉장한, 아주 멋진
- **bright**[brait] 형 밝은, 희망적인
- **cashier**[kæʃíər] 명 출납원
- **common**[kámən] 형 흔한
- **convenient**[kənvíːnjənt] 형 편리한
- **delivery**[dilívəri] 명 배달, 전달
- **destination**[dèstənéiʃən] 명 목적지, 도착지
- **difference**[dífərəns] 명 차이, 차이점
- **disaster**[dizǽstər] 명 재해, 참사, 재난
- **ensure**[inʃúər] 동 보장하다
- **equip**[ikwíp] 동 ~에 (필요한 것을) 갖추다
- **escape**[iskéip] 동 탈출하다, 달아나다, 벗어나다
- **factory**[fǽktəri] 명 공장
- **forecast**[fɔ́ːrkæst] 명 예측, 예보
- **human**[hjúːmən] 명 인간 형 인간의
- **intelligence**[intélədʒəns] 명 지능, 정보
- **invention**[invénʃən] 명 발명, 발명품
- **lab**[læb] 명 과학 실험실 (= laboratory)
- **likely**[láikli] 형 있음직한, 가능하다고 생각되는, ~할 것 같은
- **navigate**[nǽvəgèit] 동 길을 찾다, 항해하다
- **nutrient**[njúːtriənt] 명 영양소, 영양분
- **outer**[áutər] 형 외부의, 바깥쪽의
- **perceive**[pərsíːv] 동 인지하다, 감지하다

- **perform**[pərfɔ́ːrm] 동 공연하다, 실행하다
- **possible**[pásəbl] 형 가능한
- **praise**[preiz] 명 칭찬
- **present**[préznt] 형 현재의, 존재하는
- **program**[próugræm] 동 프로그램을 짜다
- **reality**[riǽləti] 명 현실
- **recipe**[résəpi] 명 요리법
- **recognize**[rékəgnàiz] 동 인식하다
- **resource**[ríːsɔːrs] 명 자원, 재원
- **route**[ruːt] 명 길, 경로
- **safety**[séifti] 명 안전, 안전한 곳
- **self-driving**[sélfdráiviŋ] 형 자율 주행하는
- **sense**[sens] 동 감지하다
- **sensor**[sénsər] 명 센서, 감지기
- **signal**[sígnəl] 명 신호
- **site**[sait] 명 위치, 장소, 용지, 부지, 현장
- **solution**[səlúːʃən] 명 해법, 해답, 해결책
- **speech**[spiːtʃ] 명 연설, 담화, 언어 능력
- **survivor**[sərváivər] 명 생존자, 살아남은 사람
- **swarm**[swɔːrm] 명 떼, 군중, 벌 떼
- **task**[tæsk] 명 일, 과제, 과업
- **technology**[teknálədʒi] 명 기술, 기계
- **threat**[θret] 명 위협, 협박

Key Expressions

- **a variety of** 다양한
- **act like** ~처럼 행동하다
- **around the world** 세계 곳곳의
- **as a group** 집단으로
- **be able to** ~할 수 있다
- **deal with** 처리하다, 다루다
- **find solutions** 해결책을 찾다
- **go into** ~에 들어가다
- **keep track of** ~의 자국을 뒤밟다

- **look toward** 앞날을 생각하다
- **make decisions** 결정을 하다
- **search and rescue** 수색 구조
- **so that ~** ~하기 위하여
- **such as** ~와 같은
- **throughout the day** 하루 종일
- **wait in line** 줄을 서서 기다리다
- **with the help of** ~의 도움으로
- **work on** ~에 노력을 들이다, 애쓰다

Word Power

※ 서로 비슷한 뜻을 가진 어휘

- □ **a variety of** ~ 다양한 : **various** 다양한
- □ **disaster** 재해, 참사, 재난 : **catastrophe** 재난, 재앙
- □ **go into** ~에 들어가다 : **enter** 들어가다
- □ **praise** 칭찬 : **compliment** 칭찬
- □ **solution** 해법, 해답 : **answer** 답, 해답

- □ **bright** 밝은, 희망적인 : **promising** 조짐이 좋은, 유망한
- □ **escape** 탈출하다, 달아나다, 벗어나다 : **flee** 도망치다, 피하다
- □ **perceive** 인지하다 : **recognize** 인지하다
- □ **signal** 신호 : **sign** 신호, 암호
- □ **task** 일, 과제, 과업 : **job** 과제, 직무, 역할

※ 서로 반대의 뜻을 가진 어휘

- □ **bright** 밝은, 희망적인 ↔ **dark** 어두운, 암울한
- □ **convenient** 편리한 ↔ **inconvenient** 불편한
- □ **possible** 가능한 ↔ **impossible** 불가능한
- □ **present** 현재의, 존재하는 ↔ **absent** 부재의

- □ **common** 흔한 ↔ **uncommon** 흔하지 않은
- □ **difference** 차이, 차이점 ↔ **similarity** 유사, 유사성
- □ **praise** 칭찬 ↔ **criticism** 비평, 비난
- □ **recognize** 인식하다 ↔ **ignore** 무시하다, 모른 체하다

English Dictionary

- □ **artificial** 인공적인, 인위적인
  → made by humans 인간에 의해 만들어진
- □ **convenient** 편리한, 간편한
  → able to be used easily 쉽게 사용될 수 있는
- □ **deal with** 처리하다, 다루다
  → to handle or solve something such as a problem 문제 같은 것을 다루거나 해결하다
- □ **disaster** 참사, 재난, 재해
  → an unfortunate event that damages a large area and may harm many people 큰 지역에 손상을 가해 많은 사람들에게 해를 입힐 수도 있는 불행한 사건
- □ **escape** 탈출하다, 달아나다, 벗어나다
  → to get free 자유롭게 되다
- □ **navigate** 길을 찾다, 항해하다
  → to make one's way through an area 한 지역의 길을 찾다
- □ **perceive** 인지하다, 감지하다
  → to notice something with the senses 감각으로 어떤 것을 알아채다
- □ **perform** 공연하다, 해 보이다; 실행[수행]하다
  → to complete an action or activity 행동이나 행위를 완결하다
- □ **route** 경로
  → a way to go from one place to another 한곳에서 다른 곳으로 가는 길
- □ **safety** 안전
  → the state of being safe from harm or danger 피해나 위험으로부터 안전한 상태
- □ **sense** 감지하다
  → to be aware of something without seeing or hearing it 보거나 듣지 않고도 어떤 것을 알다
- □ **solution** 해법, 해답
  → the answer to a problem 어떤 문제에 대한 답
- □ **survivor** 생존자
  → a person who remains alive 살아남은 사람
- □ **swarm** 떼, 군중
  → a large number of living things 많은 살아 있는 것들
- □ **threat** 협박, 위협
  → a risk or danger 위험이나 우려

서답형

01 다음 짝지어진 단어의 관계가 같도록 빈칸에 알맞은 말을 주어진 철자로 시작하여 쓰시오.

> bright : dark = c_____ : praise

02 다음 영영풀이가 가리키는 것을 고르시오.

> able to be used easily

① convenient   ② artificial
③ disaster   ④ nutrient
⑤ swarm

중요

03 다음 중 밑줄 친 부분의 뜻풀이가 바르지 <u>않은</u> 것은?

① The light bulb was a great <u>invention</u>. (발명품)
② It changes your voice into an electrical <u>signal</u>. (사인)
③ Although my sister was hiding in her room, I was able to sense her <u>presence</u>. (존재)
④ He finally <u>escaped</u> from his enemies. (도망쳤다)
⑤ It is <u>possible</u> to see the whole city from this roof. (가능한)

서답형

04 다음 우리말에 맞게 빈칸에 알맞은 말을 주어진 철자로 시작하여 쓰시오.

(1) 모든 차는 에어백을 갖추고 있다.
➡ Every car is e_____ with an airbag.
(2) 나는 한국의 역사적인 장소를 방문하는 것을 좋아한다.
➡ I like visiting historical s_____ in Korea.

(3) 그 아기는 자라면서 사물을 정확히 인지하기 시작했다.
➡ As the baby grew, he started to p_____ objects clearly.

서답형

05 다음 문장의 빈칸에 들어갈 말을 〈보기〉에서 골라 쓰시오.

> ┤ 보기 ├
> deal with / keep track of / destination / be used in / forecast

(1) Parents can _____ their children using smartphones.
(2) This tool can _____ a variety of ways.
(3) The weather _____ says there will be more snow.
(4) The _____ of our trip is Washington, D.C.
(5) You have to _____ this problem first.

중요

06 다음 주어진 문장의 밑줄 친 present와 같은 의미로 쓰인 것은?

> How do you read the <u>present</u> situation?

① 200 people were <u>present</u> at the meeting.
② Those <u>present</u> were in favour of change.
③ The local MP will start the race and <u>present</u> the prizes.
④ There's no end in sight to the <u>present</u> crisis.
⑤ She chose the <u>present</u> with loving care.

01 다음 짝지어진 단어의 관계가 같도록 빈칸에 알맞은 말을 주어진 철자로 시작하여 쓰시오.

go into : enter = p_____ : recognize

02 다음 우리말에 맞게 빈칸에 알맞은 말을 쓰시오.

(1) 그 기원에 관해서는 여러 가지 설이 있다.
➡ There are _____ _____ _____
views about its origin.

(2) 삼촌의 도움으로 그는 암호를 알아낸다.
➡ _____ _____ _____
his uncle, he figures out the password.

(3) 이것과 같은 기회가 매일 찾아오는 것은 아니었다.
➡ Opportunities _____ _____ this
did not come every day.

03 다음 우리말에 맞게 주어진 어구를 사용하여 영작하시오.

(1) 이 단어는 일상 대화에서 흔히 쓰는 말이 아니다. (casual conversation)
➡ _____
_____

(2) 전자 레인지는 편리한 요리 기구이다. (a microwave, cooking device)
➡ _____
_____

(3) 어느 길로 가는 것이 가장 좋을까? (take, route)
➡ _____
_____

04 다음 제시된 의미에 맞는 단어를 주어진 철자로 시작하여 빈칸에 쓰고, 알맞은 것을 골라 문장을 완성하시오.

- s_____ : to be aware of something without seeing or hearing it
- n_____ : to make one's way through an area
- n_____ : a chemical or food that provides what is needed to live and grow

(1) Travelers usually _____ by the stars in the old days.

(2) She _____ someone watching her at that time.

(3) Vitamins are essential _____ for us.

05 다음 우리말과 일치하도록 주어진 어구를 바르게 배열하시오.

(1) 이 개들은 그들의 높은 지능으로 잘 알려져 있다.
(their / these dogs / intelligence / known / high / are / for)
➡ _____
_____

(2) 홍수와 지진과 같은 자연 재해는 매년 수천 명의 사람에게 피해를 입힌다.
(of / natural / every / disasters / affect / such / as / floods / and / earthquakes / thousands / people / year)
➡ _____
_____

Conksation

1 설명 요청하기

Could you explain how it works? 이게 어떻게 작동하는 건지 설명해 줄 수 있니?

- 어떤 사실이나 대상에 대해 설명해 달라고 요청할 때, 'Can you explain ~?'이라는 표현을 쓸 수 있다. 이와 같은 표현으로는 'Can you tell me how to ~?', 'Can you explain how to ~?' 등이 있다. 이때, explain 또는 tell 뒤에는 보통 의문사절이나 '의문사+to 동사원형'을 써서 구체적으로 설명을 요청하는 내용을 제시한다. Can 대신에 Could를 쓰면 보다 정중한 표현이 된다.

- 상대방에게 설명을 요청 받았을 때 다음과 같이 요청을 수락한다는 의사를 표현할 수 있다.

Yes. / Okay. / Sure. / All right. / No problem. / Of course.

설명 요청하기

- Do you know how to ~? ~하는 법을 아니?
- Can[Could] you tell me how to ~? ~하는 법을 말해 주시겠어요?
- Can[Could] you explain how to ~? ~하는 법을 설명해 주시겠어요?
- What do you mean by A? A가 무슨 의미이죠?
- Can[Could] you tell me what A means? A가 무슨 의미인지 말해 줄래요?
- I'd like to know what A means. A가 무슨 의미인지 알고 싶어요.

핵심 Check

1. 다음 대화에서 밑줄 친 부분과 바꿔 쓸 수 <u>없는</u> 표현은?

A: Hey, have you played this game? It's really interesting. The developers used AI technology.

B: No, I haven't. <u>Can you explain in more detail?</u>

A: Sure. The AI characters in the game learn from what human players do and develop their skills.

B: Oh, that's very smart. I'd like to give it a try.

① Can you tell me how it works in more detail?
② Could you tell me how to play it in more detail?
③ Do you know how to learn it in more detail?
④ Could you explain how to play it in more detail?
⑤ Can you explain how it works in more detail?

② 가능성 정도 표현하기

It is likely that we will have to change how we get our food.
우리는 식량을 얻는 방법을 바꾸어야 할 가능성이 있다.

■ 'It's likely that ~'은 자신이 생각하는 어떤 일에 대한 가능성의 정도를 나타낼 때 사용하는 표현이다. It은 가주어이고 접속사 that이 이끄는 명사절이 진주어 역할을 한다. 보통 절 안에는 미래를 나타내는 조동사를 쓰는 경우가 많다.

• It's likely that he will cancel his order. 그가 주문을 취소할 가능성이 있습니다.

■ 'It is possible to ~', '~ can ~', 'It is probable that ~' 등으로 가능성의 정도를 나타낼 수도 있다.

• It is possible to get there by bus. 버스로 거기에 가는 것이 가능하다.

• Dogs can be trained to obey orders. 개는 명령을 따르도록 훈련시킬 수가 있다.

• It is probable that she will come tomorrow. 그녀가 내일 올 것으로 예상된다.

■ 미래를 나타내는 조동사로는 대표적으로 will과 'be going to'가 있다. 이때, 'be going to'는 미래에 어떤 일이 일어날 것임을 확신할 때 쓰는 반면, will은 어떤 일이 일어날 확신보다는 가능성이 있을 때 쓰는 표현이다. 따라서 가능성을 나타내는 'It's likely that ~' 구문에서는 조동사 will을 쓰는 것이 보다 적절하다.

• It's likely that you or someone you love will suffer from high blood pressure. 당신 또는 사랑하는 사람이 고혈압으로 고생할 수 있습니다.

핵심 Check

2. 다음 밑줄 친 우리말을 likely를 이용해 영작하시오.

M: As climate change is going to make farming harder, there may not be enough resources for the increasing number of people on Earth. For this reason, 우리가 식량을 얻기 위한 방식을 바꿔야 할 수도 있을 것이다. For example, we won't kill animals for food. Instead, meat will be grown in a lab using animal cells. This will require less land, water, and other resources.

➡ _____

Listen & Talk 1 A

G: Hey, have you heard of a smart umbrella?

B: No, I haven't. ❶Could you explain ❷what it is?

G: Sure. It's an umbrella ❸that gives you the weather forecast for the day. ❹If it is going to rain, the umbrella makes a sound.

B: That's very convenient.

여: 있잖아, 스마트 우산에 대해 들어 본 적 있니?
남: 아니, 들어 본 적 없어. 그게 무엇인지 설명해 줄 수 있니?
여: 물론이지. 그것은 그날의 일기 예보를 알려주는 우산이야. 만약 비가 올 예정이면, 우산에서 소리가 나.
남: 그거 참 편리하구나.

❶ 설명을 요청하는 표현이다.　❷ what it is는 간접의문문으로 explain의 목적어이다.
❸ that은 주격 관계대명사이다.　❹ If는 조건절을 이끄는 접속사이다.

Check(√) True or False

(1) The boy has heard of a smart umbrella.　　　　T ☐ F ☐

(2) If it is going to rain, the smart umbrella makes a sound.　T ☐ F ☐

Listen & Talk 1 B

G: Look at these. They are the new inventions of the month!

B: They all ❶look great. What is the invention on the first page?

G: It's a new smart refrigerator. ❷It senses the items inside ❷it and suggests ❸recipes.

B: That sounds helpful.

G: It does. What do you think of this flying camera? I want to buy it.

B: A flying camera? ❹Could you explain how it works?

G: Of course. This machine flies to a destination ❺that we have already set. While it's flying, it can take pictures from 500 meters above the location.

B: That ❻sounds awesome. What do you want to take pictures of?

G: I want to take pictures of flying birds!

여: 이것들을 봐. 이달의 새로운 발명품들이야!
남: 모두 멋져 보인다. 첫 번째 쪽에 있는 발명품은 뭐지?
여: 그건 새로 나온 스마트 냉장고야. 이 냉장고는 냉장고 내부의 음식들을 감지해서 요리법을 제시해 줘.
남: 유용하겠다.
여: 맞아. 이 플라잉 카메라에 대해서는 어떻게 생각해? 나는 이 카메라를 사고 싶어.
남: 플라잉 카메라? 이게 어떻게 작동하는 건지 설명해 줄 수 있니?
여: 물론이지. 이 기기는 우리가 미리 설정해 둔 목적지로 날아가. 비행하는 동안 이 기기는 그 지점의 500미터 상공에서 사진을 찍을 수 있어.
남: 정말 멋지다. 너는 무슨 사진을 찍고 싶니?
여: 나는 날고 있는 새들의 사진을 찍고 싶어!

❶ look+형용사: ~해 보이다　❷ It[it]은 a new smart refrigerator를 가리킨다.　❸ recipe: 요리법
❹ 설명을 요청하는 표현으로 'Can you tell me how it works?'로 바꿔 쓸 수 있다.
❺ that은 목적격 관계대명사이다　❻ sound+형용사: ~하게 들리다

Check(√) True or False

(3) The new smart refrigerator senses the items inside it and suggests recipes.　T ☐ F ☐

(4) The boy wants to take pictures of flying birds with the flying camera.　T ☐ F ☐

Listen & Talk 1 C

B: What are you watching?
G: It's a show about a man ❶who lost one of his arms in an accident. Surprisingly, he can play the drums very well.
B: How can he play the drums with only one arm?
G: Actually he uses two arms. One is a robot arm ❷controlled by his brain.
B: That's awesome. ❸Could you explain in more detail?
G: Sure. First, he thinks ❹what he wants to do with his arm. Then those thoughts are turned into electronic signals. The signals travel from his brain to his robot arm and move ❺it.
B: That's amazing! I think this technology can help many people.

❶ who는 주격 관계대명사이다.
❷ controlled가 뒤에서 a robot arm을 수식하고 있다.
❸ 설명을 요청하는 표현이다. in more detail: 더 자세히
❹ what은 선행사를 포함하는 관계대명사로 '~하는 것'으로 해석한다.
❺ it은 his robot arm을 가리킨다.

Listen & Talk 2 A

G: ❶You know what? Scientists are ❷working on a project to send people to Mars.
B: ❸It is likely that we'll live in outer space in the near future.

❶ You know what?: 그거 아니?, 있잖아.
❷ work on: ~에 노력을 들이다, 애쓰다
❸ 'It's likely that ~'은 자신이 생각하는 어떤 일에 대한 가능성의 정도를 나타낼 때 사용하는 표현이다.

Listen & Talk 2 B

M: ❶As climate change is going to make farming harder, there may not be enough resources for the increasing number of people on Earth. ❷For this reason, ❸it is likely that we will have to change how we get our food. For example, we won't kill animals for food. Instead, meat will be grown in a ❹lab using animal cells. This will require less land, water, and other resources. Also, bugs ❺such as ants will become part of our daily meals. You might not want to eat them, but they are actually very ❻rich in nutrients!

❶ As는 이유를 나타내는 부사절을 이끌고 있다.
❷ For this reason: 이러한 이유로
❸ 가능성의 정도를 나타내는 표현이다.
❹ lab: 과학 실험실(= laboratory), cell: 세포
❺ such as: ~와 같은(= like)
❻ rich: 풍부한 nutrient: 영양소, 영양분

Listen & Talk 2 C

G: I had to wait in line at the store for almost twenty minutes.
B: That's too bad. Maybe in the future we'll never have to wait in line.
G: What do you mean?
B: I read about a store without cashiers. You take ❶what you want to buy and just walk out.
G: ❷That's it? How do you pay for it?
B: There are cameras and sensors in the store. They ❸keep track of the items you choose and send the information to an app on your smartphone.
G: Then the app pays for ❹them when you leave the store?
B: Exactly. ❺It's likely that these kinds of stores will be more common in the future.

❶ what은 선행사를 포함하는 관계대명사이다.
❷ That's it?: 그게 다야?
❸ keep track of: ~의 자국을 뒤밟다
❹ the items you choose를 가리킨다.
❺ 가능성의 정도를 나타내는 표현이다. 'It is possible to ~', 'It is probable that ~' 등으로 가능성의 정도를 나타낼 수도 있다.

Do It Yourself A

B: Hey, have you played this game? It's really exciting.
G: Yes, I ❶have. That game is pretty popular these days.
B: The developers used AI technology in ❷it. The game characters are equipped with AI.
G: Oh, really? ❸Could you explain in more detail?
B: Sure. The AI characters in the game learn from what human players do and develop their skills.
G: Oh! ❹That's why I sometimes felt like they already knew my moves!
B: They're very smart. ❺It is likely that the AI in games will get stronger and stronger.

❶ have는 대동사 역할을 하고 있다.
❷ it은 'That game'을 가리킨다.
❸ 설명을 요청하는 표현이다.
❹ That's why ~.: 그것이 ~한 이유이다.
❺ 가능성의 정도를 나타내는 표현이다.

다음 우리말과 일치하도록 빈칸에 알맞은 말을 쓰시오.

해석

Listen & Talk 1 A

G: Hey, have you _____ _____ a smart umbrella?

B: No, I haven't. _____ _____ _____ _____ _____
_____?

G: Sure. It's an umbrella _____ gives you the _____ _____
for the day. If it _____ _____ _____ rain, the umbrella
_____ a sound.

B: That's very _____.

여: 있잖아, 스마트 우산에 대해 들어 본 적 있니?

남: 아니, 들어 본 적 없어. 그게 무엇인지 설명해 줄 수 있니?

여: 물론이지. 그것은 그날의 일기 예보를 알려주는 우산이야. 만약 비가 올 예정이면, 우산에서 소리가 나.

남: 그거 참 편리하구나.

Listen & Talk 1 B

G: Look at these. They are the new _____ of the month!

B: They all look _____. What is the invention on the first page?

G: It's a new smart refrigerator. It _____ the items inside _____
and _____ recipes.

B: That sounds _____.

G: It _____. What do you _____ _____ this _____ camera?
I want to buy it.

B: A flying camera? Could you explain _____ _____ _____?

G: Of course. This machine flies to a destination _____ we have
already _____. _____ _____ _____, it can take pictures
from 500 meters above the location.

B: That sounds _____. _____ do you want to take pictures
_____?

G: I want to take pictures of _____ birds!

여: 이것들을 봐. 이달의 새로운 발명품들이야!

남: 모두 멋져 보인다. 첫 번째 쪽에 있는 발명품은 뭐지?

여: 이건 새로 나온 스마트 냉장고야. 이 냉장고는 냉장고 내부의 음식들을 감지해서 요리법을 제시해 줘.

남: 유용하겠다.

여: 맞아. 이 플라잉 카메라에 대해서는 어떻게 생각해? 나는 이 카메라가 사고 싶어.

남: 플라잉 카메라? 이게 어떻게 작동하는 건지 설명해 줄 수 있니?

여: 물론이지. 이 기기는 우리가 미리 설정해 둔 목적지로 날아가. 비행하는 동안 이 기기는 그 지점의 500미터 상공에서 사진을 찍을 수 있어.

남: 정말 멋지다. 너는 무슨 사진을 찍고 싶니?

여: 나는 날고 있는 새들의 사진을 찍고 싶어!

Listen & Talk 1 C

B: What are you watching?

G: It's a show about a man _____ lost _____ _____ his
_____ in an accident. Surprisingly, he can play _____ _____
very well.

B: _____ can he play the drums _____ only one arm?

G: Actually he uses two arms. One is a robot arm _____ by his brain.

B: That's awesome. Could you explain _____ more _____?

G: Sure. First, he thinks _____ he wants to do _____ his arm.
Then those thoughts _____ _____ _____ electronic signals.
The signals _____ from his brain to his robot arm and move it.

B: That's amazing! I think this _____ can help many people.

남: 무엇을 보고 있니?

여: 이건 사고로 한쪽 팔을 잃은 한 남자에 관한 프로야. 놀랍게도 그는 드럼을 매우 잘 쳐.

남: 그는 어떻게 한쪽 팔만으로 드럼을 칠 수 있는 거지?

여: 사실 그는 두 팔을 사용해. 한쪽 팔은 그의 뇌가 제어하는 로봇 팔이야.

남: 그거 정말 멋지다. 좀 더 구체적으로 설명해 줄 수 있니?

여: 물론이지. 먼저, 그는 자신의 팔로 하고 싶은 것을 생각해. 그런 다음 그 생각들이 전기 신호로 바뀌지. 그 신호들은 그의 뇌에서 로봇 팔로 이동해서 그 팔을 움직여.

남: 놀라운데! 이 기술이 많은 사람들에게 도움을 줄 수 있을 것 같아.

Listen & Talk 2 B

M: _____ climate change is going to make farming _____, there _____ _____ _____ enough resources for the _____ number of people on Earth. _____ _____ _____, _____ _____ _____ _____ we will have to change _____ _____ _____ our food. For example, we won't kill animals for food. _____, meat _____ _____ _____ in a lab _____ animal cells. This will require less land, water, and other resources. Also, bugs _____ _____ ants will become part of our daily meals. You might not want to eat them, but they are actually very _____ in _____!

Listen & Talk 2 C

G: I _____ _____ wait _____ _____ at the store for almost twenty minutes.

B: That's too bad. Maybe in the future _____ _____ _____ wait in line.

G: What _____ _____ _____?

B: I read about a store without cashiers. You take _____ you want to buy and just walk out.

G: That's it? _____ do you pay _____ it?

B: There are cameras and sensors in the store. They _____ _____ the items you choose and _____ _____ _____ to an app on your smartphone.

G: Then the app pays for _____ when you leave the store?

B: Exactly. _____ _____ _____ these kinds of stores will be more _____ in the future.

Do It Yourself A

B: Hey, have you played this game? It's really _____.

G: Yes, I _____. That game is pretty _____ these days.

B: The developers used AI technology in _____. The game characters _____ _____ _____ AI.

G: Oh, really? Could you _____ _____ _____ _____ _____?

B: Sure. The AI characters in the game learn from _____ _____ _____ and develop their skills.

G: Oh! That's _____ I sometimes _____ _____ they already knew my moves!

B: They're very smart. _____ _____ _____ _____ _____ the AI in games will get stronger and stronger.

해석

남: 기후 변화가 농업을 더 어렵게 만들 것이기 때문에, 지구상의 점점 더 늘어나는 사람들을 위한 자원이 충분하지 않게 될지도 모른다. 이러한 이유로, 우리는 식량을 얻는 방법을 바꾸어야 할 가능성이 높다. 예를 들어, 우리는 식량을 얻기 위해 동물을 죽이지 않게 될 것이다. 대신, 동물 세포를 이용하여 실험실에서 고기가 배양될 것이다. 이는 더 적은 땅과 물, 그리고 다른 자원들을 필요로 할 것이다. 또한, 개미와 같은 곤충들이 우리 끼니의 일부가 될 것이다. 여러분은 먹고 싶지 않을 수도 있지만, 사실 곤충들은 영양분이 매우 풍부하다!

여: 매장에서 거의 20분 동안 줄을 서서 기다려야 했어.
남: 그것 참 안됐다. 어쩌면 미래에는 줄을 서서 기다릴 필요가 전혀 없을지도 몰라.
여: 그게 무슨 말이야?
남: 계산원이 없는 매장에 관한 글을 읽었거든. 사고 싶은 것을 가지고 그냥 걸어나가면 돼.
여: 그게 다야? 지불은 어떻게 해?
남: 매장 내에 카메라와 감지기가 있어. 그것들이 네가 고른 물건들을 계속 파악하면서 그 정보를 네 스마트폰에 있는 앱으로 보내.
여: 그러면 네가 매장을 나갈 때 앱이 물건 값을 지불하는 거고?
남: 바로 그거야. 미래에는 이런 종류의 매장이 더 흔해질 것 같아.

남: 저기, 이 게임 해봤니? 이거 정말 흥미진진해.
여: 응, 해봤어. 그 게임은 요즘 꽤 인기가 있어.
남: 개발자들이 이 게임에 인공지능 기술을 사용했어. 게임 캐릭터들에 인공지능이 탑재되어 있지.
여: 아, 정말? 좀 더 구체적으로 설명해 줄 수 있니?
남: 물론이지. 게임 속 인공지능 캐릭터들은 인간 플레이어가 하는 행동을 통해 배우고 자신의 기술을 발전시켜.
여: 아! 그래서 이따금씩 캐릭터들이 이미 내 움직임을 알고 있는 것처럼 느껴졌던 거구나!
남: 그들은 매우 똑똑해. 게임 속 인공지능은 점점 더 강화될 가능성이 높아.

[01~02] 다음 대화를 읽고 물음에 답하시오.

G: Look at these. They are the new inventions of the month!
B: They all look great. (①) What is the invention on the first page?
G: It's a new smart refrigerator. (②)
B: That sounds helpful. (③)
G: It does. What do you think of this flying camera? I want to buy it.
B: A flying camera? (④) Could you explain how it works?
G: Of course. (⑤) This machine flies to a destination that we have already set. While it's flying, it can take pictures from 500 meters above the location.

01 위 대화의 (①)~(⑤) 중 다음 문장이 들어가기에 적절한 곳은?

> It senses the items inside it and suggests recipes.

①   ②   ③   ④   ⑤

02 위 대화의 내용과 일치하지 <u>않는</u> 것은?

① G는 새로 나온 스마트 냉장고에 대해 이미 알고 있다.
② 스마트 냉장고는 냉장고 내부의 음식들을 감지해서 요리법을 제시해 준다.
③ G는 플라잉 카메라를 사고 싶어한다.
④ B는 플라잉 카메라의 작동법을 알고 있었다.
⑤ 플라잉 카메라는 500미터 상공에서 사진을 찍을 수 있었다.

[03~04] 다음 대화를 읽고 물음에 답하시오.

G: Hey, have you heard of a smart umbrella?
B: No, I haven't. (A)Could you explain what it is?
G: Sure. It's an umbrella that gives you the weather forecast for the day. If it is going to rain, the umbrella makes a sound.
B: (B)That's very convenient.

03 위 대화의 밑줄 친 (A)를 tell을 이용하여 바꿔 쓰시오.

➡ _____

04 위 대화의 밑줄 친 (B)That이 가리키는 것을 우리말로 쓰시오.

➡ _____

서답형

01 다음 주어진 대화 사이의 (A)~(E)가 자연스럽게 이어지도록 순서대로 배열하시오.

> B: What are you watching?
>
> (A) Actually he uses two arms. One is a robot arm controlled by his brain.
>
> (B) How can he play the drums with only one arm?
>
> (C) It's a show about a man who lost one of his arms in an accident. Surprisingly, he can play the drums very well.
>
> (D) That's awesome. Could you explain in more detail?
>
> (E) Sure. First, he thinks what he wants to do with his arm. Then those thoughts are turned into electronic signals. The signals travel from his brain to his robot arm and move it.
>
> B: That's amazing! I think this technology can help many people.

➡ _____

[02~05] 다음 글을 읽고 물음에 답하시오.

M: As climate change is going to make farming harder, there may not be enough resources for the ⓐincreased number of people on Earth. For this reason, it is likely that we ⓑwill have to change how we get our food. _____(A)_____, we won't kill animals for food. Instead, meat ⓒwill grow in a lab ⓓused animal cells. This will require less land, water, and other resources. Also, (B)개미와 같은 곤충들이 우리 끼니의 일부가 될 것이다 (meals, bugs, ants, part, such, will, our, become, daily, of, as). You might not want to eat ⓔit, but they are actually very rich in nutrients!

02 위 글의 빈칸 (A)에 알맞은 것을 고르시오.

① For example ② Therefore
③ As a result ④ However
⑤ In addition

서답형

03 위 글의 밑줄 친 ⓐ~ⓔ 중 어색한 것을 모두 찾아 바르게 고치시오.

➡ _____

_____

04 위 글의 내용과 일치하지 않는 것은?

① 기후 변화가 농업을 더 어렵게 만들 것이다.
② 지구상의 점점 더 늘어나는 사람들을 위한 자원이 충분하지 않게 될지도 모른다.
③ 우리는 식량을 얻는 방법을 바꾸어야 할 가능성이 높다.
④ 고기가 동물 세포를 이용하여 실험실에서 배양될 것이다.
⑤ 영양분이 매우 풍부하기 때문에 곤충은 인기 있는 음식이 될 것이다.

서답형

05 위 글의 밑줄 친 (B)의 우리말에 맞게 괄호 안에 주어진 어휘를 알맞게 배열하여 영작하시오.

➡ _____

_____

[06~08] 다음 대화를 읽고 물음에 답하시오.

G: I had to wait in line at the store for almost twenty minutes.

B: (A)That's too bad. Maybe in the future we'll never have to wait in line.

G: What do you mean?

B: I read about (B)a store without cashiers. You take what you want to buy and just walk out.

G: That's it? How do you pay for it?

B: There are cameras and sensors in the store. They keep track of the items you choose and send the information to an app on your smartphone.

G: Then the app pays for them when you leave the store?

B: Exactly. (C)미래에는 이런 종류의 매장이 더 흔해질 것 같아. (likely, that, common)

06 밑줄 친 (A)를 대신하여 쓸 수 있는 것은?

① That depends on you.
② That's cool.
③ I'm sorry to hear that.
④ Don't be so disappointed.
⑤ Can you tell me why you waited in line?

서답형

07 밑줄 친 (B)a store without cashiers에서는 어떻게 물건 값을 지불하는지 40자 내외의 우리말로 쓰시오.

➡ _____

_____

서답형

08 위 대화의 밑줄 친 우리말 (C)를 주어진 어휘를 활용하여 영작하시오.

➡ _____

_____

[09~11] 다음 대화를 읽고 물음에 답하시오.

B: Hey, have you played this game? It's really exciting.

G: Yes, I (A)[do / have]. That game is pretty popular these days.

B: The developers used AI technology in it. The game characters are equipped with AI.

G: Oh, really? (a)Could you explain in more detail?

B: Sure. The AI characters in the game learn from (B)[that / what] human players do and develop their skills.

G: Oh! That's (C)[because / why] I sometimes felt like they already knew my moves!

B: They're very smart. (b)It is likely that the AI in games will get stronger and stronger. (possible)

09 위 대화의 괄호 (A)~(C)에 알맞은 말이 바르게 짝지어진 것은?

	(A)	(B)	(C)
①	do	that	because
②	do	what	because
③	have	what	because
④	have	what	why
⑤	have	that	why

중요

10 위 대화의 밑줄 친 (a)가 의도하는 것은?

① 소원 묻기　　　　② 설명 요청하기
③ 궁금증 표현하기　④ 의견 묻기
⑤ 가능성 정도 표현하기

서답형

11 위 대화의 밑줄 친 (b)를 주어진 어휘를 이용하여 바꿔 쓰시오.

➡ _____

_____

01 다음 대화가 자연스럽게 이어지도록 순서대로 배열하시오.

> (A) How do you think they will change?
> (B) It is likely that there will be 3D printed food in restaurants.
> (C) I think that restaurants will change a lot.
> (D) How will our lives change in the future?

➡ _____

[02~04] 다음 대화를 읽고 물음에 답하시오.

G: Look at these. They are the new inventions of the month!

B: They all look great. What is the invention on the first page?

G: It's a new smart refrigerator. It senses the items inside it and suggests recipes.

B: That sounds helpful.

G: It does. What do you think of this flying camera? I want to buy it.

B: A flying camera? (A)이게 어떻게 작동하는 건지 설명해 줄 수 있니? (how, work, could, explain)

G: Of course. This machine flies to a destination that we have already set. While it's flying, it can take pictures from 500 meters above the location.

B: That sounds awesome. What do you want to take pictures of?

G: I want to take pictures of flying birds!

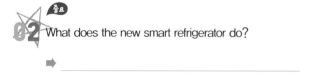

02 What does the new smart refrigerator do?

➡ _____

03 What can we do with the flying camera?

➡ _____
_____

04 위 대화의 밑줄 친 우리말 (A)를 주어진 어휘를 활용하여 영작하시오.

➡ _____

[05~07] 다음 대화를 읽고 물음에 답하시오.

G: Hey, have you heard of a smart umbrella?

B: No, I haven't. Could you explain what it is?

G: Sure. It's an umbrella that gives you the ____(A)____ for the day. If it is going to rain, the umbrella makes a sound.

B: That's very ___(B)___.

05 위 대화의 빈칸 (A)에 알맞은 말을 두 단어로 쓰시오.

➡ _____

06 다음 문장의 X에 해당하는 단어를 위 대화의 빈칸 (B)에 쓰시오.

> If a way of doing something is X, it is easy, or very useful or suitable for a particular purpose.

➡ _____

07 How does the smart umbrella work? Explain in Korean.

➡ _____

Grammar

① **가정법 과거: 'If+주어+동사 과거형 ~, 주어+would/could+동사원형 …'**

- Cooking and cleaning **would be** easier **if** you **had** a robot.
  만약 당신이 로봇 하나를 가지고 있다면, 요리와 청소가 더 쉬워질 텐데.
- **If** I **had** a self-driving car, I **would** not drive. 자율주행차가 있다면, 나는 운전을 안 할 텐데.

■ **가정법 과거:** 현재 사실을 반대로 가정하거나 실현 가능성이 없는 일을 가정한다. 'If+주어+동사 과거형 ~, 주어+would/could+동사원형 …' 형태로, '만약 ~라면 …할 텐데'의 뜻이다.

- **If** I **raise** a pet robot, I **will play** with it. 내가 펫 로봇을 키운다면, 함께 놀 것이다. (조건문)
- **If** I **raised** a pet robot, I **would play** with it. 내가 펫 로봇을 키운다면, 함께 놀 텐데. (가정법)
  = **As** I **don't raise** a pet robot, I **won't play** with it. 내가 펫 로봇을 키우지 않아, 함께 놀 수 없다. (직설법)

■ **가정법 과거완료:** 일어난 과거 사실을 반대로 가정한다. 'If+주어+had+과거분사 ~, 주어+would/could+have+과거분사 …'의 형태이다.

- **If** Foster **had not invented** the robot, Mina **would have ignored** him.
  Foster가 그 로봇을 발명하지 않았더라면, Mina가 그를 무시했을 텐데.

■ 'I wish' 가정법은 현재 사실에 반대되는 소망 또는 현재 사실에 대한 유감을 나타낸다.

- **I wish** I **were** a great musician like Bach. 내가 바흐같은 훌륭한 음악가라면 좋을 텐데.
  = **I'm sorry that** I'm **not** a great musician like Bach.

■ 가정법의 다양한 표현들로 직설법의 의미를 나타낼 수 있다.

- **As** there **is** an AI speaker, he **can** play music for you. (직설법) 인공지능 스피커가 있어서, 그가 당신을 위해 음악을 재생할 수 있다.
  → **If** there **were no** AI speaker, he **couldn't play** music for you. (가정법) 인공지능 스피커가 없다면, 그가 당신을 위해 음악을 재생할 수 없을 텐데.
  → **Were** there **no** AI speaker, he **couldn't play** music for you. (If 생략 후 도치)
  → **Without** an AI speaker, he **couldn't play** music for you.
  → **If it were not for** an AI speaker, **he couldn't play** music for you.
  → **Were it not for** an AI speaker, **he couldn't play** music for you. (If 생략 후 도치)

핵심 Check

1. 다음 우리말에 맞게 괄호 안의 어구를 바르게 배열하여 빈칸을 채우시오.
   (1) 내가 로봇이라면, 그녀의 말을 들을 텐데. (her, to, would, were, I, listen, a robot)
      ➡ If I _____.
   (2) 돈이 좀 있으면, 서울에 아파트를 살 텐데. (if, an apartment, money, buy, Seoul, would, had, some, I, in)
      ➡ I _____.

② '목적'이나 '의도'를 나타내는 so that

- It can navigate roads for you **so that** you can relax and enjoy the ride.
  그것은 당신이 쉬면서 주행을 즐길 수 있도록, 당신을 위해 길을 찾아갈 수 있다.

- I'll do something **so that** she can cheer up. 나는 그녀가 기운낼 수 있도록, 뭔가 할 것이다.

■ so that은 '~하기 위해', '~하고자', '~하도록'의 의미로 '목적'이나 '의도'를 나타낸다. 일반적으로 '주절 +so that+주어+can/will(조동사)+동사원형 ~'의 구조로 쓰인다.

  - We sat at the front **so that** we **could** see the stage well. 우리는 무대를 잘 볼 수 있도록, 앞에 앉았다.
  - The singer did her best in the performance **so that** she **would** satisfy herself. 그 가수는 스스로 만족할 수 있도록 공연에서 최선을 다했다.

■ so that은 다양한 표현들로 같은 의미를 나타낼 수 있다.

  - He donated money **so that** he **could help** others. 그는 다른 사람들을 돕고자 돈을 기부했다.
    = He donated money **in order that** he **could help** others.
    = He donated money **to help** others. 〈to부정사의 부사적 용법 – 목적〉
    = He donated money **so as to help** others.
    = He donated money **in order to help** others.
  - She studied hard **so that she wouldn't** fail. 그녀는 낙제하지 않으려고 열심히 공부했다.
    = She studied hard **in order that she wouldn't** fail.
    = She studied hard **(in order) not to** fail.
    = She studied hard **so as not to** fail.

■ so that을 기준으로 앞과 뒤의 시제를 일치시킨다.

  - Sujin **works** hard **so that** she **can** support her sisters. 수진이는 동생들을 부양하기 위해 열심히 일한다.
  - Sujin **worked** hard **so that** she **could** support her sisters.

■ so that이 '결과'의 의미를 갖는 접속사로 쓰이기도 한다. 이때는 대개 so that 앞에 쉼표가 온다.

  - Minkyoung overate every day, **so that** she **became** overweight. 민경이는 매일 과식했고, 결국 과체중이 되었다.

■ so ~ that 사이에 수식어가 오면, '너무 ~해서 결국 …하다'라는 뜻이 된다.

  - The road was **so** dark **that** the drivers could see nothing. 도로가 너무 캄캄해서 운전자들이 아무것도 볼 수 없었다.

핵심 Check

2. 다음 괄호 안에서 알맞은 말을 고르시오.

  (1) Sana came to Korea so (that / where) she could be an idol star.

  (2) Be quiet please (for that / so that) the audience can focus on the music.

01 다음 각 가정법 문장에서 어법상 <u>어색한</u> 단어를 한 개씩만 찾아 고치시오.

(1) If the robots are smarter, they could think like humans.

_____ ➡ _____

(2) If the machine had AI, it can make decisions.

_____ ➡ _____

(3) It would be better if the patient eats some healthy food.

_____ ➡ _____

(4) I will find solutions if the robots caused problems.

_____ ➡ _____

02 다음 두 문장의 의미가 같도록 빈칸에 알맞은 말을 쓰시오.

(1) They built the dam to prevent the flood.

➡ They built the dam so _____ they _____ prevent the flood.

(2) Since it was very cold, Tom turned on the heater.

➡ It was _____ _____ _____ Tom turned on the heater.

(3) Jihun's friends will run in order to save the baby ducks.

➡ Jihun's friends will run so _____ _____ _____ save the baby ducks.

03 다음 빈칸에 들어갈 말로 알맞은 것은?

If the car _____ cameras, sensors, and software, it could navigate the roads for you.

① can have   ② will have   ③ have had   ④ had   ⑤ has had

04 다음 각 문장의 빈칸에 공통으로 들어갈 말로 알맞은 것은?

• People invented search-and-rescue robots _____ that they could go into the dangerous areas.

• Turn the volume down _____ that I can enjoy the meal.

• The question is _____ easy that you can answer in two seconds.

① enough   ② too   ③ so   ④ such   ⑤ quite

01 다음 중 같은 뜻을 가진 문장끼리 짝지어진 것은?

① The robots would help you do the science homework if they had artificial intelligence.
= The robots didn't have artificial intelligence, so they wouldn't help you do the science homework.

② If it snows tomorrow morning, Nelly would stay in her hotel room.
= It is going to snow tomorrow morning, so Nelly will stay in her hotel room.

③ If Chris could run faster than usual, he would arrive at the meeting in time.
= Chris can't run faster than usual, so he won't arrive at the meeting in time.

④ If my uncle saw the truck coming, he could avoid the accident.
= My uncle didn't see the truck coming, so he couldn't avoid the accident.

⑤ The little girl could write a letter to the composer of the song if she knew his mail address.
= The little girl can't write a letter to the composer of the song though she knows his mail address.

[02~03] 다음 우리말을 어법상 알맞게 영작한 것을 고르시오.

02

> 그 노인은 소녀가 기운 낼 수 있도록 나뭇잎 그림을 그렸다.

① The old man drew a picture of the leaf that she so could cheer up.
② The old man drew a picture of the leaf so what she could cheer up.
③ The old man drew a picture of the leaf such that she could cheer up.
④ The old man drew a picture of the leaf so that she could cheer up.
⑤ The old man drew a picture of the leaf so order that she could cheer up.

03

> 우리는 무대 위 배우들의 연기를 더 잘 보기 위해서 앞에 앉았다.

① We sat at the front so that we can see the actors' performance on the stage better.
② We sat at the front in order that we can see the actors' performance on the stage better.
③ We sat at the front for that we could see the actors' performance on the stage better.
④ We sat at the front so as we saw the actors' performance on the stage better.
⑤ We sat at the front so that we could see the actors' performance on the stage better.

04 다음 중 어법상 어색한 문장은?

① If I knew the truth, I would tell it to you.
② If the fish knew the way to their home, they could go up against the river.
③ If the lady were in Spain, she could attend her father's funeral.
④ If the robot had AI, it won't do the bad thing to human children.
⑤ If it were not for the shoes you bought for me, I would not able to survive.

서답형

[05~08] 다음 우리말과 일치하도록 괄호 안에 주어진 어구들을 바르게 배열하시오.

05
진호의 반 친구들 모두가 어려운 사람들이 도움을 얻도록, 그들의 용돈을 기부했다.
→ All of Jinho's classmates (in, that, get, their, so, donated, people, could, need, help, allowances).

➡ _____

_____

06
수업 시간 동안에 집중할 수 있도록 충분히 잠을 자라구!
→ Be sure (sleep, order, to, can, that, you, enough, focus, in, get) during class!

➡ _____

_____

07
날씨가 맑다면, 우리는 놀이 공원에 갈 수 있을 텐데.
→ If (sunny, the amusement park, go, we, it, to, were, could).

➡ _____

_____

08
펫 로봇을 키운다면, 그 어린이 환자는 더 이상 심심하지 않을 텐데.
→ If the child patient (bored, wouldn't, she, a pet robot, be, raised) anymore.

➡ _____

_____

[09~10] 다음 각 가정법 과거 문장에서 어법상 옳은 것을 고르시오.

09
① I wish Sam follows her father's advice when she gets in trouble.
② I wish I had been at her concert playing the songs this coming Sunday.
③ I wish Brian can memorize the form so well that he could pass the test.
④ I wish all my relatives don't live far from the town my family will move to.
⑤ I wish people in my country knew a lot about the heroes in our history.

중요

10
① If Jessica has the car, she could pick my kids up on her way home.
② If the girl I met yesterday were rich, she could travel all around the world.
③ I wish the new cleaning robots will remove the dirty matter from the river.
④ If the scientists had invented the AI robot, you can deal with it easily.
⑤ I wish I know the correct answers to the final term exam.

서답형

11 다음 가정법 과거 문장에서 어법상 어색한 부분을 찾아서 고치시오. (총 4곳)

If you are a scientist developed robots, what kinds of robots will you be designed?

➡ ① _____ ② _____
③ _____ ④ _____

12 다음 두 문장의 의미가 같도록 바꿔 쓸 때 적절하지 않은 것은?

① Lisa works out regularly in order for her daddy not to get worried.
= Lisa works out regularly so that her daddy won't get worried.

② Jinsu left the dance party quite early not to meet his girlfriend.
= Jinsu left the dance party quite early, so he could not meet his girlfriend.

③ Wendy left for London so that she would get a better job in design.
= Wendy left for London so as to get a better job in design.

④ Thomas made cookies for Marianne so that he would feel happy.
= Thomas made cookies for Marianne in order to feel happy.

⑤ Karen waved her hand so that her study members could find her with ease.
= Karen waved her hand in order for her study members to find her with ease.

13 다음 문장의 빈칸 (A)~(C)에 들어갈 말로 가장 적절한 것은?

• If the gentleman __(A)__ some money, he could help you to support the victims.
• Were it not for the sun, all the living things on earth __(B)__ not survive.
• If the show __(C)__ early, Frank would come and help me with the project.

	(A)	(B)	(C)
①	has	would	ends
②	had	could	ends
③	had had	could	will end
④	had	would	ended
⑤	has	could	ended

14 다음 중 주어진 문장과 의미가 다른 것은?

Scientists try to make the robots able to recognize human emotions so that they can act like real friends.

① Scientists try to make the robots able to recognize human emotions in order that they can act like real friends.

② Scientists try to make the robots able to recognize human emotions in order for them to act like real friends.

③ Scientists try to make the robots able to recognize human emotions to have them act like real friends.

④ Scientists try to make the robots able to recognize human emotions in case that they can act like real friends.

⑤ Scientists try to make the robots able to recognize human emotions so as to have them act like real friends.

15 다음 〈보기〉의 밑줄 친 부분과 쓰임이 다른 하나는?

보기
I wish robots could be able to think and act like humans.

① If the officer knew the driver's number, he could make a phone call.

② Could you make me a robot pet for my little daughter?

③ I wish I could speak as many foreign languages as possible.

④ Were it not for your help, they could not complete the assignment.

⑤ The prisoner could get freedom if the witness told the truth to the judge.

Grammar **83**

01 다음 각 가정법 문장에서 어법상 어색한 단어를 한 개씩만 찾아 바르게 고치시오. (고친 부분은 두 단어라도 상관 없음.)

(1) Without artificial intelligence, robots won't be able to think like humans.

_____ ➡ _____

(2) If the police officer is in the driver's situation, he would understand how urgently she should get to the hospital.

_____ ➡ _____

(3) Samuel wouldn't be late for the P.E. class yesterday if his bike had not been broken.

_____ ➡ _____

(4) I wish I make a smarter robot so that it could help me with my homework.

_____ ➡ _____

(5) If robots could recognize the emotions of humans, they can act like real friends.

_____ ➡ _____

(6) If it were not for the effort of the medical staff around the country, we will be in a big trouble from the covid 19.

_____ ➡ _____

(7) I wish the robots can talk with my family members and sense their emotions.

➡ _____

02 다음 우리말과 일치하도록 괄호 안에 주어진 단어들을 바르게 배열하여 문장을 완성하시오.

(1) 그 로봇이 사람의 감정을 느낀다면, 우리는 그 것과 친구처럼 지낼 수 있을 텐데.

➡ If the robot _____

_____ with it like a friend. (could, human, along, we, sensed, get, emotions)

(2) 수색-구조 로봇들이 없다면, 사람들이 위험한 재난 현장으로 들어갈 텐데.

➡ If there _____

_____ .

(would, areas, search-and-rescue, go, into, humans, robots, disaster, were, no)

(3) 그 발명가는 외로운 사람들을 도울 수 있게 펫 로봇을 만들었다.

➡ The inventor made _____

_____ .

(the lonely people, so, could, a pet robot, help, he, that).

03 다음 문장과 같은 뜻이 되도록 괄호 안의 주어진 조건에 맞게 빈칸을 채우시오.

> Without cameras and the GPS system, the self-driving cars could not navigate roads.

(1) _____ cameras and the GPS system, the self-driving cars could not navigate roads. (it, be동사 활용, 5 단어)

(2) _____ cameras and the GPS system, the self-driving cars could not navigate roads. (there, no 활용, 4 단어)

(3) _____ cameras and the GPS system, the self-driving cars could not navigate roads. (it, be동사 활용, 4 단어)

(4) _____

_____ navigate roads. (직설법, there, 접속사 as 활용, 12 단어, self-driving은 한 단어로 간주)

04 다음 〈보기〉와 같이 두 문장이 같은 의미가 되도록 주어진 단어를 활용하여 다시 쓰시오.

┌─── 보기 ├───
Some people exercise regularly to stay healthy. (so, that)
➡ Some people exercise regularly so that they can stay healthy.
└─────────────

(1) Mom returned home so as to take the umbrella with her. (that, in, could, order)

➡ _____

_____

(2) Abigail runs every day to join his sports club. (that, so, can, she)

➡ _____

_____

(3) Semi left for Italy to learn cooking. (that, in, could, she, order)

➡ _____

_____

(4) Be sure to get enough sleep to focus during class. (that, so, you)

➡ _____

_____

(5) Sean ran fast in order not to be late for the wedding. (that, would, so, he)

➡ _____

_____

05 다음 〈보기〉와 같이 직설법 문장을 가정법으로 고치시오.

┌─── 보기 ├───
Since Paul isn't an eagle, he can't fly high.
→ If Paul were an eagle, he could fly high.
└─────────────

(1) Since the coronavirus isn't in my town, we feel relieved.

➡ _____

_____

(2) As Brian had an invitation, it was easy for them to enter the castle.

➡ _____

_____

(3) Because she is not rich enough, she will sell her books on the street market.

➡ _____

_____

(4) As there is no money left, Mr. Robert won't join the party.

➡ _____

_____

06 다음 그림을 보고, 그림에 나온 단어를 활용하여, 우리말에 맞게 가정법 문장으로 빈칸을 채우시오.

When the last leaf falls, it will be my last day.

┌─────────────
마지막 잎이 떨어진다면, 그게 나의 마지막 날이 될 텐데.
→ If _____.
(가정법 과거, If 포함 총 11 단어)
└─────────────

Reading

Life with Robots

Where Do We See Robots?

Robots are not only in movies and books anymore. Around the world, robots are doing a variety of tasks. There are delivery robots flying in the sky, robot arms in factories, and service robots in public places.

앞의 명사 delivery robots를 수식하는 현재분사

- A delivery robot in the sky
- Robot arms in a factory
- A service robot at the PyeongChang Olympics

Robots Are Becoming Smart

목적격 관계대명사절을 이끌며 선행사 only easy tasks를 수식함.

In the past, robots performed only easy tasks that humans programmed them to do. However, robots are now getting "smarter," and soon they might be able to think like humans. What makes this possible is artificial intelligence (AI).

What은 선행사를 포함하는 관계대명사.
주어 역할을 하는 명사절을 이끈다.

Robots that have AI can perceive environments and make decisions. They can also recognize speech, tell jokes, and play games with humans.

AI Speakers

They can answer your questions, control machines in your home, and play music for you.

AI Pets

They act just like real dogs. They walk and play with their owners and recognize praise.

---

a variety of 다양한

task 일, 과제, 과업

delivery 배달

factory 공장

perform 실행하다, 공연하다

program 프로그램을 짜다

artificial 인공적인

intelligence 지능

perceive 인지하다, 감지하다

recognize 알아보다, 인정하다

speech 연설, 말

📎 **확인문제**

● 다음 문장이 본문의 내용과 일치하면 T, 일치하지 <u>않으면</u> F를 쓰시오.

1 Around the world, robots are doing a variety of tasks. ☐

2 There are delivery robots in public places. ☐

3 In the past, robots performed only easy tasks that humans programmed them to do. ☐

4 Robots that have AI can recognize speech, tell jokes, and play games with each other. ☐

Robots around Us – Present and Future

Robots are making things faster and easier. They can help us anywhere—in our homes, on roads, or in disaster areas.

Home Helper Robot: This robot helps your family throughout the day. Cooking and cleaning would be easier if you had one. It also talks with family members and can sense emotions.

Self-Driving Car: A self-driving car doesn't need a driver. With cameras, sensors, and software, it can navigate roads for you so that you can relax and enjoy the ride.

Robot Swarm: A robot swarm is a large group of robots that can communicate with one another, like ants or bees. They can be used in a variety of places, including farms or building sites. They work on tasks and find solutions as a group.

Search-and-Rescue Robot: Search-and-rescue robots can go into disaster areas that are dangerous for humans. They find survivors, deal with dangers, and clear routes so that people can escape to safety.

Looking toward the Future

Our future with robots looks bright but not perfect. Some people expect life to become more convenient with the help of robots. However, other people worry about problems they might cause, such as threats to our jobs and safety. The important thing is to find possible solutions and to ensure that robots are only used for good.

present 현재의
disaster 재난, 재해
sense 감지하다; 감각
navigate 길을 찾다, 항해하다
swarm 떼, 군중
site 위치, 현장
solution 해법, 해결책
survivor 생존자, 살아남은 사람
deal with ~을 다루다, 처리하다
route 길, 경로
escape 탈출하다, 달아나다
safety 안전(함), 안전한 곳
look toward 앞날을 생각하다
convenient 편리한, 간편한
threat 위협
possible 가능한

확인문제

● 다음 문장이 본문의 내용과 일치하면 T, 일치하지 <u>않으면</u> F를 쓰시오.

1 Robots are making things faster and easier. ☐

2 A home helper robot can help us in disaster areas. ☐

3 A self-driving car doesn't need a driver. ☐

4 The robots in a robot swarm work on tasks and find solutions alone. ☐

5 Search-and-rescue robots can go into disaster areas that are dangerous for humans. ☐

6 Our future with robots looks bright and perfect. ☐

● 우리말을 참고하여 빈칸에 알맞은 말을 쓰시오.

1 Life _____ _____

2 _____ Do We See Robots?

3 Robots are _____ only in movies and books _____ .

4 Around the world, robots are doing _____ _____ _____ tasks.

5 There are delivery robots _____ in the sky, robot arms in factories, and service robots _____ _____ _____ .

6 A _____ robot in the sky

7 Robot arms in a _____

8 _____ _____ _____ at the PyeongChang Olympics

9 **Robots Are** _____ _____

10 In the past, robots performed only easy tasks that humans _____ _____ _____ _____ .

11 However, robots are now _____ "_____," and soon they might be able to think like humans.

12 _____ _____ _____ _____ is artificial intelligence (AI).

13 Robots that have AI can _____ _____ and make decisions.

14 They can also _____ _____ , tell jokes, and play games with humans.

15 **AI Speakers:** They can answer your questions, _____ _____ in your home, and play music for you.

16 **AI Pets:** They _____ _____ _____ real dogs.

17 They walk and play with their owners and _____ _____ .

18 **Robots** _____ _____ **– Present and Future**

19 Robots are making things _____ and _____ .

1	로봇과 함께하는 삶
2	우리는 어디에서 로봇을 보는가?
3	로봇은 더는 영화와 책 속에만 있는 것은 아니다.
4	전 세계적으로 로봇은 다양한 임무를 수행하고 있다.
5	하늘에는 날아다니는 배달 로봇, 공장에는 로봇 팔, 그리고 공공장소에는 서비스 로봇이 있다.
6	하늘에서 날아다니는 배달 로봇
7	공장의 로봇 팔들
8	평창 올림픽의 서비스 로봇
9	로봇이 똑똑해지고 있다
10	과거에 로봇은 인간이 로봇에게 실행하도록 프로그램을 설정한 단순 업무만을 수행했다.
11	그러나 로봇은 이제 '더 똑똑'해지고 있으며, 곧 인간처럼 생각할 수 있을지도 모른다.
12	이러한 것을 가능하게 만드는 것은 인공 지능(AI)이다.
13	인공 지능을 가진 로봇은 환경을 인식하고 의사 결정을 할 수 있다.
14	그들은 또한 인간의 말을 인지하고, 농담을 건네며, 인간과 게임을 할 수 있다.
15	〈인공 지능 스피커〉 그들은 당신의 질문에 대답할 수 있고, 당신의 집에 있는 기계들을 조종할 수 있으며, 당신을 위해 음악을 재생할 수도 있다.
16	〈인공 지능 반려동물〉 그들은 마치 진짜 개처럼 행동한다.
17	그들은 그들의 주인과 함께 걷고 놀며 칭찬을 알아챈다.
18	우리 주변의 로봇들 – 현재와 미래
19	로봇은 일을 더 빠르고 더 쉽게 해 주고 있다.

20 They can help us _____ — in our homes, on roads, or _____ _____ _____.

21 **Home Helper Robot:** This robot helps your family _____ the day.

22 Cooking and cleaning _____ _____ _____ if you _____ _____.

23 It also talks with family members and can _____ _____.

24 **Self-Driving Car:** A self-driving car doesn't need _____ _____.

25 With cameras, sensors, and software, it can navigate roads for you _____ _____ you _____ relax and enjoy the ride.

26 **Robot Swarm:** A robot swarm is _____ _____ _____ _____ that can communicate with one another, like ants or bees.

27 They _____ _____ _____ in a variety of places, _____ farms or building sites.

28 They work on tasks and find solutions _____ _____ _____.

29 **Search-and-Rescue Robot:** Search-and-rescue robots can go into disaster areas that are _____ _____ _____.

30 They find survivors, deal with dangers, and clear routes _____ _____ people _____ escape to safety.

31 _____ _____ the Future

32 Our future with robots looks bright but _____ _____.

33 Some people expect life _____ _____ more convenient with the help of robots.

34 However, other people worry about problems _____ _____, such as threats to our jobs and safety.

35 The important thing is _____ _____ possible solutions and _____ _____ that robots are only used for _____.

20 그들은 어디에서나 우리를 도울 수 있다. 우리의 집에서, 길에서 또는 재난 지역에서 말이다.

21 〈집안일 도우미 로봇〉 이 로봇은 온종일 당신의 가족을 돕는다.

22 만약 당신이 이 로봇 하나를 가지고 있다면 요리와 청소가 더 쉬워질 것이다.

23 이 로봇은 또한 가족 모두와 이야기를 나누며 감정을 파악할 수 있다.

24 〈자율 주행 자동차〉 자율 주행 자동차는 운전자를 필요로 하지 않는다.

25 카메라, 감지기 그리고 소프트웨어를 갖춘 채, 이 자동차는 당신이 쉬면서 주행을 즐길 수 있도록 당신을 위해 길을 찾아갈 수 있다.

26 〈로봇 군집〉 로봇 군집은 개미나 벌처럼, 서로 의사소통할 수 있는 로봇의 대규모 집단을 말한다.

27 이 로봇들은 농장이나 건설 현장을 포함한 다양한 장소에서 사용될 수 있다.

28 그들은 하나의 집단으로서 임무를 완수하고 해결책을 찾는다.

29 〈수색 구조 로봇〉 수색 구조 로봇은 사람에게 위험한 재난 지역에 투입될 수 있다.

30 그들은 생존자를 찾고 위험한 상황을 처리하며, 사람들이 안전한 곳으로 대피할 수 있도록 길을 확보한다.

31 미래에 대한 전망

32 로봇과 함께하는 우리의 미래는 밝지만 완벽하지는 않다.

33 어떤 사람들은 로봇의 도움으로 삶이 더욱 편리해질 것을 기대한다.

34 그러나 다른 사람들은 우리의 일자리와 안전에 대한 위협과 같이, 로봇이 일으킬지 모르는 문제들에 대해 걱정한다.

35 중요한 것은 가능한 해결책을 찾아내는 것과 로봇이 오로지 좋은 일을 위해서만 쓰이게 됨을 확실히 하는 것이다.

● 우리말을 참고하여 본문을 영작하시오.

1 로봇과 함께하는 삶
➡ _____

2 우리는 어디에서 로봇을 보는가?
➡ _____

3 로봇은 더는 영화와 책 속에만 있는 것은 아니다.
➡ _____

4 전 세계적으로 로봇은 다양한 임무를 수행하고 있다.
➡ _____

5 하늘에는 날아다니는 배달 로봇, 공장에는 로봇 팔, 그리고 공공장소에는 서비스 로봇이 있다.
➡ _____

6 하늘에서 날아다니는 배달 로봇
➡ _____

7 공장의 로봇 팔들
➡ _____

8 평창 올림픽의 서비스 로봇
➡ _____

9 로봇이 똑똑해지고 있다
➡ _____

10 과거에 로봇은 인간이 로봇에게 실행하도록 프로그램을 설정한 단순 업무만을 수행했다.
➡ _____

11 그러나 로봇은 이제 '더 똑똑'해지고 있으며, 곧 인간처럼 생각할 수 있을지도 모른다.
➡ _____

12 이러한 것을 가능하게 만드는 것은 인공 지능(AI)이다.
➡ _____

13 인공 지능을 가진 로봇은 환경을 인식하고 의사 결정을 할 수 있다.
➡ _____

14 그들은 또한 인간의 말을 인지하고, 농담을 건네며, 인간과 게임을 할 수 있다.
➡ _____

15 〈인공 지능 스피커〉 그들은 당신의 질문에 대답할 수 있고, 당신의 집에 있는 기계들을 조종할 수 있으며, 당신을 위해 음악을 재생할 수도 있다.
➡ _____
_____

16 〈인공 지능 반려동물〉 그들은 마치 진짜 개처럼 행동한다.
➡ _____

17 그들은 그들의 주인과 함께 걷고 놀며 칭찬을 알아챈다.
➡ _____

18 우리 주변의 로봇들 – 현재와 미래
➡ _____

19 로봇은 일을 더 빠르고 더 쉽게 해 주고 있다.

➡ _____

20 그들은 어디에서나 우리를 도울 수 있다. 우리의 집에서, 길에서 또는 재난 지역에서 말이다.

➡ _____

21 〈집안일 도우미 로봇〉 이 로봇은 온종일 당신의 가족을 돕는다.

➡ _____

22 만약 당신이 이 로봇 하나를 가지고 있다면 요리와 청소가 더 쉬워질 것이다.

➡ _____

23 이 로봇은 또한 가족 모두와 이야기를 나누며 감정을 파악할 수 있다.

➡ _____

24 〈자율 주행 자동차〉 자율 주행 자동차는 운전자를 필요로 하지 않는다.

➡ _____

25 카메라, 감지기 그리고 소프트웨어를 갖춘 채, 이 자동차는 당신이 쉬면서 주행을 즐길 수 있도록 당신을 위해 길을 찾아갈 수 있다.

➡ _____

_____

26 〈로봇 군집〉 로봇 군집은 개미나 벌처럼, 서로 의사소통할 수 있는 로봇의 대규모 집단을 말한다.

➡ _____

_____

27 이 로봇들은 농장이나 건설 현장을 포함한 다양한 장소에서 사용될 수 있다.

➡ _____

28 그들은 하나의 집단으로서 임무를 완수하고 해결책을 찾는다.

➡ _____

29 〈수색 구조 로봇〉 수색 구조 로봇은 사람에게 위험한 재난 지역에 투입될 수 있다.

➡ _____

_____

30 그들은 생존자를 찾고 위험한 상황을 처리하며, 사람들이 안전한 곳으로 대피할 수 있도록 길을 확보한다.

➡ _____

31 미래에 대한 전망

➡ _____

32 로봇과 함께하는 우리의 미래는 밝지만 완벽하지는 않다.

➡ _____

33 어떤 사람들은 로봇의 도움으로 삶이 더욱 편리해질 것을 기대한다.

➡ _____

34 그러나 다른 사람들은 우리의 일자리와 안전에 대한 위협과 같이, 로봇이 일으킬지 모르는 문제들에 대해 걱정한다.

➡ _____

_____

35 중요한 것은 가능한 해결책을 찾아내는 것과 로봇이 오로지 좋은 일을 위해서만 쓰이게 됨을 확실히 하는 것이다.

➡ _____

_____

[01~03] 다음 글을 읽고 물음에 답하시오.

> ⓐ
>
> Robots are not only in movies and books anymore. Around the world, robots are doing ⓑa variety of tasks. There are delivery robots ⓒflying in the sky, robot arms in factories, and service robots in public places.
> • A delivery robot in the sky
> • Robot arms in a factory
> • A service robot at the PyeongChang Olympics

01 위 글의 빈칸 ⓐ에 들어갈 제목으로 알맞은 것을 고르시오.

① Robots Are Becoming Smart
② Looking toward the Future
③ Where Do We See Robots?
④ Robots in Movies
⑤ Robots around Us – Present and Future

02 위 글의 밑줄 친 ⓑ의 임무를 수행하는 로봇 세 종류를 우리말로 쓰시오.

➡ (1) _____
(2) _____
(3) _____

03 위 글의 밑줄 친 ⓒflying과 문법적 쓰임이 같은 것을 모두 고르시오.

① He is good at flying in the sky.
② Two birds are flying in the sky.
③ My dream is flying in the sky.
④ Look at the man flying in the sky.
⑤ Flying in the sky, the eagle looked down at the tree.

[04~06] 다음 글을 읽고 물음에 답하시오.

Robots Are Becoming Smart

> In the past, robots performed only easy tasks that humans programmed (A)them to do. ⓐ , robots are now getting "smarter," and soon they might be able to think like humans. (B)What makes this possible is artificial intelligence (AI).
> Robots that have AI can perceive environments and make decisions. (C)They can also recognize speech, tell jokes, and play games with humans.

04 위 글의 빈칸 ⓐ에 들어갈 알맞은 말을 고르시오.

① In addition   ② In other words
③ For example   ④ Therefore
⑤ However

05 다음 빈칸에 위 글의 밑줄 친 (A)them과 (C)They가 가리키는 것을 쓰시오. (한 칸에 한 단어씩 쓸 것.)

➡ (A) _____ of _____ _____
(C) _____ _____ _____

06 위 글의 밑줄 친 (B)What과 문법적 쓰임이 같은 것을 고르시오.

① What is the matter with you?
② What kind of fruit do you like best?
③ What he needs is a good meal.
④ What do you think of that film?
⑤ I know what plan he will try.

[07~09] 다음 글을 읽고 물음에 답하시오.

Search-and-Rescue Robot

ⓐSearch-and-rescue robots can go into disaster areas that are safe for humans. They find survivors, deal with dangers, and clear routes ⓑso that people can escape to safety.

Looking toward the Future

Our future with robots looks bright but not perfect. Some people expect life to become more convenient with the help of robots. However, other people worry about problems they might cause, such as threats to our jobs and safety. The important thing is to find possible solutions and to ensure that robots are only used for good.

서답형

07 위 글의 밑줄 친 ⓐ에서 흐름상 어색한 부분을 찾아 고치시오.

➡ _____ ➡ _____

서답형

08 위 글의 밑줄 친 ⓑ를 다음과 같이 바꿔 쓸 때 빈칸에 들어갈 알맞은 말을 두 단어로 쓰시오.

➡ for people _____ to safety

09 According to the passage, which is NOT true?

① Search-and-rescue robots find survivors, deal with dangers, and clear routes so that people can escape to safety.

② Our future with robots looks bright and perfect.

③ There are some people who expect life to become more convenient with the help of robots.

④ Other people worry about problems that robots might cause.

⑤ The important thing is finding possible solutions and ensuring that robots are only used for good.

[10~12] 다음 글을 읽고 물음에 답하시오.

Robots around Us – Present and Future

(A)로봇은 일을 더 빠르고 더 쉽게 해 주고 있다. They can help us anywhere — in our homes, on roads, or in disaster areas.

Home Helper Robot

This robot helps your family throughout the day. Cooking and cleaning would be easier if you ___ⓐ___ one. It also talks with family members and can sense emotions.

서답형

10 위 글의 빈칸 ⓐ에 have를 알맞은 형태로 쓰시오.

➡ _____

11 위 글의 밑줄 친 (A)의 우리말에 맞게 주어진 어휘를 알맞게 배열하시오.

> making / easier / things / robots / and / are / faster

➡ _____

12 According to the passage, which is NOT true?

① Thanks to robots, things are becoming faster and easier.

② It is not easy to use robots in such places as disaster areas.

③ A home helper robot helps your family throughout the day.

④ A home helper robot would make cooking easier.

⑤ A home helper robot talks with family members and can sense emotions.

[13~15] 다음 글을 읽고 물음에 답하시오.

Robots Are Becoming Smart

In the past, robots performed only easy tasks _____ⓐ_____ humans programmed them to do. However, robots are now getting "smarter," and soon they might be able to think like humans. (A)이러한 것을 가능하게 만드는 것은 인공 지능(AI)이다.

Robots _____ⓑ_____ have AI can perceive environments and make decisions. They can also recognize speech, tell jokes, and play games with humans.

13 위 글의 빈칸 ⓐ와 ⓑ에 공통으로 들어갈 알맞은 말을 모두 고르시오.

① which ② what
③ who ④ that
⑤ whom

서답형

14 위 글의 밑줄 친 (A)의 우리말에 맞게 주어진 어휘를 이용하여 영작하시오.

> what, this, (AI)

➡ _____

중요

15 According to the passage, which is NOT true?

① In the past, robots performed only easy tasks humans programmed them to do.
② Robots are now getting "smarter."
③ Artificial intelligence can make it possible for robots to think like humans.
④ Every robot can perceive environments and make decisions.
⑤ Robots having AI can also recognize speech, tell jokes, and play games with humans.

[16~18] 다음 글을 읽고 물음에 답하시오.

Self-Driving Car

A self-driving car doesn't need a driver. With cameras, sensors, and software, ⓐit can navigate roads for you so that you can relax and enjoy the ride.

Robot Swarm

A robot swarm is a large group of robots that can communicate with one another, like ants or bees. They can be used in a variety of places, including farms or building sites. They work on tasks and find solutions ⓑas a group.

서답형

16 위 글의 밑줄 친 ⓐit이 가리키는 것을 본문에서 찾아 쓰시오.

➡ _____

17 위 글의 밑줄 친 ⓑas와 같은 의미로 쓰인 것을 고르시오.

① As I was tired, I soon fell asleep.
② This box will serve as a table.
③ Do in Rome as the Romans do.
④ Susan is not as pretty as Jane.
⑤ She sang as she walked.

중요

18 According to the passage, which is NOT true?

① A self-driving car doesn't need a driver.
② A self-driving car can navigate roads for you.
③ A robot swarm is a large group of robots.
④ A robot swarm can communicate with ants or bees.
⑤ A robot swarm works on tasks and finds solutions as a group.

[19~22] 다음 글을 읽고 물음에 답하시오.

Self-Driving Car

A self-driving car doesn't need a driver.
____ⓐ____ cameras, sensors, and software, it can navigate roads for you so that you can relax and enjoy the ride.

Robot Swarm

A robot swarm is a large group of robots that can communicate ___ⓑ___ one another, like ants or bees. ⓒThey can be used in a variety of places, including farms or building sites. They work on tasks and find solutions as a group.

19 위 글의 빈칸 ⓐ와 ⓑ에 공통으로 들어갈 알맞은 전치사를 고르시오. (대 · 소문자 무시)

① On   ② With   ③ For
④ About   ⑤ By

서답형

20 주어진 영영풀이에 해당하는 단어를 본문에서 찾아 쓰시오.

> It means finding a direction across, along, or over an area of water or land, often by using a map.

➡ _____

서답형

21 위 글의 밑줄 친 ⓒ를 다음과 같이 바꿔 쓸 때 빈칸에 들어갈 알맞은 말을 두 단어로 쓰시오.

➡ They can be used in a variety of places, _____ _____ farms or building sites.

22 Which question CANNOT be answered after reading the passage?

① Does a self-driving car need a driver?
② What is a robot swarm?
③ How many robots are there in a robot swarm?
④ Where can a robot swarm be used?
⑤ Does each robot in a robot swarm work alone?

[23~26] 다음 글을 읽고 물음에 답하시오.

Looking toward the Future

Our future with robots looks bright but not perfect. Some people expect life to become more convenient _____(A)_____ robots. However, other people worry about problems ⓐthey might cause, ⓑsuch as threats to our jobs and safety. The important thing is to find possible solutions and to ensure that robots are only used for good.

서답형

23 위 글의 빈칸 (A)에 '~의 도움으로'의 뜻을 갖는 4 단어를 쓰시오.

➡ _____

서답형

24 위 글의 밑줄 친 ⓐthey가 가리키는 것을 본문에서 찾아 쓰시오.

➡ _____

서답형

25 위 글의 밑줄 친 ⓑsuch as와 바꿔 쓸 수 있는 한 단어를 쓰시오.

➡ _____

서답형

26 What are the problems that robots might cause? Answer in English. (8 words)

➡ _____

[01~04] 다음 글을 읽고 물음에 답하시오.

Robots Are Becoming Smart

In the past, robots performed only easy tasks that humans programmed them to do. (A)However, robots are now getting "sillier," and soon they might be able to think like humans. ⓐ makes this possible is artificial intelligence (AI).

Robots that have AI can perceive environments and make decisions. They can also recognize speech, tell jokes, and play games with humans.

01 위 글의 빈칸 ⓐ에 들어갈 알맞은 한 단어를 쓰시오.

➡ _____

02 위 글의 밑줄 친 (A)에서 흐름상 어색한 부분을 찾아 고치시오.

_____ ➡ _____

03 What kinds of tasks did the robots do in the past? Fill in the blanks (A) and (B) with suitable words.

> In the past, humans (A)_____ easy tasks that robots would perform, and then robots (B)_____ only those tasks.

04 본문의 내용과 일치하도록 다음 빈칸 (A)와 (B)에 공통으로 들어갈 알맞은 단어를 쓰시오.

> Robots that can perceive environments and make decisions have (A)_____.
> Thanks to (B)_____, they can also recognize speech, tell jokes, and play games with humans.

[05~07] 다음 글을 읽고 물음에 답하시오.

AI Speakers

They can answer your questions, control machines in your home, and play music for you.

AI Pets

ⓐ그들은 마치 진짜 개처럼 행동한다. They walk and play with their owners and recognize praise.

05 위 글의 밑줄 친 ⓐ의 우리말에 맞게 주어진 어휘를 이용하여 6 단어로 영작하시오.

> act, just

➡ _____

06 What activities can AI pets do? Answer in English in a full sentence. (11 words)

➡ _____
_____

07 다음 빈칸 (A)와 (B)에 알맞은 단어를 넣어 '인공 지능 스피커'에 대한 소개를 완성하시오.

> AI Speakers can reply to (A)_____ _____, manage (B)_____ in your home, and play music for you.

[08~11] 다음 글을 읽고 물음에 답하시오.

Search-and-Rescue Robot

Search-and-rescue robots can go into disaster areas that are dangerous for humans. They find ___ⓐ___, (A)deal with dangers, and clear routes so that people can escape to ___ⓑ___ .

Looking toward the Future

Our future with robots looks bright but not perfect. Some people expect life to become more convenient with the help of robots. However, other people worry about problems they might cause, such as threats to our jobs and safety. (B)The important thing is to find possible solutions and to ensure that robots are only used for good.

08 주어진 영영풀이를 참고하여 빈칸 ⓐ에 철자 s로 시작하는 단어를 쓰시오.

> people who continue to live afterwards in spite of coming close to death

➡ _____

09 위 글의 빈칸 ⓑ에 safe를 알맞은 형태로 쓰시오.

➡ _____

10 위 글의 밑줄 친 (A)deal with와 바꿔 쓸 수 있는 한 단어를 쓰시오.

➡ _____ 또는 _____

11 위 글의 밑줄 친 (B)The important thing에 해당하는 두 가지를 우리말로 쓰시오.

➡ (1) _____
　 (2) _____

[12~15] 다음 글을 읽고 물음에 답하시오.

Self-Driving Car

A self-driving car doesn't need a driver. With cameras, sensors, and software, (A)it can navigate roads for you so that you can relax and enjoy the ride.

Robot Swarm

A robot swarm is a large group of robots that can communicate with one another, like ants or bees. They can be used in a variety of places, including farms or building sites. They work ___ⓐ___ tasks and find solutions as a group.

12 위 글의 빈칸 ⓐ에 알맞은 전치사를 쓰시오.

➡ _____

13 위 글의 밑줄 친 (A)를 다음과 같이 바꿔 쓸 때 빈칸에 들어갈 알맞은 말을 세 단어로 쓰시오.

➡ it can navigate roads for you _____ _____ _____ you can relax and enjoy the ride

14 Why does a self-driving car need no driver? Answer in English in a full sentence beginning with "Because".

➡ _____
　 _____

15 With whom can a robot swarm communicate? Answer in English in a full sentence beginning with "It". (6 words)

➡ _____

Presentation Time Step 3

What do you think this painting shows? I think it shows a machine helping

<small>machine을 수식하는 현재분사</small>

people clean their houses. The machine looks similar to today's robot vacuum

<small>help의 목적격보어(= to clean)</small> <small>'거리, 시간, 가격, 무게' 등의 경우 무생물이라도 아포스트로피('s)로 소유격을 나타낼 수 있음.</small>

cleaners, but they have some differences. For example, unlike today's robot

<small>전치사: ~와는 달리</small>

vacuum cleaners, the machine in the painting is controlled by a human.

<small>the machine이 주어이므로 수동태</small>

구문해설 • machine: 기계 • similar: 비슷한 • difference: 차이 • robot vacuum cleaner: 로봇 진공청소기 • unlike: ~와 다른, ~와는 달리 • control: 조정[조절]하다

After You Read B

home helper robot: I tried to cheer up a child of the family I work for. He felt

<small>try+to부정사: ~하려고 노력하다</small>

sad because of his bad grades.

<small>because of 뒤에는 '주어+동사'가 올 수 없다.</small>

search-and-rescue robot: Last week, after a storm hit, I cleared a route to

help a boy to escape.

<small>help+목적어+(to)부정사</small>

robot swarm: We communicated with one another and built a tower

<small>서로</small>

by working together.

<small>by ~ing: ~하는 것에 의해, ~함으로써</small>

구문해설 • cheer up: 기운을 내다, ~을 격려하다 • grade: 성적 • rescue: 구조 • escape: 탈출하다 • communicate with: ~와 연락하다

Think and Write Step 3

School Life in 30 Years

In 30 years, school life will be very different from now. It is likely

<small>가주어</small>

that there will be a big change in location. Students won't have to go to school.

<small>진주어</small> <small>= will not</small>

Instead, they will study at home using a variety of apps. One positive effect of

<small>분사구문</small> <small>= various</small>

such a change would be that students could save time because they would not

<small>가정법(미래 상황)</small>

have to go to school and come back. However, there could be some negative

<small>가정법</small>

effects too. For example, students wouldn't be able to meet their friends as

<small>가정법</small> <small>= can</small> <small>원급 비교</small>

often. We don't know exactly what school life will be like in the future, but I

<small>what A will be like: A가 어떻게 될지</small>

hope it will be as fun and meaningful as it is now.

<small>원급 비교</small> <small>지금과 같이</small>

구문해설 • a variety of: 다양한 • exactly: 정확하게 • meaningful: 의미 있는

해석

여러분은 이 그림이 무엇을 보여준다고 생각하나요? 저는 이것이 사람들이 집을 청소하는 것을 도와주는 기계를 보여준다고 생각합니다. 그 기계는 오늘날의 로봇 진공청소기와 비슷하게 보이지만 약간의 차이가 있습니다. 예를 들어, 오늘날의 로봇 진공청소기와는 다르게 그림에 있는 기계는 인간에 의해 조종됩니다.

집안일 도우미 로봇: 나는 내가 일하는 가족의 한 아이의 기운을 북돋워주려고 했다. 그는 나쁜 점수 때문에 슬픔을 느꼈다.

수색 구조 로봇: 지난주에 나는 폭풍이 강타한 뒤에 한 소년이 탈출하는 것을 돕기 위해 길을 청소했다.

로봇 군집: 우리는 서로 의사소통하고, 함께 일함으로써 탑을 지었다.

30년 후의 학교 생활

30년 후에, 학교 생활은 지금과 많이 달라질 것이다. 장소에 큰 변화가 있을 것이다. 학생들은 학교에 갈 필요가 없게 될 것이다. 대신, 그들은 집에서 다양한 앱을 이용하여 공부할 것이다. 그러한 변화의 한 가지 긍정적인 효과는 학생들이 학교에 다녀올 필요가 없기 때문에 시간을 절약할 수 있다는 것이다. 하지만, 부정적인 효과 또한 있을 수 있다. 예를 들어, 학생들이 전과 같이 자주 친구들을 만날 수 없을 것이다. 우리는 미래에 학교 생활이 어떻게 될지 정확하게 알 수 없다. 그렇지만, 나는 오늘날과 마찬가지로 재미있고, 의미 있기를 희망한다.

Words & Expressions

01 밑줄 친 부분과 바꿔 쓸 수 있는 말을 주어진 철자로 시작하여 쓰시오.

> He is 59 years old, and uses his fake arms well.

➡ a_____

02 다음 영영풀이가 가리키는 것을 고르시오.

> an unfortunate event that damages a large area and may harm many people

① delivery   ② intelligence   ③ program
④ signal   ⑤ disaster

03 다음 중 밑줄 친 부분의 뜻풀이가 바르지 않은 것은?

① He performs an important role in this group. (공연하다)
② A swarm of bees passed over the field. (떼)
③ The solution to last week's puzzle is on page 12. (해답)
④ You should think of your safety before anything else. (안전)
⑤ The president's speech continued for more than an hour. (연설)

04 다음 짝지어진 단어의 관계가 같도록 빈칸에 알맞은 말을 쓰시오.

> praise : compliment = _____ : flee

05 다음 문장의 빈칸에 들어갈 말을 〈보기〉에서 골라 쓰시오.

> ┌── 보기 ──┐
> make decisions / work on / find solutions / look toward / deal with

(1) Moody people are very difficult to _____.
(2) We _____ based on our experiences.
(3) _____ the future and make a plan.
(4) Which subject do you want to _____?
(5) I have to face my problems and learn to _____ for them.

Conversation

[06~08] 다음 대화를 읽고 물음에 답하시오.

G: Look at these. They are the new inventions of the month!
B: They all look great. What is the invention on the first page?
G: It's a new smart refrigerator. It senses the items inside it and suggests recipes.
(A) It does. What do you think of this flying camera? I want to buy it.
(B) That sounds awesome. What do you want to take pictures of?
(C) A flying camera? Could you explain how it works?
(D) ⓐThat sounds helpful.
(E) ⓑOf course. This machine flies to a destination that we have already set. While it's flying, it can take pictures from 500 meters above the location.
G: I want to take pictures of flying birds!

06 위 대화의 (A)~(E)가 자연스럽게 이어지도록 순서대로 배열한 것을 고르시오.

① (B) – (A) – (C) – (E) – (D)
② (C) – (B) – (D) – (A) – (E)
③ (C) – (D) – (A) – (E) – (B)
④ (D) – (A) – (C) – (E) – (B)
⑤ (D) – (B) – (A) – (C) – (E)

07 위 대화의 밑줄 친 ⓐThat이 가리키는 것을 우리말로 쓰시오.

➡ _____

_____

08 위 대화의 밑줄 친 ⓑOf course.와 바꿔 쓸 수 없는 것을 고르시오.

① Yes.   ② That's all right.
③ Okay.   ④ Sure.
⑤ No problem.

[09~11] 다음 대화를 읽고 물음에 답하시오.

B: What are you watching?
G: It's a show about a man who lost one of his ⓐarm in an accident. Surprisingly, he can play the drums very well.
B: How can he play the drums with only one arm?
G: Actually he uses two arms. ⓑOne is a robot arm ⓒcontrolled by his brain.
B: That's awesome. Could you explain in more detail?
G: Sure. First, he thinks ⓓwhat he wants to do with his arm. Then those thoughts are turned into electronic signals. The signals travel from his brain to his robot arm and move ⓔit.
B: That's amazing! I think this technology can help many people.

09 위 대화의 밑줄 친 ⓐ~ⓔ 중에서 어법상 어색한 것은?

① ⓐ   ② ⓑ   ③ ⓒ   ④ ⓓ   ⑤ ⓔ

10 위 대화에서 다음의 영영풀이가 나타내는 말을 찾아 쓰시오.

information sent in the form of light, sound, electricity, etc., by a machine

➡ _____

11 위 대화의 내용과 일치하도록 다음 빈칸에 알맞은 말을 쓰시오.

➡ He thinks _____ with his arm. → Those thoughts are changed to _____. → The signals are transported from his brain _____.

Grammar

12 다음 주어진 문장을 가정법으로 바르게 고친 것은?

As Anne didn't pay the bill, she couldn't use light and water last year.

① If Anne paid the bill, she could use light and water last year.
② If Anne paid the bill last year, she could have used light and water.
③ If Anne had paid the bill, she couldn't have used light and water last year.
④ If Anne had paid the bill, she could have used light and water last year.
⑤ If Anne had paid the bill, she could have been used light and water last year.

13 다음 대화를 참고하여 아래 주어진 빈칸에 적절한 단어를 쓰시오.

> Tommy: Did you call me yesterday? Why?
> Sandy: To get you ready for the presentation.

➡ Sandy called Tommy yesterday in _____ _____ he might _____ _____ _____ the presentation.

[14~15] 다음 가정법으로 주어진 우리말에 맞게 아래 어구들을 어법상 적절한 형태로 바꿔 배열하고, 직설법 문장으로도 바꾸시오.

14
> 비가 세차게 오면, 우리가 응원하러 야구장에 갈 수 없을 텐데. (hard, to, can, go, we, the stadium, it, to, rain, cheer, not)

➡ (1) If _____

_____ .

(2) 직설법: As _____

_____ .

15
> 인공지능이 개발되지 않았다면, 컴퓨터가 인간을 이길 수 없었을 텐데. (be developed, can't, win over, artificial intelligence, humans)

➡ (1) If _____

_____ .

(2) 직설법: As _____

_____ .

16 다음 우리말을 영작할 때, 어법상 어색한 문장을 모두 고르시오.

> 로봇이 없다면, 많은 사람들이 그 위험한 작업을 해야 할 텐데.

① Without robots, many people should have done the dangerous work.

② If there were no robots, many people would have to do the dangerous work.

③ If it were not for robots, many people would have to do the dangerous work.

④ Were it not for robots, many people would have to do the dangerous work.

⑤ If there are no robots, many people would have to do the dangerous work.

[17~18] 다음 중 어법상 어색한 문장을 고르시오.

17 ① If he told that to his friends, they would be upset with the teacher.

② If the boy succeeded in catching the school bus this morning, he would not have been late for school.

③ If you were the president, you could make a rule to respect one another.

④ If Mary got up earlier, she could be at the meeting in time.

⑤ If Yuna had put that coat on, she wouldn't have caught a cold.

18
① Could you share your method of studying so that the students can improve their scores in a math test?

② Jamie practiced playing the cello hard so that for her to get a scholarship.

③ Julie prepared rice and water so that she could make Juk, the Korean porridge.

④ The genius majored in the computer science so as to make a better machine.

⑤ Mr. Lee got up early so as not to miss the airplane.

19 다음 그림을 보고 괄호 안의 어구를 바르게 배열하여 빈칸을 알맞게 채우시오.

(1)

➡ The rescue robot is approaching the burning building _____ _____ of human firefighters.
(the risks, order, can, it, reduce, that, in)

(2)

➡ The robots in a robot swarm communicate with one another _____ _____.
(tasks, as, on, they, that, so, can, work, a group)

[20~22] 다음 글을 읽고 물음에 답하시오.

Robots around Us – Present and Future
Robots are making things faster and easier. They can help us anywhere—in our homes, on roads, or in disaster areas.

Home Helper Robot
This robot helps your family throughout the day. Cooking and cleaning ___ⓐ___ be easier if you had ⓑone. It also talks with family members and can sense emotions.

20 위 글의 빈칸 ⓐ에 들어갈 알맞은 조동사를 쓰시오.

➡ _____

21 Where can robots help us? Answer in English in a full sentence.

➡ _____
_____

22 위 글의 밑줄 친 ⓑone과 문법적 쓰임이 같은 것을 고르시오.

① There's only one thing we can do.
② They all went off in one direction.
③ She was wearing her new dress, the red one.
④ Do you want one biscuit or two?
⑤ One must obey one's parents.

[23~24] 다음 글을 읽고 물음에 답하시오.

_____ⓐ_____

Our future with robots looks bright but not perfect. Some people expect life to become more convenient with the help of robots. _____ⓑ_____, other people worry about problems they might cause, such as threats to our jobs and safety. The important thing is to find possible solutions and to ensure that robots are only used for good.

23 위 글의 빈칸 ⓐ에 들어갈 제목으로 알맞은 것을 고르시오.

① Looking toward the Future
② Threats to Our Safety Caused by Robots
③ Robots around Us – Present and Future
④ Robots Are Becoming Smart
⑤ Where Do We See Robots?

24 위 글의 빈칸 ⓑ에 들어갈 알맞은 말을 고르시오.

① Similarly   ② However
③ Thus   ④ That is
⑤ As a result

[25~27] 다음 글을 읽고 물음에 답하시오.

School Life in 30 Years

In 30 years, school life will be very different from now. (①) It is likely that there will be ⓐ a big change in location. (②) Students won't have to go to school. (③) One positive effect of such a change would be that students could save time because they would not have to go to school and come back. (④) However, there could be some negative effects too. (⑤) For example, students wouldn't be able to meet their friends as often. We don't know exactly what school life will be like in the future, but I hope it will be as fun and meaningful as it is now.

25 위 글의 흐름으로 보아, 주어진 문장이 들어가기에 가장 적절한 곳은?

> Instead, they will study at home using a variety of apps.

①   ②   ③   ④   ⑤

26 위 글의 밑줄 친 ⓐ의 구체적인 내용을 우리말로 쓰시오.

➡ _____

27 According to the passage, which is NOT true?

① In 30 years, school life will be very different from now.
② Students will study at home using a variety of apps.
③ Students could save time because they would not have to go to school and come back.
④ Students wouldn't be able to meet their friends as often.
⑤ School life in the future will be as fun and meaningful as it is now.

01 출제율 90%

다음 영영풀이가 가리키는 것을 고르시오.

> to attach something or put something on, especially something useful

① escape
② equip
③ recognize
④ navigate
⑤ ensure

02 출제율 95%

다음 주어진 문장의 밑줄 친 common과 같은 의미로 쓰인 것은?

> Jackson is a common English name.

① They combined against a common enemy.
② This decision was taken for the common good.
③ It's a common mistake among learners of English.
④ Just use your common sense!
⑤ We went for a walk on the common.

03 출제율 100%

다음 문장의 빈칸 (A)~(C)에 들어갈 말로 바르게 짝지어진 것은?

> • It was not an easy ___(A)___ , and I couldn't finish it on time.
> • The machine ___(B)___ my question and answered it.
> • There is a ___(C)___ of stormy weather during the flight.

① task – ensured – delivery
② destination – ensured – delivery
③ task – recognized – delivery
④ destination – recognized – threat
⑤ task – recognized – threat

[04~06] 다음 대화를 읽고 물음에 답하시오.

G: I had to wait in line at the store for almost twenty minutes.

B: That's too bad. (①) Maybe in the future we'll never have to wait in line.

G: (②) What do you mean?

B: (③) I read about (a)a store without cashiers. You take what you want to buy and just walk out.

G: (④) _____(A)_____

B: There are cameras and sensors in the store. (⑤) They keep track of the items you choose and send the information to an app on your smartphone.

G: Then the app pays for them when you leave the store?

B: Exactly. It's likely that these kinds of stores will be more common in the future.

04 출제율 90%

위 대화의 (①)~(⑤) 중 다음 문장이 들어가기에 적절한 곳은?

> That's it?

①   ②   ③   ④   ⑤

05 출제율 90%

위 대화의 빈칸 (A)에 알맞은 것은?

① How do you pay for it?
② How do you think they will change?
③ Have you heard of it before?
④ Could you tell me if they are equipped with AI?
⑤ Could you explain what it is?

06 출제율 95%

밑줄 친 (a)a store without cashiers의 특징을 45자 내외의 우리말로 서술하시오.

➡ _____

_____

[07~08] 다음 대화를 읽고 물음에 답하시오.

B: Hey, have you played this game? It's really exciting.

G: Yes, I have. That game is pretty popular these days.

B: The developers used AI technology in it. The game characters are equipped with AI.

G: Oh, really? Could you explain in more detail?

B: Sure. The AI characters in the game learn from what human players do and develop their skills.

G: Oh! That's why I sometimes felt like they already knew my moves!

B: They're very smart. (A)It is likely that the AI in games will get stronger and stronger.

07 위 대화의 밑줄 친 (A)와 바꾸어 쓸 수 있는 것을 모두 고르시오.

① It is notable that the AI in games will get stronger and stronger.

② It is probable that the AI in games will get stronger and stronger.

③ It is expected that the AI in games will get stronger and stronger.

④ It is possible that the AI in games will get stronger and stronger.

⑤ It is doubtful that the AI in games will get stronger and stronger.

08 위 대화의 내용과 일치하지 않는 것은?

① G는 그 게임을 해봤다.

② 개발자들이 그 게임에 인공지능 기술을 사용했다.

③ 게임 캐릭터들에 인공지능이 탑재되어 있다.

④ 게임 속 인공지능 캐릭터들은 인간 플레이어가 하는 행동을 통해 배우고 자신의 기술을 발전시킨다.

⑤ B는 이따금씩 캐릭터들이 이미 자신의 움직임을 알고 있는 것처럼 느꼈다.

09 다음 가정법 문장 중 어법상 옳은 것을 고르시오.

① His father would feel proud if David makes it to the finals of the national athletic competition.

② If it had not been for the Chinese characters, the ancient people would be difficult to read and write.

③ If the student were not so hungry, he can share his sandwich with you.

④ What would Mr. Kang do if it rained on his daughter's marathon day?

⑤ Mary will feel disappointed if her dogs and cats left the area.

10 다음 각 빈칸에 공통으로 들어갈 단어 중 나머지 넷과 성격이 다른 하나는?

① They woke up early _____ that they could see their mom off.

② Yejin hurried _____ that she couldn't miss the train her husband was in.

③ Carlson Jr. was _____ busy that he couldn't hear my requests.

④ The member of city council talked louder _____ that everyone present could understand.

⑤ Please switch on the light _____ that I can get out of here.

출제율 90%

11 다음 주어진 우리말을 어법에 맞게 바르게 영작한 것은?

> 비가 충분히 오지 않으면 곡식들이 전보다 덜 자랄 텐데. (그러나 비가 충분히 안 온다.)

① If it didn't rain enough, the crops would grow less than before.

② If it had not rained enough, the crops would have grown less than before.

③ Had it not rained enough, the crops would grow less than before.

④ Didn't it rain enough, the crops will grow less than before.

⑤ If it rained not enough, the crops would have grown less than before.

출제율 100%

12 다음 문장의 밑줄 친 so that의 쓰임이 흐름상 어색한 것은?

① Sumi's father baked some bread for her friends so that they could enjoy.

② The performer played the guitar on the street so that the passers-by could listen to the beautiful music.

③ Minju practiced hard so that she could pass the P.E. test.

④ Wendy failed to get the doctor's certificate so that she had studied harder.

⑤ The actress wore sunglasses so that she could hide her face.

출제율 100%

13 다음 중 어법상 옳은 문장은?

① Jane has saved changes for 8 months so to buy a pretty doll.

② Bob has been exercising regularly in order that he could lose some weight.

③ The penguin was so sadness that it wouldn't show up above the water.

④ Kate came out earlier so that she not being late for the concert.

⑤ Henderson took the umbrellas in order for his kids could use them.

출제율 100%

14 다음 우리말을 주어진 어구들과 조건에 맞게 영작하시오.

> 한국의 역사를 배우면, 그들이 독도를 더욱 이해할 수 있을 텐데.
> (learn, understand, much, can, Dokdo, the history of Korea 활용. If로 시작, 단어 변형 가능, 총 12 단어로 할 것)

➡ _____

_____

출제율 100%

15 다음 주어진 문장과 같은 뜻이 되도록 각각 주어진 조건에 맞게 빈칸을 채우시오.

> Beth watched the movie three times so that she would not forget the touching scenes.

(1) Beth watched the movie three times _____ the touching scenes.
(to부정사의 부사적 용법 활용, 3 단어)

(2) Beth watched the movie three times _____ the touching scenes.
(so as 활용, 5 단어)

(3) Beth watched the movie three times _____ she would not forget the touching scenes. (in 활용, 3 단어)

16 다음 그림을 보고 자연스러운 문장이 되도록 괄호 안에 주어진 단어를 바르게 배열하여 빈칸을 완성하시오.

(1)

Self-Driving Car

➡ Mike bought a self-driving car _____ _____ himself. (would, that, drive, he, not, so)

(2)

➡ Gutenberg invented the printing press _____ and wider. (that, information, in order, spread, faster, could, much)

[17~18] 다음 중에서 틀린 문장을 찾아 기호를 쓰고, 바르게 고쳐 문장을 다시 쓰시오.

17 ① If the professor could be awarded for her work, I would be very proud of her.
② If Sujin told the truth to her mom, she would be touched with what her daughter had been doing for her.
③ If Teresa had got up earlier than usual this morning, she wouldn't have missed the train.
④ If Sehee missed the school bus, she would not have been late for class.

⑤ If Ralph had put on the glasses, he would have noticed the girl.

➡ _____
_____
_____

18 ① The priest has gone to the poor town so that he would help the kids there.
② The old maid saved some money in order that her son could study abroad.
③ I called the special cleaning service so that my car would get washed.
④ The players tried their best in order to beat the other players.
⑤ The shopper didn't buy a thing so as that she could save money.

➡ _____
_____

19 괄호 안의 조건과 가정법을 이용하여 아래 대화의 빈칸을 알맞게 채우시오.

(1) A: Do the girls see the show?
   B: No, but if they _____, they _____ happy. (see, will, feel 활용)

(2) A: Does Jenny have my number?
   B: No, but if she _____, she _____ you. (know, can, contact 활용)

(3) A: Was the lady healthy?
   B: No, but if she _____, she _____ the short marathon last week. (be, complete, can 활용)

[20~22] 다음 글을 읽고 물음에 답하시오.

_____ ⓐ _____

(①) In the past, robots performed only easy tasks that humans programmed them to do. (②) However, robots are now getting "smarter," and soon they might be able to think ⓑlike humans. (③)

Robots that have AI can perceive environments and make decisions. (④) They can also recognize speech, tell jokes, and play games with humans. (⑤)

🖋 출제율 100%

20 위 글의 빈칸 ⓐ에 들어갈 제목으로 알맞은 것을 고르시오.

① Robots around Us – Present and Future
② Where Do We See Robots?
③ Humans Programmed Tasks for Robots
④ Looking toward the Future
⑤ Robots Are Becoming Smart

🖋 출제율 90%

21 위 글의 흐름으로 보아, 주어진 문장이 들어가기에 가장 적절한 곳은?

> What makes this possible is artificial intelligence (AI).

①　　　②　　　③　　　④　　　⑤

🖋 출제율 95%

22 위 글의 밑줄 친 ⓑlike와 같은 의미로 쓰인 것을 고르시오.

① What's it like studying in Spain?
② He ran like the wind.
③ I didn't like noisy music.
④ No one sings the blues like she did.
⑤ She responded in like manner.

[23~24] 다음 글을 읽고 물음에 답하시오.

Robot Swarm

A robot swarm is a large group of robots that can communicate with one another, like ants or bees. (A)They can ____ⓐ____ in a variety of places, including farms or building sites. They work on tasks and find solutions as a group.

🖋 출제율 90%

23 위 글의 빈칸 ⓐ에 use를 알맞은 형태로 쓰시오.

➡ _____

🖋 출제율 95%

24 위 글의 밑줄 친 (A)They가 가리키는 것을 본문에서 찾아 쓰시오.

➡ _____

[25~26] 다음 글을 읽고 물음에 답하시오.

The Smartphone

• When was it invented?
- The smartphone was invented in the United States in 1992.
• What changes did it bring?
- The smartphone allows people to do many different things with just their phone. ⓐIt can be used not only for calls but also for sending messages, taking pictures, and more. Also, it lets people access the Internet any time and anywhere.

25 위 글의 밑줄 친 ⓐ를 다음과 같이 바꿔 쓸 때 빈칸에 들어갈 알맞은 말을 세 단어로 쓰시오.

➡ It can be used for sending messages, taking pictures, and more _____ _____ _____ for calls.

26 위 글을 읽고 알 수 없는 것을 고르시오.

① When was the smartphone invented?
② Who invented the smartphone?
③ Can people do many different things with just their smartphone?
④ Can people take pictures with their smartphone?
⑤ Can people access the Internet any time and anywhere with the smartphone?

27 주어진 문장 다음에 이어질 글의 순서로 가장 적절한 것은?

In the past, robots performed only easy tasks that humans programmed them to do.
(A) What makes this possible is artificial intelligence (AI).
(B) Robots that have AI can perceive environments and make decisions. They can also recognize speech, tell jokes, and play games with humans.
(C) However, robots are now getting "smarter," and soon they might be able to think like humans.

① (A) – (C) – (B)　　② (B) – (A) – (C)
③ (B) – (C) – (A)　　④ (C) – (A) – (B)
⑤ (C) – (B) – (A)

[28~30] 다음 글을 읽고 물음에 답하시오.

School Life in 30 Years

In 30 years, school life will be very different from now. It is likely that there will be ⓐa big change in textbooks. Students won't use paper books anymore. Instead, they will use a tablet PC and files (A)[downloading / downloaded] from the cloud. One positive effect of (B)[so / such] a change would be that students won't have to carry heavy backpacks with books and notebooks. However, there could be some negative effects too. For example, students' eyesight could get (C)[better / worse] because they have to look at the tablet PC screen all day long. We don't know exactly ⓑ학교 생활이 어떤 모습일지 in the future, but I hope it will be as fun and meaningful as it is now.

28 위 글의 밑줄 친 ⓐ의 구체적인 내용을 우리말로 쓰시오.

➡ _____

29 위 글의 괄호 (A)~(C)에서 문맥이나 어법상 알맞은 낱말을 골라 쓰시오.

➡ (A) _____ (B) _____ (C) _____

30 위 글의 밑줄 친 ⓑ의 우리말에 맞게 주어진 어휘를 알맞게 배열하시오.

will / school life / like / what / be

➡ _____

[01~03] 다음 대화를 읽고 물음에 답하시오.

G: I had to wait in line at the store for almost twenty minutes.

B: That's too bad. Maybe in the future we'll never have to wait in line.

G: What do you mean?

B: I read about a store without cashiers. You take what you want to buy and just walk out.

G: That's it? How do you pay for it?

B: There are cameras and sensors in the store. They keep track of the items you choose and send the information to an app on your smartphone.

G: Then the app pays for them when you leave the store?

B: Exactly. It's likely that these kinds of stores will be more common in the future.

01 What is likely to disappear at stores in the future? Use the phrase "It is likely that".

➡ _____

_____

02 What will pay for the items you choose at the store without cashiers?

➡ _____

_____

03 What are there in the store without cashiers?

➡ _____

_____

04 다음 우리말을 영작할 때, 〈보기〉의 어구들을 사용하여 빈칸에 알맞게 써 넣으시오. (중복 사용 불가)

┌─ 보기 ─────────────────────────┐
could / would / order / in order to / that / raise / so that / satisfy / show / his thirst / it / I / them
└────────────────────────────────┘

(1) 그는 갈증을 채우기 위해서 시원한 음료수를 주문했다.

➡ He ordered cold beverage _____

_____.

(2) 유진이는 아빠에게 보여드리기 위해서 춤 동작들을 연습했다.

➡ Yujin practiced the dance movements _____ to her daddy.

(3) 나는 강아지를 기를 수 있도록 하기 위해서, 애완 동물 학교에 등록했다.

➡ I signed up for a pet school in _____

_____ a puppy.

[05~06] 아래 각 두 문장을 가정법의 한 문장으로 합치되, 주어진 단어로 시작하시오.

05
┌──────────────────────────────────┐
• Jihun doesn't know the actor's name.
• He wants to search him online.
└──────────────────────────────────┘

➡ If _____

_____.

06
┌──────────────────────────────────┐
• I'm sorry that I'm not as smart as Bill.
• I want to be as smart as Bill.
└──────────────────────────────────┘

➡ I _____.

Robots Are Becoming Smart

In the past, robots performed only easy tasks (A)[that / what] humans programmed them to do. However, robots are now getting "smarter," and soon they might be able to think like humans. What makes ⓐthis possible (B)[is / are] artificial intelligence (AI).

Robots that have AI can perceive environments and (C)[make / makes] decisions. They can also recognize speech, tell jokes, and play games with humans.

07 위 글의 괄호 (A)~(C)에서 어법상 알맞은 낱말을 골라 쓰시오.

➡ (A) _____ (B) _____ (C) _____

08 위 글의 밑줄 친 ⓐthis가 가리키는 것을 본문에서 찾아 쓰시오.

➡ _____

_____

09 위 글을 읽고, (1) '과거에 로봇이 할 수 있던 일'과 (2) '미래에 인공 지능을 가진 로봇이 할 수 있는 일'을 각각 우리말로 쓰시오.

➡ (1) _____

_____

(2) _____

_____

Search-and-Rescue Robot

Search-and-rescue robots can go into disaster areas that are dangerous for humans. They find survivors, deal with dangers, and clear routes so that people can escape to safety.

Looking toward the Future

Our future with robots looks bright but ⓐnot perfect. ⓑSome people expect life becoming more convenient with the help of robots. However, other people worry about problems they might cause, such as threats to our jobs and safety. The important thing is to find possible solutions and to ensure that robots are only used for good.

10 위 글의 밑줄 친 ⓐnot perfect를 한 단어로 바꿔 쓰시오.

➡ _____

11 위 글의 밑줄 친 ⓑ에서 어법상 틀린 부분을 찾아 고치시오.

_____ ➡ _____

12 본문의 내용과 일치하도록 다음 빈칸 (A)와 (B)에 알맞은 단어를 쓰시오.

> Search-and-rescue robots can be used in (A)_____ _____ that are dangerous for humans, where they find survivors, deal with dangers, and (B)_____ _____ for people to escape to safety.

01 다음 그림을 보고 '가능성 정도 표현하기'를 이용하여 자신의 생각을 쓰시오.

(1) 　(2) 　(3)

(1) _____

(2) _____

(3) _____

02 다음 내용을 바탕으로 30년 후의 학교 생활을 상상하여 쓰시오.

---

1. How will school life be different in 30 years?

There will be a big change in location.

2. Give some details about the change.

Students won't have to go to school. Instead, they will study at home using a variety of apps.

3. What would be a positive effect of the change?

Students could save time because they would not have to go to school and come back.

4. Would there be any negative effects? If so, describe one.

Students wouldn't be able to meet their friends as often.

School Life in 30 Years

In 30 years, school life will be very different from now. It is likely that there will be a big change in (A)_____. Students won't have to go to school. Instead, they will study at home (B)_____. One positive effect of such a change would be that students could (C)_____ because they would not have to go to school and come back. However, there could be some (D)_____ too. For example, students wouldn't be able to (E)_____ as often. We don't know exactly what school life will be like in the future, but I hope it will be as fun and meaningful as it is now.

단원별 모의고사

01 다음 우리말에 맞게 빈칸에 알맞은 말을 쓰시오. (철자가 주어진 것도 있음.)

(1) 그가 그 사고의 유일한 생존자였다.
➡ He was the only _____ of the accident.

(2) 거실에는 몇 개의 조화가 장식용으로 사용되었다.
➡ Some _____ flowers were used to decorate the living room.

(3) 이것이 학교로 가는 가장 짧은 길이다.
➡ This is the shortest r_____ to the school.

(4) 주문하신 상품을 이번 주에 배달해 드릴 것을 약속드립니다.
➡ We guarantee _____ of your order this week.

02 다음 문장의 빈칸에 들어갈 말을 〈보기〉에서 골라 쓰시오.

┌─ 보기 ─┐
likely / resource / safety / sense / signal
└──────┘

(1) Oil is not a renewable energy _____.

(2) They have a casual attitude towards _____.

(3) The siren was a _____ for everyone to leave the building.

(4) The computer will be able to _____ other cars on the road.

(5) The exchange rate is _____ to fall in the near future.

03 다음 제시된 의미에 맞는 단어를 주어진 철자로 시작하여 빈칸에 쓰고, 그 뜻을 마지막의 빈칸에 쓰시오.

(1) d_____ _____ : to handle or solve something such as a problem: _____

(2) s_____ : the answer to a problem: _____

(3) s_____ : the state of being safe from harm or danger: _____

(4) s_____ : a large number of living things: _____

(5) e_____ : to get free: _____

(6) p_____ : to notice something with the senses: _____

04 다음 중 짝지어진 대화가 어색한 것은?

① A: The space balloon is an interesting invention.
  B: I haven't heard of it before.

② A: Could you explain how it works in more detail?
  B: Sure. That sounds awesome.

③ A: How will our lives change in the future?
  B: I think that restaurants will change a lot.

④ A: What do you want to take pictures of?
  B: I want to take pictures of flying birds!

⑤ A: Then the app pays for them when you leave the store?
  B: Exactly. It's likely that these kinds of stores will be more common in the future.

[05~06] 다음 대화를 읽고 물음에 답하시오.

B: What are you watching?

G: It's a show about a man who lost one of his arms in an accident. Surprisingly, he can play the drums very well.

B: How can he play the drums with only one arm?

G: Actually he uses two arms. One is a robot arm controlled by his brain.

B: That's awesome. Could you explain in more detail?

G: Sure. First, he thinks what he wants to do with his arm. Then those thoughts are turned into electronic signals. The signals travel from his brain to his robot arm and move it.

B: That's amazing! I think this technology can help many people.

5 What is the show G is watching about?

➡ _____

_____

6 위 대화의 내용과 일치하지 <u>않는</u> 것은?

① G는 사고로 한쪽 팔을 잃은 남자에 관한 프로그램을 보고 있다.

② 그 남자는 드럼을 매우 잘 칠 수 있다.

③ 사실 그 남자는 두 팔을 사용해서 드럼을 친다.

④ 그 남자가 자신의 팔로 하고 싶은 것을 생각하면 그 생각들이 전기 신호로 바뀐다.

⑤ 로봇 팔이 바뀐 전기 신호를 뇌로 전달한다.

[07~08] 다음 대화를 읽고 물음에 답하시오.

B: Hey, have you played this game? It's really exciting.

G: Yes, I have. That game is pretty popular these days.

B: The developers used AI technology in it. The game characters are equipped with AI.

G: Oh, really? Could you explain in more detail?

B: Sure. The AI characters in the game learn from what human players do and develop their skills.

G: Oh! (a)<u>그래서 이따금씩 그들이 이미 내 움직임을 알고 있는 것처럼 느껴졌던 거구나!</u> (my moves, sometimes, that's, feel, already)

B: They're very smart. It is ___(A)___ that the AI in games will get stronger and stronger.

7 위 대화의 빈칸 (A)에 알맞지 <u>않은</u> 것을 <u>모두</u> 고르시오.

① probable　　② possible

③ likely　　　④ imaginable

⑤ appropriate

8 위 대화의 밑줄 친 우리말 (a)를 주어진 어휘를 활용하여 11단어로 영작하시오.

➡ _____

_____

[09~10] 다음 글을 읽고 물음에 답하시오.

M: As climate change is going to make farming harder, there may not be enough resources for the increasing number of people on Earth. For this reason, _____(A)_____. For example, we won't kill animals for food. ___(B)___, meat will be grown in a lab using animal cells. This will require less land, water, and other resources. ___(C)___, bugs such as ants will become part of our daily meals. You might not want to eat them, but they are actually very rich in nutrients!

09 〈보기〉에 주어진 어휘를 알맞게 배열하여 위 글의 빈칸 (A)에 들어갈 말을 쓰시오.

> ┤ 보기 ├
>
> we, we, our, it, food, get, change, have, is, will, likely, how, that, to

➡ _____

_____

10 위 글의 빈칸 (B)와 (C)에 알맞은 것으로 바르게 짝지어진 고르시오.

	(B)	(C)
①	Instead	Also
②	Instead	That is
③	In addition	Also
④	In addition	That is
⑤	As a result	However

[11~12] 다음 중 밑줄 친 부분의 쓰임이 나머지와 다른 것은?

11 ① The ballerina would get a full scholarship to the college if she practiced harder than before.
② If Henry were an actor in the movie, you could find him at least once.
③ The kids in the kinderagarten would go out to play if it stopped raining.
④ Nancy had no idea if the rumor about Jessy would turn out true.
⑤ The secretary could call his boss if he needed advice about the report.

12 ① My aunt turned off the radio so that she could concentrate on the study.
② Those flowers open up in early spring so that they can avoid the competition.
③ Jordan's friends tried their best so that they could win the final match.
④ Marianne took a taxi so that she wouldn't be late for work.
⑤ She made a great fortune, so that she could buy a big house in New York.

13 다음 중 〈보기〉의 밑줄 친 would와 쓰임이 같은 것은?

> ┤ 보기 ├
>
> Lynn would give up the job opportunity from abroad if her family didn't agree on their being apart.

① Would you bring me the red umbrella while I'm holding this dog?
② The math teacher said that he would buy me a good meal the next day.
③ Michael's family would go on a picnic to the lake park when I was young.
④ The students would like to eat the Bulgogi pizza for the birthday party.
⑤ The applicant would get the position if he improved the skill in persuading others.

14 다음 주어진 우리말을 영작한 것으로 옳지 않은 것은?

> Paul은 세계적인 가수가 되기 위해 밤낮으로 노래 연습을 했다.

① Paul practiced singing day and night in order to become a world-class singer.
② Paul practiced singing day and night so that he became a world-class singer.
③ Paul practiced singing day and night so as to become a world-class singer.
④ Paul practiced singing day and night so that he could become a world-class singer.
⑤ Paul practiced singing day and night in order that he would become a world-class singer.

15 다음 중 내용상 〈보기〉의 밑줄 친 부분과 바꿔 쓸 수 없는 것은?

┌─ 보기 ─┐

If it were not for Artificial Intelligence, the robots could not decide what to do.

① Were it not for Artificial Intelligence,
② Without Artificial Intelligence,
③ Had it not been for Artificial Intelligence,
④ But for Artificial Intelligence,
⑤ If there were no Artificial Intelligence,

16 다음 중 〈보기〉의 문장과 의미가 가장 가까운 것을 고르시오.

┌─ 보기 ─┐

If Kobe were in good condition, he would make three times as many clean shots as any other players.

① As Kobe was not in good condition, he didn't make three times as many clean shots as any other players.
② As Kobe is not in good condition, he doesn't make three times as many clean shots as any other players.
③ Though Kobe was not in good condition, he made three times as many clean shots as any other players.
④ As Kobe isn't in good condition, he didn't make three times as many clean shots as any other players.
⑤ As Kobe was in good condition, he made three times as many clean shots as any other players.

17 다음 우리말을 주어진 어구들과 조건에 맞게 영작하시오.

로봇들이 인간의 감정을 느낄 수 있다면, 우리는 그들과 함께 놀 수 있을 텐데
(can, sense, with, human emotions 활용. If로 시작, 단어 변형 가능, 총 10 단어로 할 것.)

➡ _____

_____

[18~20] 다음 글을 읽고 물음에 답하시오.

Where Do We See Robots?

Robots are not only in movies and books ____ⓐ____ . Around the world, robots are doing (A)a variety of tasks. There are delivery robots ____ⓑ____ in the sky, robot arms in factories, and service robots in public places.

• A delivery robot in the sky
• Robot arms in a factory
• A service robot at the PyeongChang Olympics

18 위 글의 빈칸 ⓐ에 들어갈 알맞은 말을 모두 고르시오.

① no longer   ② anymore
③ anywhere   ④ no more
⑤ any longer

19 위 글의 빈칸 ⓑ에 fly를 알맞은 형태로 쓰시오.

➡ _____

20 위 글의 밑줄 친 (A)a variety of와 바꿔 쓸 수 있는 한 단어를 쓰시오.

➡ _____

[21~23] 다음 글을 읽고 물음에 답하시오.

_____ ⓐ _____

Robots are making things faster and easier. They can help us anywhere — in our homes, on roads, or in disaster areas.

Home Helper Robot

This robot helps your family throughout the day. Cooking and cleaning would be easier if you had ⓑone. It also talks with family members and can sense emotions.

21 위 글의 빈칸 ⓐ에 들어갈 제목으로 알맞은 것을 고르시오.

① Looking toward the Future
② Life with a Home Helper Robot
③ Robots Are Becoming Smart
④ Robots around Us – Present and Future
⑤ Let's Enjoy Talking with Robots

22 위 글의 밑줄 친 ⓑone이 가리키는 것을 본문에서 찾아 쓰시오.

➡ _____

23 다음 중 '집안일 도우미 로봇'이 할 수 있는 일이 <u>아닌</u> 것을 고르시오.

① 요리
② 재난 지역 복구
③ 청소
④ 가족과 이야기하기
⑤ 가족의 감정을 파악하기

[24~25] 다음 글을 읽고 물음에 답하시오.

Looking toward the Future

Our future with robots looks bright but not perfect. Some people expect life to become more convenient with the help of robots. However, _____ ⓐ _____ worry about problems they might cause, such as threats to our jobs and safety. The important thing is ⓑto find possible solutions and to ensure that robots are only used for good.

24 위 글의 빈칸 ⓐ에 들어갈 알맞은 말을 고르시오.

① the other
② another
③ the others
④ each other
⑤ other people

25 아래 〈보기〉에서 위 글의 밑줄 친 ⓑ와 to부정사의 용법이 <u>다른</u> 것의 개수를 고르시오.

┌─── 보기 ───┐
① I need a pencil <u>to write</u> with.
② I have to study hard <u>to pass</u> the exam.
③ He grew up <u>to be</u> a doctor.
④ It is very important <u>to study</u> English hard.
⑤ She must be stupid <u>to marry</u> him.
└─────────┘

① 1개   ② 2개   ③ 3개   ④ 4개   ⑤ 5개

MEMO

Lesson

8

Which Is the Best Way?

Words & Expressions

Key Words

- **agree**[əgríː] 동 동의하다, 찬성하다
- **attack**[ətǽk] 동 공격하다
- **bottom**[bátəm] 명 밑, 바닥
- **climb**[klaim] 동 오르다, 올라가다
- **compare**[kəmpέər] 동 비교하다
- **correct**[kərékt] 형 옳은
- **create**[kriéit] 동 창조하다
- **destination**[dèstənéiʃən] 명 목적지, 도착지
- **disagree**[dìsəgríː] 동 동의하지 않다, 의견이 다르다
- **further**[fə́ːrðər] 부 더 멀리 형 더 먼
- **gone**[gɔ(ː)n] 형 가버린, 떠난
- **guide**[gaid] 명 안내인, 가이드
- **hunger**[hʌ́ŋgər] 명 굶주림
- **hurry**[hə́ːri] 동 서두르다, 서둘러 가다
- **kindness**[káindnis] 명 친절
- **move**[muːv] 동 움직이다, 감동시키다
- **path**[pæθ] 명 길

- **pioneer**[pàiəníər] 명 선구자, 개척자
- **protect**[prətékt] 동 보호하다
- **reach**[riːtʃ] 동 ~에 이르다[닿다], 도착하다
- **realize**[ríːəlàiz] 동 깨닫다, 자각하다
- **separate**[sépərèit] 형 분리된, 서로 다른
- **solve**[sɑlv] 동 (문제, 곤경을) 해결하다, 풀다
- **someday**[sʌ́mdei] 부 (미래의) 언젠가, 훗날
- **straight**[streit] 부 똑바로
- **strongly**[strɔ́ːŋli] 부 강경히, 강하게
- **survival**[sərváivəl] 명 생존
- **take**[teik] 동 (시간이) 걸리다
- **thick**[θik] 형 두꺼운, (나무가) 울창한
- **thief**[θiːf] 명 도둑
- **travel**[trǽvəl] 명 여행 동 여행하다
- **whole**[houl] 형 전체의, 모든
- **wisdom**[wízdəm] 명 지혜, 슬기
- **wise**[waiz] 형 지혜로운, 현명한

Key Expressions

- **a group of** ~의 집단
- **act on** ~에 따라 행동하다
- **become lost** 길을 잃다
- **die of** ~으로 죽다
- **even though** ~일지라도
- **for a while** 잠시 동안
- **go on forever** 무한정 계속되다
- **in the end** 마침내, 결국

- **keep ~ing** 계속 ~하다
- **make one's way to ~** ~로 나아가다
- **on the way** 가는 길에
- **shake one's head** 고개를 가로젓다
- **thanks to ~** ~ 덕분에
- **the way out** 나가는 길, 출구
- **without ~ing** ~하지 않고

Word Power

※ 서로 비슷한 뜻을 가진 어휘

☐ **climb** 오르다, 올라가다 : **ascend** 올라가다, 오르다

☐ **in the end** 마침내, 결국 : **finally** 마침내, 결국

☐ **move** 옮기다, 감동시키다 : **touch** 마음을 움직이다, 감동시키다

☐ **separate** 분리된 : **divided** 분리된

☐ **thick** 두꺼운, (나무가) 울창한 : **dense** 밀집한, 빽빽한

☐ **hurry** 서두르다 : **rush** 급히 움직이다, 서두르다

☐ **kindness** 친절 : **goodwill** 선의, 친절

☐ **path** 길 : **way** 길, 도로

☐ **someday** (미래의) 언젠가 : **one day** 어느 날, 언젠가

☐ **wisdom** 지혜, 슬기 : **knowledge** 지식, 지혜

※ 서로 반대의 뜻을 가진 어휘

☐ **agree** 동의하다 ↔ **disagree** 동의하지 않다, 의견이 다르다

☐ **climb** 오르다, 올라가다 ↔ **descend** 내려가다

☐ **separate** 분리된 ↔ **connected** 연결된, 일관된

☐ **whole** 전체의 ↔ **partial** 일부의, 부분적인

☐ **bottom** 밑, 바닥 ↔ **top** 꼭대기, 정상

☐ **kindness** 친절 ↔ **unkindness** 불친절, 몰인정

☐ **thick** 두꺼운, (나무가) 울창한 ↔ **thin** 얇은, 가느다란

☐ **wisdom** 지혜, 슬기 ↔ **foolishness** 어리석음

※ 접두사 dis-

☐ **dis-+use** → **disuse** 사용하지 않음

☐ **dis-+cover** → **discover** 발견하다

☐ **dis-+count** → **discount** 할인하다

☐ **dis-+like** → **dislike** 싫어하다

☐ **dis-+close** → **disclose** 밝히다, 폭로하다

※ 접미사 -ness

☐ **bright+-ness** → **brightness** 빛남, 밝음

☐ **kind+-ness** → **kindness** 친절함

☐ **good+-ness** → **goodness** 선량함

☐ **busy+-ness** → **business** 사업, 업무

☐ **happy+-ness** → **happiness** 행복

☐ **weak+-ness** → **weakness** 약함, 약점

☐ **ill+-ness** → **illness** 병

English Dictionary

☐ **agree** 동의하다, 찬성하다
→ to accept an idea suggested by someone else
다른 어떤 사람이 제안한 아이디어를 받아들이다

☐ **attack** 공격하다
→ to try to hurt or damage 피해를 입히거나 다치게 하다

☐ **destination** 목적지, 도착지
→ the place where somebody or something is going or being sent
어떤 사람이나 사물이 가고 있는 혹은 보내지고 있는 장소

☐ **hunger** 굶주림
→ the feeling of needing food 음식을 필요로 하는 느낌

☐ **kindness** 친절
→ the quality of behaving in a thoughtful, helpful, or friendly way
사려 깊고, 도움이 되거나 친절한 방식으로 행동하는 성질

☐ **move** 감동시키다
→ to cause someone to feel strong emotions
어떤 사람에게 강렬한 감정을 불러일으키게 하다

☐ **pioneer** 선구자, 개척자
→ one of the first people to do something or to travel to a new area
어떤 일을 하거나 새로운 곳을 여행하는 최초의 사람들 중의 하나

☐ **realize** 깨닫다, 자각하다
→ to know and understand that something is true or has happened
어떤 것이 사실이거나 일어났다는 것을 알고 이해하다

☐ **separate** 분리된
→ not together or the same 같이 있지 않거나 같지 않은

☐ **survival** 생존
→ the state of continuing to live, after despite difficult conditions
어려운 상황에도 불구하고 이후에 계속 살아남는 상태

The Five Wise Men

One day, five wise men met on the road. They agreed to travel
<small>to부정사를 목적어로 취하는 동사</small>
together. On the way, however, they became lost in a thick forest.
Before walking any further, they decided to stop and find the best
<small>to stop과 (to) find out이 등위접속사
and로 병렬 연결되어 있음.</small>
way out.

After thinking for a while, the first man said, "I strongly feel that
<small>명사절을 이끄는 접속사</small>
we should go left."

The second man said, "We should go right, because *right* also means
'correct.'"

Then the third man said, "Let's walk back. We came that way, so we
<small>뒤돌아서</small>
can leave that way. Then we can walk around the forest."

The fourth man disagreed and said, "I think we should keep walking
<small>동사 think 뒤에 명사절을 이끄는 접속사 that이 생략   동명사를 목적어로 취하는 동사, ~을 계속하다</small>
straight. The forest cannot go on forever. A new path will open."

Looking at them all, the fifth man shook his head and said, "I know
<small>동시동작을 나타내는 분사구문: ~하면서</small>
how to solve this. Just wait."
<small>'의문사+to부정사'가 동사 know의 목적어로 쓰임.</small>

---

wise 지혜로운, 현명한

agree 동의하다, 찬성하다

travel 여행하다

thick 두꺼운, (나무가) 울창한

further 더 멀리

correct 옳은

disagree 동의하지 않다, 의견이 다르다

straight 똑바로

path 길

shake one's head 고개를 가로젓다

solve (문제·곤경을) 해결하다

📎 **확인문제**

● 다음 문장이 본문의 내용과 일치하면 T, 일치하지 <u>않으면</u> F를 쓰시오.

1 One day, five wise men met on the road. ☐

2 Five wise men agreed to travel separately. ☐

3 On the way, they became lost in a thick forest. ☐

4 After thinking for a while, the first man felt that he should go right. ☐

5 The fourth man said he should keep walking straight. ☐

6 The fifth man just kept silent. ☐

He started to climb the tallest tree he could find. As he climbed,

everyone else decided to go their separate ways.

When the fifth man reached the top, he could see the whole forest.

Looking at all the paths, he found the shortest way out. He hurried

down to tell the others. However, when he got to the bottom, everyone

was gone. He thought to himself, *Where did they go? I found the best*

way out. He thought they were all wrong and he was the only wise

man.

climb 오르다, 올라가다

separate 분리된, 서로 다른

reach ~에 이르다[닿다]

whole 전체의, 모든

hurry 서두르다

bottom 밑, 바닥

확인문제

● 다음 문장이 본문의 내용과 일치하면 T, 일치하지 <u>않으면</u> F를 쓰시오.

1   The fifth man started to climb the tallest tree he could find. ☐

2   As the fifth man climbed, everyone else decided to go together. ☐

3   Reaching the top, the fifth man could see the whole forest. ☐

4   Looking at all the paths, the fifth man found the safest way out. ☐

5   When the fifth man got to the bottom, everyone was gone. ☐

6   The fifth man thought he was wrong and the others were wise. ☐

However, he was wrong. Everyone was wise. Each man had chosen

과거완료로 과거 시점을 기준으로 그 이전에 일어난 일이 과거의 한 시점까지 영향을 미치는 것을 나타낼 때 씀.

his path and created his future.

The man who went to the left walked deeper into the forest. He was

주격 관계대명사

attacked by wild animals and almost died of hunger. Soon he learned

거의

how to protect himself and find food. In the end, he made his way out

재귀대명사(재귀 용법)

of the forest and taught others survival skills.

수여동사　간접목적어　직접목적어

The man who went to the right met a group of thieves. They took

everything from him and made him join them. While he was with

them, he showed them great kindness. The thieves were moved by his

kindness and learned from his wisdom. Later, they also became wise

men.

The man who walked back created a safe path around the forest.

Using this path, people could get where they were going without

때를 나타내는 분사구문: ~할 때

getting lost, even though the trip took a little longer.

양보의 부사절을 이끄는 접속사: (비록) ~임에도

---

attack 공격하다
die of ~로 죽다
hunger 굶주림
protect 보호하다
make one's way (to) (~로) 나아가다
survival 생존
thief 도둑 (*pl.* thieves)
kindness 친절함
move 움직이다, 감동시키다
wisdom 지혜, 슬기

📎 **확인문제**

● 다음 문장이 본문의 내용과 일치하면 T, 일치하지 <u>않으면</u> F를 쓰시오.

1　Each man had chosen his path and created his future. ☐

2　The man who went to the right walked deeper into the forest. ☐

3　After the man who went to the left made his way out of the forest, he taught others survival skills. ☐

4　The man who went to the left met a group of thieves. ☐

5　The thieves were moved by the kindness of the man who went to the right and learned from his wisdom. ☐

The man who went straight became a pioneer. He left the forest and discovered places no one else had been before. Thanks to him, people could enjoy these new beautiful lands.

places 뒤에 선행사 places를 수식하는 관계부사 where가 생략

과거 시점을 기준으로 그 이전에 일어난 일이 과거의 한 시점까지 영향을 미치는 상태를 나타내는 과거완료

The man who climbed the tree became a guide. Since he had found many different paths, he was able to teach people how to find the quickest ways to their destinations.

과거 시점을 기준으로 그 이전에 있었던 일을 나타낼 때 쓰인 과거완료

'의문사+to부정사'는 '의문사+주어+should/can+동사'로 바꿔 쓸 수 있다.

This is how the five men found their own paths. Like them, we are each on our own journey in life, and we cannot compare one journey to another. You have to create your own path. Listen to yourself, make a decision, and act on it. Then, someday, you will realize that you have been living the life that is right for you.

이것이 (주어)가 ~한 방법이다. the way how(×)

각자(we와 동격)

realize의 목적어 역할을 하는 명사절을 이끄는 접속사

have been V-ing(현재완료 진행형): 과거부터 현재까지 동작이 계속되고 있음을 나타냄.

주격 관계대명사

pioneer 선구자, 개척자
discover 발견하다
guide 안내인, 가이드
destination 목적지, 도착지
on one's journey 여행 중에
compare 비교하다
create 창조하다
make a decision 결정하다
act on ~에 따라 행동하다
realize 깨닫다

 확인문제

● 다음 문장이 본문의 내용과 일치하면 T, 일치하지 않으면 F를 쓰시오.

1 The man who went straight became a pioneer and discovered places no one else had been before. ☐

2 Thanks to the man who climbed the tree, people could enjoy the new beautiful lands. ☐

3 The man who climbed the tree was able to teach people how to find the quickest ways to their destinations. ☐

4 We should compare one journey to another. ☐

5 You have to create your own path. ☐

6 If you listen to yourself, make a decision, and act on it, you will realize that you have been living the best life in the world. ☐

● 우리말을 참고하여 빈칸에 알맞은 말을 쓰시오.

1 The Five _____ Men

2 One day, five wise men _____ on the road.

3 They _____ to travel together.

4 On the way, however, they _____ _____ in a thick forest.

5 Before walking _____ _____, they decided to stop and find the best way out.

6 After thinking _____ _____ _____, the first man said, "I strongly feel that we should go left."

7 The second man said, "We should go right, because *right* also means '_____.'"

8 Then the third man said, "Let's _____ _____.

9 We came that way, so we can _____ _____ _____.

10 Then we can _____ _____ the forest."

11 The fourth man disagreed and said, "I think we should _____ _____ straight.

12 The forest cannot _____ _____ _____.

13 A _____ _____ will open."

14 Looking at them all, the fifth man _____ _____ _____ and said, "I know how to solve this. Just wait."

15 He started to climb the tallest tree he _____ _____.

16 As he climbed, everyone else decided to go their _____ ways.

1 5명의 지혜로운 사람들

2 어느 날 5명의 지혜로운 사람들이 길에서 만났다.

3 그들은 여행을 함께 하기로 했다.

4 그러나 도중에 그들은 울창한 숲속에서 길을 잃게 되었다.

5 더 멀리 가기 전에 그들은 멈추고 빠져나갈 최선의 방법을 찾기로 결정했다.

6 잠시 동안 생각한 후, 첫 번째 남자는 "우리가 왼쪽으로 가야 한다는 생각이 강하게 들어요." 라고 말했다.

7 두 번째 남자가 "우리는 오른쪽으로 가야 해요. 왜냐하면 '오른쪽'은 또한 '옳은'이라는 의미이기 때문이죠."라고 말했다.

8 그러자 세 번째 남자가 "뒤로 돌아갑시다.

9 우리가 그 길로 왔으니 그 길로 나갈 수 있을 겁니다.

10 그러면 우리는 숲을 한 바퀴 돌 수 있고요."라고 말했다.

11 네 번째 남자가 이의를 제기하며 "나는 우리가 똑바로 계속 걸어 나가야 한다고 생각해요.

12 숲이 영원히 계속될 수는 없으니까요.

13 새로운 길이 열릴 것입니다."라고 말했다.

14 모두를 바라보면서 다섯 번째 남자가 고개를 저으며 "나는 이것을 해결하는 방법을 알아요. 잠깐 기다려 보세요."라고 말했다.

15 그는 그가 찾을 수 있는 가장 높은 나무를 오르기 시작했다.

16 그가 올라가자 다른 모든 사람들은 각자 서로 다른 길을 가기로 결정했다.

17 When the fifth man _____ the top, he could see the _____ forest.

18 Looking at all the paths, he found the _____ _____ _____.

19 He _____ _____ to tell the others.

20 However, when he got to the bottom, everyone _____ _____.

21 He _____ _____ _____, *Where did they go? I found the* _____ _____ _____.

22 He thought they were all _____ and he was _____ _____ _____ man.

23 However, he was _____.

24 _____ was wise.

25 Each man had chosen his path and _____ _____ _____.

26 The man who went to the left _____ _____ into the forest.

27 He _____ _____ by wild animals and almost _____ _____ hunger.

28 Soon he learned how to _____ _____ and find food.

29 In the end, he _____ _____ _____ _____ _____ the forest and taught others survival skills.

30 The man who went to the right met _____ _____ _____ thieves.

31 They took everything from him and made him _____ _____.

32 While he was with them, he showed them _____ _____.

---

17 다섯 번째 남자가 꼭대기에 이르자 그는 전체 숲을 볼 수 있었다.

18 모든 길을 바라보며 그는 빠져나갈 가장 짧은 길을 찾았다.

19 그는 다른 사람들에게 알리기 위해 급히 내려갔다.

20 하지만 그가 밑으로 내려왔을 때, 모든 사람들은 이미 가 버리고 없었다.

21 그는 '다들 어디 간 거야? 내가 빠져나갈 최선의 길을 찾았는데.'라고 마음속으로 생각했다.

22 그는 그들이 모두 틀렸고 자신이 유일하게 현명한 사람이라고 생각했다.

23 그러나 그가 틀렸다.

24 모두가 지혜로웠다.

25 각자 자신의 길을 선택했고 자신의 미래를 만들었다.

26 왼쪽으로 간 남자는 숲속으로 더 깊이 걸어 들어갔다.

27 그는 야생 동물들의 습격을 받았고 거의 굶어 죽을 뻔했다.

28 머지않아 그는 자신을 지키고 먹을 것을 찾는 방법을 터득했다.

29 결국 그는 숲 밖으로 빠져나왔고 다른 사람들에게 생존 기술을 가르쳤다.

30 오른쪽으로 간 남자는 도둑 무리를 만났다.

31 그들은 그에게서 모든 것을 가져갔고 그를 그들과 합류시켰다.

32 그는 그들과 함께 있는 동안 그들에게 많은 친절을 베풀었다.

33 The thieves _____ _____ by his kindness and learned from his wisdom.

34 _____, they also became wise men.

35 The man who walked back created _____ _____ _____ around the forest.

36 Using this path, people could get where they were going _____ _____ _____, even though the trip took a little longer.

37 The man who _____ _____ became a pioneer.

38 He left the forest and discovered places no one else _____ _____ before.

39 _____ _____ him, people could enjoy these new beautiful lands.

40 The man _____ _____ the tree became a guide.

41 Since he had found many different paths, he was able to teach people how to find _____ _____ _____ to their destinations.

42 _____ _____ _____ the five men found their own paths.

43 Like them, we are each on our own journey in life, and we cannot compare _____ _____ to _____.

44 You have to create _____ _____ _____.

45 Listen to yourself, make a decision, and _____ _____ _____.

46 Then, someday, you will realize that you _____ _____ the life that is right for you.

33 그 도둑들은 그의 친절에 감동을 받았고 그의 지혜에서 배우게 되었다.

34 나중에 그들 또한 지혜로운 사람들이 되었다.

35 뒤돌아 간 남자는 숲 주변에 안전한 길을 만들었다.

36 사람들은 이 길을 이용할 때 길을 잃지 않고 자신이 가고자 하는 길에 다다를 수 있었다. 비록 이동 시간이 약간 더 오래 걸려도 말이다.

37 똑바로 간 남자는 개척자가 되었다.

38 그는 숲을 벗어나 아무도 이전에 가 본 적이 없는 곳을 발견했다.

39 그 남자 덕분에, 사람들은 이 새롭고 아름다운 지역을 즐길 수 있었다.

40 나무 위로 올라간 남자는 가이드가 되었다.

41 그는 여러 다양한 길을 발견했었기 때문에, 사람들에게 자신의 목적지에 이르는 가장 빠른 길을 찾는 법을 가르쳐 줄 수 있었다.

42 이런 식으로 다섯 남자는 자신만의 길을 찾아냈다.

43 그들처럼 우리는 각각 인생에서 자기 자신만의 여행을 하고 있고, 우리는 한 여정을 다른 것과 비교할 수 없다.

44 당신은 당신 자신만의 길을 만들어가야 한다.

45 자신의 목소리를 듣고, 결정하고, 그 결정에 따라 행동하라.

46 그러면 언젠가 당신은 당신에게 맞는 삶을 살아가고 있다는 것을 깨닫게 될 것이다.

● 우리말을 참고하여 본문을 영작하시오.

1 5명의 지혜로운 사람들

➡ _____

2 어느 날 5명의 지혜로운 사람들이 길에서 만났다.

➡ _____

3 그들은 여행을 함께 하기로 했다.

➡ _____

4 그러나 도중에 그들은 울창한 숲속에서 길을 잃게 되었다.

➡ _____

5 더 멀리 가기 전에 그들은 멈추고 빠져나갈 최선의 방법을 찾기로 결정했다.

➡ _____

6 잠시 동안 생각한 후, 첫 번째 남자는 "우리가 왼쪽으로 가야 한다는 생각이 강하게 들어요."
라고 말했다.

➡ _____

7 두 번째 남자가 "우리는 오른쪽으로 가야 해요. 왜냐하면 '오른쪽'은 또한 '옳은'이라는 의미이기
때문이죠."라고 말했다.

➡ _____

8 그러자 세 번째 남자가 "뒤로 돌아갑시다.

➡ _____

9 우리가 그 길로 왔으니 그 길로 나갈 수 있을 겁니다.

➡ _____

10 그러면 우리는 숲을 한 바퀴 돌 수 있고요."라고 말했다.

➡ _____

11 네 번째 남자가 이의를 제기하며 "나는 우리가 똑바로 계속 걸어 나가야 한다고 생각해요.

➡ _____

12 숲이 영원히 계속될 수는 없으니까요.

➡ _____

13 새로운 길이 열릴 것입니다."라고 말했다.

➡ _____

14 모두를 바라보면서 다섯 번째 남자가 고개를 저으며 "나는 이것을 해결하는 방법을 알아요.
잠깐 기다려 보세요."라고 말했다.

➡ _____

15 그는 그가 찾을 수 있는 가장 높은 나무를 오르기 시작했다.

➡ _____

16 그가 올라가자 다른 모든 사람들은 각자 서로 다른 길을 가기로 결정했다.

➡ _____

17 다섯 번째 남자가 꼭대기에 이르자 그는 전체 숲을 볼 수 있었다.

➡ _____

18 모든 길을 바라보며 그는 빠져나갈 가장 짧은 길을 찾았다.

➡ _____

19 그는 다른 사람들에게 알리기 위해 급히 내려갔다.

➡ _____

20 하지만 그가 밑으로 내려왔을 때, 모든 사람들은 이미 가 버리고 없었다.

➡ _____

21 그는 '다들 어디 간 거야? 내가 빠져나갈 최선의 길을 찾았는데.'라고 마음속으로 생각했다.

➡ _____

22 그는 그들이 모두 틀렸고 자신이 유일하게 현명한 사람이라고 생각했다.

➡ _____

23 그러나 그가 틀렸다.

➡ _____

24 모두가 지혜로웠다.

➡ _____

25 각자 자신의 길을 선택했고 자신의 미래를 만들었다.

➡ _____

26 왼쪽으로 간 남자는 숲속으로 더 깊이 걸어 들어갔다.

➡ _____

27 그는 야생 동물들의 습격을 받았고 거의 굶어 죽을 뻔했다.

➡ _____

28 머지않아 그는 자신을 지키고 먹을 것을 찾는 방법을 터득했다.

➡ _____

29 결국 그는 숲 밖으로 빠져나왔고 다른 사람에게 생존 기술을 가르쳤다.

➡ _____

30 오른쪽으로 간 남자는 도둑 무리를 만났다.

➡ _____

31 그들은 그에게서 모든 것을 가져갔고 그를 그들과 합류시켰다.

➡ _____

32 그는 그들과 함께 있는 동안 그들에게 많은 친절을 베풀었다.

➡ _____

33 그 도둑들은 그의 친절에 감동을 받았고 그의 지혜에서 배우게 되었다.

➡ _____

34 나중에 그들 또한 지혜로운 사람들이 되었다.

➡ _____

35 뒤돌아 간 남자는 숲 주변에 안전한 길을 만들었다.

➡ _____

36 사람들은 이 길을 이용할 때 길을 잃지 않고 자신이 가고자 하는 길에 다다를 수 있었다. 비록 이동 시간이 약간 더 오래 걸려도 말이다.

➡ _____

_____

37 똑바로 간 남자는 개척자가 되었다.

➡ _____

38 그는 숲을 벗어나 아무도 이전에 가 본 적이 없는 곳을 발견했다.

➡ _____

39 그 남자 덕분에, 사람들은 이 새롭고 아름다운 지역을 즐길 수 있었다.

➡ _____

40 나무 위로 올라간 남자는 가이드가 되었다.

➡ _____

41 그는 여러 다양한 길을 발견했었기 때문에, 사람들에게 자신의 목적지에 이르는 가장 빠른 길을 찾는 법을 가르쳐 줄 수 있었다.

➡ _____

_____

42 이런 식으로 다섯 남자는 자신만의 길을 찾아냈다.

➡ _____

43 그들처럼 우리는 각각 인생에서 자기 자신만의 여행을 하고 있고, 우리는 한 여정을 다른 것과 비교할 수 없다.

➡ _____

44 당신은 당신 자신만의 길을 만들어가야 한다.

➡ _____

45 자신의 목소리를 듣고, 결정하고, 그 결정에 따라 행동하라.

➡ _____

46 그러면 언젠가 당신은 당신에게 맞는 삶을 살아가고 있다는 것을 깨닫게 될 것이다.

➡ _____

01 다음 빈칸에 알맞은 단어를 〈보기〉에서 골라 쓰시오. (필요하면 어형을 바꿀 것.)

> ┤ 보기 ├
>
> move   hunger   discover   wisdom

(1) _____ causes great suffering in the world.

(2) Columbus wasn't the first person to _____ America.

(3) It is good to hear the _____ of great people.

(4) I was _____ by her songs and her beautiful voice.

02 주어진 단어의 영영풀이가 잘못된 것을 고르시오.

① agree: to accept an idea suggested by someone else

② attack: to prevent someone or something from being harmed or damaged

③ survival: the state of continuing to live, after despite difficult conditions

④ pioneer: one of the first people to do something or to travel to a new area

⑤ destination: the place where somebody or something is going or being sent

03 다음 우리말에 맞게 주어진 어휘를 모두 사용하여 분사구문으로 시작하는 문장을 만드시오. (동사만 변형 가능)

(1) 그들 모두를 바라보며, 다섯 번째 남자가 고개를 저었다. (the fifth man, his head, them all, look at, shake)

➡ _____

_____

(2) 당신 자신의 목소리를 들으면, 당신의 삶이 옳다는 것을 깨닫게 될 것이다. (you, yourself, your life, listen to, is, realize, will, that, right)

➡ _____

_____

(3) 그의 친절에 감동 받아, 도둑들은 그의 지혜에서 배우게 되었다. (the thieves, his kindness, his wisdom, learn, move, by, from)

➡ _____

_____

04 다음 글에서 어법상 어색한 부분을 찾아 바르게 고치시오.

> Since he has found many different paths, he was able to teach people how to find the quickest ways to their destinations.

➡ _____

_____

05 다음 우리말과 일치하도록 괄호 안의 단어를 활용하여 빈칸을 채우시오.

그는 야생 동물들의 습격을 받았고 거의 굶어 죽을 뻔했다. 머지않아 그는 자신을 지키고 먹을 것을 찾는 방법을 터득했다.

➡ He _____ _____ _____ wild animals and almost died of hunger. Soon he learned _____ _____ _____ _____ and find food.

(how, attack, protect, to)

After thinking for a while, the first man said, "I strongly feel that we should go left."

The second man said, "We should go right, because *right* also means 'correct.'"

Then the third man said, "Let's walk back. We came that way, so we can leave that way. Then we can walk around the forest."

The fourth man disagreed and said, "I think we should keep ___ⓐ___ straight. The forest cannot go on forever. A new path will open."

ⓑLooking at them all, the fifth man shook his head and said, "I know how to solve this. Just wait."

06 위 글의 빈칸 ⓐ에 walk를 알맞은 형태로 쓰시오.

➡ _____

07 위 글의 밑줄 친 분사구문 ⓑ를 부사절로 고치시오.

➡ _____ 또는

_____

08 두 번째 남자가 "우리는 오른쪽으로 가야 해요."라고 말한 이유를 우리말로 쓰시오.

➡ _____

[09~10] 다음 글을 읽고 물음에 답하시오.

The man who went to the right met a group of thieves. They took everything from him and made him join them. While he was with them, he showed ⓐthem great kindness. ⓑ The thieves were moved by his kindness and learned from his wisdom. Later, they also became wise men.

The man who walked back created a safe path around the forest. Using this path, people could get where they were going without getting lost, even though the trip took a little longer.

09 위 글의 밑줄 친 ⓐthem이 가리키는 것을 본문에서 찾아 쓰시오.

➡ _____

10 위 글의 밑줄 친 ⓑ를 능동태로 고치시오.

➡ _____

[11~12] 다음 글을 읽고 물음에 답하시오.

ⓐThis is the way how the five men found their own paths. Like them, we are each on our own journey in life, and we cannot compare one journey to another. You have to create your own path. Listen to yourself, make a decision, and act on it. Then, someday, you will realize that you have been living the life that is right for you.

11 위 글의 밑줄 친 ⓐ에서 어법상 틀린 부분을 찾아 고치시오.

_____ ➡ _____

_____

12 본문의 내용과 일치하도록 다음 빈칸 (A)와 (B)에 알맞은 단어를 쓰시오.

Each of you are on (A)_____ _____

_____ in life, and you cannot compare one journey to another. You have to create (B)_____ _____ _____ by listening to yourself, making a decision, and acting on it.

출제율 95%

01 다음 빈칸에 공통으로 들어갈 말을 쓰시오.

> • You'll pass a bank _____ the way to the train station.
> • If you only act _____ instinct, you are an animal.

출제율 90%

02 다음 빈칸에 알맞은 단어를 〈보기〉에서 골라 쓰시오. (필요하면 어형을 바꿀 것.)

> ┌─ 보기 ─┐
> climb   realize   compare   disagree

(1) I will _____ the prices of several digital cameras online.

(2) Janet _____ with her parents on everything.

(3) It is not easy to _____ the mountain.

(4) They didn't _____ how creative their work was.

출제율 95%

03 다음 짝지어진 단어의 관계가 같도록 빈칸에 알맞은 말을 주어진 철자로 시작하여 쓰시오.

(1) move – touch : separate – d_____

(2) bottom – top : kindness – u_____

(3) agree – disagree : t_____ – thin

출제율 90%

04 밑줄 친 부분과 바꿔 쓸 수 있는 말을 고르시오.

> We can't arrive at the airport in time.

① realize   ② compare   ③ disagree
④ solve   ⑤ reach

출제율 100%

05 다음 우리말에 맞도록 빈칸에 알맞은 말을 쓰시오. (철자가 주어진 것도 있음.)

(1) 우리는 대기 오염 문제를 해결해야 한다.
➡ We should s_____ the problem of air pollution.

(2) 모든 동물들은 그들만의 생존 방법이 있다.
➡ All animals have their own ways of _____.

(3) 코페르니쿠스는 시대를 앞선 선구자라는 점에서 개척자로 여겨졌다.
➡ Corpernicus was considered a p_____ because he was ahead of his time.

(4) 나는 제시간에 목적지에 도착했다.
➡ I reached my d_____ on time.

출제율 95%

06 다음 영영풀이를 보고 빈칸에 알맞은 단어를 주어진 철자로 시작하여 쓰시오.

> to know and understand that something is true or has happened

> I don't think you r_____ how important this is to her.

출제율 95%

07 다음 밑줄 친 to부정사들 중 쓰임이 다른 것을 고르시오.

① One day, five wise men agreed to travel together.

② Before walking any further, they decided to stop and find the best way out.

③ The fifth wise man started to climb the tallest tree he could find.

④ The fifth wise man hurried down from the tree to tell the others.

⑤ Each man left there and chose to create his own future.

08 다음 중 〈보기〉의 밑줄 친 부분을 같은 의미로 알맞게 바꾼 것은?

┌─── 보기 ┐

He was able to teach people how to find the quickest ways to their destinations.

① He was able to teach people how they found the quickest ways to their destinations.
② He was able to teach people how they had found the quickest ways to their destinations.
③ He was able to teach people how he had found the quickest ways to their destinations.
④ He was able to teach people how could they find the quickest ways to their destinations.
⑤ He was able to teach people how they should find the quickest ways to their destinations.

09 다음 밑줄 친 부분 중 어법상 어색한 것을 고르시오.

① He left the forest and discovered places no one else had been before.
② Since he had found many different paths, he was able to teach people how to find the ways to their destinations.
③ When he got to the bottom of the tree, everyone had already gone.
④ When the fifth man reached the top, he had seen the whole forest.
⑤ He asked himself when and where they had gone.

10 다음 중 주어진 〈보기〉의 문장에서 밑줄 친 부분을 분사구문으로 알맞게 바꾼 것을 고르시오.

┌─── 보기 ┐

When he met the thieves, the man gave them his all money.

① Meeting the thieves, the man gave them his all money.
② He meeting the thieves, the man gave them his all money.
③ His meeting the thieves, the man gave them his all money.
④ Having met the thieves, the man gave them his all money.
⑤ When he meeting the thieves, the man gave them his all money.

11 다음 〈보기〉의 두 문장을 하나의 문장으로 만들 때 어법상 옳지 않은 것은?

┌─── 보기 ┐

• This is the way.
• The five men found their own paths in the way.

① This is the way the five men found their own paths.
② This is the way in which the five men found their own paths.
③ This is the way that the five men found their own paths.
④ This is the way in that the five men found their own paths.
⑤ This is how the five men found their own paths.

✏️ 출제율 90%

12 다음 주어진 우리말에 맞게 괄호 안의 단어를 알맞게 배열하여 빈칸에 넣으시오.

> 언젠가 당신은 당신에게 맞는 삶을 살아가고 있다는 것을 깨닫게 될 것이다.
> (you, that, that, realize, living, right, the life, been, is, have)

➡️ Someday, you will _____
_____ for you.

[13~14] 다음 〈보기〉에 주어진 어구들을 사용하여, 각 번호의 그림에 대한 우리말 설명에 맞게 빈칸을 채우시오.

┌─ 보기 ┐
(중복 사용 가능, 동사 변형 가능)
where / without / find / create / walk / get / even though / who / the / how / quick / they / tree / use / back / be / climb / to
└─────┘

✏️ 출제율 95%

13

> 나무 위로 올라간 남자는 가이드가 되었다. 그는 여러 다양한 길을 발견했었기 때문에, 사람들에게 자신의 목적지에 이르는 가장 빠른 길을 찾는 법을 가르쳐 줄 수 있었다.

➡️ The man _____ _____ _____
_____ became a guide. Since he
_____ _____ many different
paths, he was able to teach people
_____ _____ _____ _____
_____ ways to their destinations.

✏️ 출제율 95%

14

> 뒤돌아 간 남자는 숲 주변에 안전한 길을 만들었다. 사람들은 이 길을 이용할 때 길을 잃지 않고 자신이 가고자 하는 길에 다다를 수 있었다. 비록 이동 시간이 약간 더 오래 걸려도 말이다.

➡️ The man _____ _____ _____
_____ a safe path around the forest.
_____ this path, people could
_____ _____ _____
going _____ _____ lost, _____
_____ the trip took a little longer.

[15~17] 다음 글을 읽고 물음에 답하시오.

> After thinking for a while, the first man said, "I strongly feel that we should go left."
> The second man said, "We should go right, because *right* also means 'correct.'"
> Then the third man said, "Let's walk back. We came that way, so we can leave that way. Then we can walk around the forest."
> The fourth man disagreed and said, "I think we should keep walking straight. The forest cannot go on forever. A new path will open."
> ⓐLooking at them all, the fifth man nodded his head and said, "I know how to solve this. Just wait."

15 출제율 90%

Why did the fourth man suggest that they should keep walking straight? Fill in the blanks (A) and (B) with suitable words.

> Because he believed the forest could not go on (A)_____ and that (B)_____ _____ would open.

16 출제율 95%

위 글의 밑줄 친 ⓐ에서 흐름상 어색한 부분을 찾아 고치시오.

➡ _____ ➡ _____

17 출제율 100%

According to the passage, which is NOT true?

① The first man strongly felt that they should go left.
② The second man said they should go right.
③ The word 'right' means 'to the right side' and 'correct.'
④ The third man suggested that they should walk straight.
⑤ The fifth man said he knew how to solve the problem.

[18~20] 다음 글을 읽고 물음에 답하시오.

He started to climb the tallest tree he could find. (①) As he climbed, everyone else decided to go their separate ways. (②)

When the fifth man reached the top, he could see the whole forest. (③) He hurried down to tell the others. (④) ____ⓐ____, when he got to the bottom, everyone was gone. (⑤) He thought to himself, *Where did* ⓑ*they* go? *I found the best way out.* He thought they were all wrong and he was the only wise man.

18 출제율 95%

위 글의 빈칸 ⓐ에 들어갈 알맞은 말을 고르시오.

① For example ② That is
③ Moreover ④ However
⑤ Therefore

19 출제율 100%

위 글의 흐름으로 보아, 주어진 문장이 들어가기에 가장 적절한 곳은?

> Looking at all the paths, he found the shortest way out.

①   ②   ③   ④   ⑤

20 출제율 90%

위 글의 밑줄 친 ⓑ*they*가 가리키는 것을 본문에서 찾아 쓰시오.

➡ _____

[21~24] 다음 글을 읽고 물음에 답하시오.

The man who went to the left walked deeper into the forest. He was attacked by wild animals and almost died ____ⓐ____ hunger. (A) Soon he learned how to protect him and find food. In the end, he made his way out of the forest and taught others survival skills.

The man who went to the right met a group of thieves. They took everything ____ⓑ____ him and made him join them. While he was with them, he showed them great kindness. The thieves were (B)moved by his kindness and learned from his wisdom. Later, they also became wise men.

21 출제율 95%

위 글의 빈칸 ⓐ와 ⓑ에 들어갈 전치사가 바르게 짝지어진 것은?

	ⓐ	ⓑ		ⓐ	ⓑ
①	for	from	②	of	from
③	from	to	④	for	to
⑤	of	for			

출제율 90%

22 위 글의 밑줄 친 (A)에서 어법상 틀린 부분을 찾아 고치시오.

➡ _____

출제율 95%

23 위 글의 밑줄 친 (B)moved와 같은 의미로 쓰인 것을 고르시오.

① Time <u>moved</u> on.
② He <u>moved</u> to Seoul last week.
③ We <u>moved</u> our chairs a little nearer.
④ I <u>moved</u> that the meeting should start.
⑤ The sight <u>moved</u> me to tears.

출제율 100%

24 Which question CANNOT be answered after reading the passage?

① What attacked the man who went to the left?
② What did the man who went to the left do after he made his way out of the forest?
③ Whom did the man who went to the right meet?
④ How long did the man who went to the right live with the thieves?
⑤ How did the thieves become wise?

[25~26] 다음 글을 읽고 물음에 답하시오.

The man who went straight became a pioneer. He left the forest and discovered places no one else ___ⓐ___ before. Thanks to him, people could enjoy these new beautiful lands.

The man who climbed the tree became a guide. Since he had found many different paths, ⓑhe was able to teach people how to find the quickest ways to their destinations.

출제율 90%

25 위 글의 빈칸 ⓐ에 be를 알맞은 형태로 쓰시오.

➡ _____

출제율 95%

26 위 글의 밑줄 친 ⓑ를 다음과 같이 바꿔 쓸 때 빈칸에 들어갈 알맞은 말을 두 단어로 쓰시오.

➡ he was able to teach people how _____ _____ find the quickest ways to their destinations

[27~28] 다음 글을 읽고 물음에 답하시오.

This is how the five men found their own paths. Like them, we are each on our own journey in life, and we cannot compare one journey to another. You have to create your own path. Listen to yourself, make a decision, and act on it. Then, someday, you will realize that you have been living the life that is right for you.

출제율 95%

27 위 글의 분위기로 가장 알맞은 것을 고르시오.

① instructive   ② cynical
③ confusing   ④ skeptical
⑤ festive

출제율 100%

28 위 글의 주제로 알맞은 것을 고르시오.

① the way the five men found their own paths
② the benefit of comparing one journey to another
③ how to live harmoniously with others
④ living the life that is right for you
⑤ how to make a unique decision

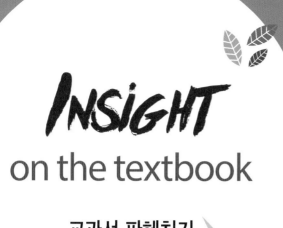

INSIGHT
on the textbook

교과서 파헤치기

※ 다음 영어를 우리말로 쓰시오.

01 refund		22 experience	
02 user		23 fee	
03 weakness		24 choose	
04 issue		25 freely	
05 lender		26 improve	
06 negative		27 return	
07 regularly		28 owner	
08 positive		29 personal	
09 broken		30 download	
10 condition		31 economy	
11 provide		32 purpose	
12 upset		33 reliable	
13 concern		34 borrow	
14 reasonable		35 for free	
15 upload		36 look after	
16 exact		37 be aware of	
17 wherever		38 out of town	
18 communicate		39 take care of	
19 discount		40 on sale	
20 resource		41 less than	
21 balanced		42 What if ~?	
		43 search for	

※ 다음 우리말을 영어로 쓰시오.

01 선택하다, 고르다 _____

02 믿을 수 있는 _____

03 향상하다, 개선하다 _____

04 정확한, 정밀한 _____

05 균형 잡힌 _____

06 의사소통하다 _____

07 다운로드하다 _____

08 경제 _____

09 우려, 근심 _____

10 타당한, 합리적인, (값이) 적당한 _____

11 빌리다 _____

12 약점 _____

13 할인 _____

14 업로드하다, 전송하다 _____

15 자유롭게 _____

16 환불 _____

17 망가진, 고장 난 _____

18 정기적으로 _____

19 문제(점), 쟁점 _____

20 상태, 조건 _____

21 자원 _____

22 긍정적인 _____

23 사용자 _____

24 빌려주는 사람 _____

25 경험하다 _____

26 개인의, 개인적인 _____

27 어디든지 _____

28 요금, 수수료 _____

29 부정적인, 나쁜 _____

30 주인, 소유주 _____

31 제공하다 _____

32 목적 _____

33 함께 쓰다, 공유하다 _____

34 돌려주다, 반납하다 _____

35 ~보다 적은, ~ 미만의 _____

36 무료로 _____

37 할인 중인 _____

38 ~를 찾다 _____

39 ~을 요청하다, 필요로 하다 _____

40 ~을 찾아오다 _____

41 ~을 돌보다 _____

42 ~을 알고 있다 _____

43 도시를 떠나, 다른 곳으로 떠나 _____

※ 다음 영영풀이에 알맞은 단어를 <보기>에서 골라 쓴 후, 우리말 뜻을 쓰시오.

1 _____ : not working properly: _____

2 _____ : many times or in large quantities: _____

3 _____ : to repair or correct something: _____

4 _____ : the state or condition of lacking strength: _____

5 _____ : an amount of money that must be paid: _____

6 _____ : a fact or situation that worries you: _____

7 _____ : unpleasant, depressing, or harmful: _____

8 _____ : to decide which person or thing you want to have: _____

9 _____ : to move data to a smaller computer system from a larger one: _____

10 _____ : an amount of money that is taken off the usual cost of something: _____

11 _____ : to give something that someone needs or wants to them, or make it available: _____

12 _____ : able to be trusted, or consistently good in quality or performance: _____

13 _____ : to bring, give, put, or send something back to someone or something: _____

14 _____ : to achieve or produce something of a better standard or quality than before: _____

15 _____ : the system according to which the money, industry and trade of a country or region are organized: _____

16 _____ : based on or using good judgment and therefore fair, practical and sensible: _____

보기

improve	choose	reasonable	negative
discount	freely	provide	broken
return	concern	economy	fee
reliable	fix	download	weakness

※ 다음 우리말과 일치하도록 빈칸에 알맞은 말을 쓰시오.

Listen & Talk 1 A

G: These two _____ of shoes are _____ _____! _____ _____ _____ _____?

B: Well, I _____ the white shoes _____ the _____ _____.

G: Why is that? The black ones are _____.

B: Yes, but I like the _____ of the _____ _____ _____.

여: 이 두 켤레의 신발이 세일 중이네! 어떤 것이 더 좋으니?
남: 음, 나는 검은색 신발보다 흰색 신발이 더 좋아.
여: 왜? 검은색 신발이 더 저렴하잖아.
남: 맞아, 하지만 나는 흰색 신발의 디자인이 더 좋아.

Listen & Talk 1 B

G: _____ do you _____, the Special Sandwich _____ the Classic Sandwich?

B: Well, the Special Sandwich is the _____ _____. It's _____ _____ lots of fresh vegetables and _____ healthy _____.

G: But it's _____ more _____ _____ _____ the Classic Sandwich.

B: I know, but I _____ the Special Sandwich _____ the Classic Sandwich. _____ _____ is important _____ me.

G: I prefer the _____ one. I'll _____ my money _____ books _____.

B: I guess _____ _____ _____ are _____.

여: 스페셜 샌드위치와 클래식 샌드위치 중 어떤 것이 더 좋으니?
남: 음, 스페셜 샌드위치가 더 건강한 선택이야. 그것은 신선한 야채들과 다른 건강한 재료들로 만들어졌어.
여: 하지만 그건 클래식 샌드위치보다 훨씬 더 비싸잖아.
남: 맞아, 하지만 나는 클래식 샌드위치보다 스페셜 샌드위치가 더 좋아. 나에게는 건강하게 먹는 것이 중요하거든.
여: 나는 더 저렴한 것이 더 좋아. 대신 나는 내 돈을 책 사는 데 쓸래.
남: 우리는 소비 습관이 다른 것 같구나.

Listen & Talk 1 C

G1: I think my hair is too _____. I want to _____ my hair. Can you _____ a _____ _____?

G2: Sure. I know two places, Styles Studio and Hair Castle.

G1: Is there any _____ _____ the _____?

G2: Well, Styles Studio provides _____ _____ _____ your hair _____.

G1: That's great. _____ _____ Hair Castle?

G2: Hair Castle doesn't _____ treatment _____ _____, but they give _____ _____.

G1: Okay. _____ do you _____?

G2: I _____ Styles Studio _____ Hair Castle. It's important _____ me _____ get hair treatment _____.

여1: 내 머리가 너무 곱슬곱슬한 것 같아. 머리카락을 곧게 펴고 싶어. 좋은 곳을 추천해 줄 수 있니?
여2: 물론이지. 난 스타일 스튜디오와 헤어 캐슬, 두 군데를 알고 있어.
여1: 두 군데의 차이점이 있니?
여2: 음, 스타일 스튜디오는 머리카락을 건강하게 유지해 주는 트리트먼트를 무료로 제공해 줘.
여1: 그것 좋으네. 헤어 캐슬은 어때?
여2: 헤어 캐슬은 트리트먼트를 무료로 제공해 주지는 않지만, 학생 할인을 해 줘.
여1: 그렇구나. 넌 어느 곳을 선호하니?
여2: 나는 헤어 캐슬보다 스타일 스튜디오를 선호해. 나한텐 헤어 트리트먼트를 규칙적으로 받는 것이 중요해.

Listen & Talk 2 A

B: I'm going to _____ _____ _____ for these clothes this evening. I found I have _____ ones.

W: Okay. _____ _____ to bring your _____. Last time you couldn't _____ _____ _____ because you didn't bring it.

B: Okay, Mom. I _____ _____ it this time.

Listen & Talk 2 B

G: What should we sell at the _____ _____ next month?

B: Before we choose anything _____ _____, I think we need to do some _____ _____.

G: _____ _____? Why do we need _____?

B: _____ it helps us _____ out _____ _____ _____ _____ these days.

G: I see. Then we can _____ _____ _____ _____ _____ _____ at the market.

B: That's right. It will also help us _____ _____ _____ for our items.

G: Cool. Is there _____ _____ we should do?

B: Oh, don't forget _____ _____ our names _____ this Friday.

G: Right. Thanks for _____ me.

Listen & Talk 2 C

G: I tried Spring Chips recently, and now I want to _____ them.

B: That sounds fun. _____ will you do your _____?

G: I'll make a video. I want to _____ _____ their delicious taste!

B: Okay, but _____ _____ _____ _____ _____ about their _____ _____ too.

G: I _____. I want to give a _____ _____.

B: Good. Your video will make _____ _____ _____ people _____ _____ _____ _____ _____.

G: That's exactly _____ I want. I'd _____ _____ give people more _____ _____ about the product.

Do It Yourself

G: Jinho, look! These two _____ look _____ _____.

B: Yeah, they do. _____ _____ _____ _____ _____, the red one or the _____ _____?

G: I prefer the red one _____ the black one. It's only 20 dollars, and it comes with a _____ _____ for music downloads.

B: _____ the black one is 40 dollars, I think it's the _____ one for me. I heard it has _____ _____ _____.

남: 저 오늘 저녁에 이 옷들을 환불하려고 해요. 제가 비슷한 옷들을 갖고 있다는 것을 발견했거든요.

여: 그래. 영수증 갖고 가는 것 잊지 마렴. 저번에 네가 영수증을 가지고 가지 않는 바람에 환불을 못 받았잖니.

남: 알겠어요, 엄마. 이번에는 잊지 않을게요.

여: 우리 다음 달에 벼룩시장에서 무엇을 판매해야 할까?

남: 우리가 판매할 물건을 선택하기 전에 시장 조사부터 좀 해야 할 것 같아.

여: 시장 조사? 우리가 그게 왜 필요한데?

남: 왜냐하면 우리가 시장 조사를 통해 요즘 어떤 물건이 인기 있는지 알아내는 데 도움이 되기 때문이지.

여: 그렇구나. 그럼 벼룩시장에서 무엇을 판매할지 정할 수 있겠다.

남: 맞아. 그리고 시장 조사를 통해 우리는 판매할 물건에 합리적인 가격을 정하는 데 도움이 될 거야.

여: 좋아. 그 외에 우리가 해야 할 다른 게 있을까?

남: 오, 우리 이름을 이번 주 금요일까지 등록하는 것을 잊지 마.

여: 맞아. 알려 줘서 고마워.

여: 내가 요새 스프링 칩스를 먹어봤는데, 이제 그것을 비평해 보고 싶어.

남: 그거 재밌겠다. 어떻게 비평할 거니?

여: 나는 동영상을 만들려고 해. 스프링 칩스의 맛있는 맛에 초점을 맞추고 싶어!

남: 그래, 하지만 그것의 단점에 대해서도 이야기하는 것을 잊지 마.

여: 잊지 않을 거야. 나는 균형 잡힌 비평을 보여주고 싶어.

남: 좋아. 네 동영상 덕분에 사람들이 더 나은 제품을 선택하는 것이 쉬워지겠구나.

여: 그것이 바로 내가 원하는 거야. 나는 사람들에게 제품에 대한 더 유용한 정보를 주고 싶어.

여: 진호, 이것 봐! 이 스피커 두 개 꽤 멋져 보이는데.

남: 응, 정말 그러네. 빨간색 스피커와 검은색 스피커 중에서 어떤 것이 더 좋니?

여: 나는 검은색 스피커보다 빨간색 스피커가 더 좋아. 그것은 20달러밖에 안 하고, 음악 다운로드를 할인해 주는 쿠폰도 같이 있잖아.

남: 검은색 스피커가 40달러이지만, 그것이 나한테 맞는 것 같아. 그게 더 나은 음질을 갖고 있다고 들었거든.

※ 다음 우리말에 맞도록 대화를 영어로 쓰시오.

Listen & Talk 1 A

G: _____

B: _____

G: _____

B: _____

여: 이 두 컬레의 신발이 세일 중이네! 어떤 것이 더 좋으니?

남: 음, 나는 검은색 신발보다 흰색 신발이 더 좋아.

여: 왜? 검은색 신발이 더 저렴하잖아.

남: 맞아, 하지만 나는 흰색 신발의 디자인이 더 좋아.

Listen & Talk 1 B

G: _____

B: _____
_____

G: _____

B: _____
_____

G: _____

B: _____

여: 스페셜 샌드위치와 클래식 샌드위치 중 어떤 것이 더 좋으니?

남: 음, 스페셜 샌드위치가 더 건강한 선택이야. 그것은 신선한 야채들과 다른 건강한 재료들로 만들어졌어.

여: 하지만 그건 클래식 샌드위치보다 훨씬 더 비싸잖아.

남: 맞아, 하지만 나는 클래식 샌드위치보다 스페셜 샌드위치가 더 좋아. 나에게는 건강하게 먹는 것이 중요하거든.

여: 나는 더 저렴한 것이 더 좋아. 대신 나는 내 돈을 책 사는 데 쓸래.

남: 우리는 소비 습관이 다른 것 같구나.

Listen & Talk 1 C

G1: _____
_____

G2: _____

G1: _____

G2: _____

G1: _____

G2: _____

G1: _____

G2: _____
_____

여1: 내 머리가 너무 곱슬곱슬한 것 같아. 머리카락을 곧게 펴고 싶어. 좋은 곳을 추천해 줄 수 있니?

여2: 물론이지. 난 스타일 스튜디오와 헤어 캐슬, 두 군데를 알고 있어.

여1: 두 군데의 차이점이 있니?

여2: 음, 스타일 스튜디오는 머리카락을 건강하게 유지해 주는 트리트먼트를 무료로 제공해 줘.

여1: 그것 좋으네. 헤어 캐슬은 어때?

여2: 헤어 캐슬은 트리트먼트를 무료로 제공해 주지는 않지만, 학생 할인을 해줘.

여1: 그렇구나. 넌 어느 곳을 선호하니?

여2: 나는 헤어 캐슬보다 스타일 스튜디오를 선호해. 나한텐 헤어 트리트먼트를 규칙적으로 받는 것이 중요해.

Listen & Talk 2 A

B: _____

_____

W: _____

_____

B: _____

Listen & Talk 2 B

G: _____

B: _____

G: _____

B: _____

G: _____

B: _____

G: _____

B: _____

G: _____

Listen & Talk 2 C

G: _____

B: _____

G: _____

B: _____

G: _____

B: _____

G: _____

Do It Yourself

G: _____

B: _____

G: _____

B: _____

남: 저 오늘 저녁에 이 옷들을 환불하려고 해요. 제가 비슷한 옷들을 갖고 있다는 것을 발견했거든요.

여: 그래. 영수증 갖고 가는 것 잊지 마렴. 저번에 네가 영수증을 가지고 가지 않는 바람에 환불을 못 받았잖니.

남: 알겠어요, 엄마. 이번에는 잊지 않을게요.

여: 우리 다음 달에 벼룩시장에서 무엇을 판매해야 할까?

남: 우리가 판매할 물건을 선택하기 전에 시장 조사부터 좀 해야 할 것 같아.

여: 시장 조사? 우리가 그게 왜 필요한데?

남: 왜냐하면 우리가 시장 조사를 통해 요즘 어떤 물건이 인기 있는지 알아내는 데 도움이 되기 때문이지.

여: 그렇구나. 그럼 벼룩시장에서 무엇을 판매할지 정할 수 있겠다.

남: 맞아. 그리고 시장 조사를 통해 우리는 판매할 물건에 합리적인 가격을 정하는 데 도움이 될 거야.

여: 좋아. 그 외에 우리가 해야 할 다른 게 있을까?

남: 오, 우리 이름을 이번 주 금요일까지 등록하는 것을 잊지 마.

여: 맞아. 알려 줘서 고마워.

여: 내가 요새 스프링 칩스를 먹어봤는데, 이제 그것을 비평해 보고 싶어.

남: 그거 재밌겠다. 어떻게 비평할 거니?

여: 나는 동영상을 만들려고 해. 스프링 칩스의 맛있는 맛에 초점을 맞추고 싶어!

남: 그래, 하지만 그것의 단점에 대해서도 이야기하는 것을 잊지 마.

여: 잊지 않을 거야. 나는 균형 잡힌 비평을 보여주고 싶어.

남: 좋아. 네 동영상 덕분에 사람들이 더 나은 제품을 선택하는 것이 쉬워지겠구나.

여: 그것이 바로 내가 원하는 거야. 나는 사람들에게 제품에 대한 더 유용한 정보를 주고 싶어.

여: 진호, 이것 봐! 이 스피커 두 개 꽤 멋져 보이는데.

남: 응, 정말 그러네. 빨간색 스피커와 검은색 스피커 중에서 어떤 것이 더 좋니?

여: 나는 검은색 스피커보다 빨간색 스피커가 더 좋아, 그것은 20달러밖에 안 하고, 음악 다운로드를 할인해 주는 쿠폰도 같이 있잖아.

남: 검은색 스피커가 40달러이지만, 그것이 나한테 맞는 것 같아. 그게 더 나은 음질을 갖고 있다고 들었거든.

※ 다음 우리말과 일치하도록 빈칸에 알맞은 것을 골라 쓰시오.

1 _____ in the _____ _____

   A. Economy   B. Life   C. Sharing

2 Son: _____ _____ _____ _____ this weekend, Dad?

   A. do   B. what   C. we   D. should

3 Dad: _____ _____ _____ go camping?

   A. we   B. don't   C. why

4 Son: But we _____ _____ a _____.

   A. tent   B. have   C. don't

5 _____ we _____ _____ ?

   A. one   B. should   C. buy

6 _____, who will _____ _____ _____ our dog?

   A. care   B. also   C. of   D. take

7 Dad: _____ _____. I know some _____ that can _____ us.

   A. apps   B. worry   C. help   D. don't

8 _____ _____ **your** _____ !

   A. neighbors   B. borrow   C. from

9 Ask Your Neighbors _____ people _____ _____ items that they can borrow from _____.

   A. others   B. easily   C. find   D. helps

10 First, users _____ the app and _____ for _____ user that has the _____ they need.

   A. item   B. search   C. download   D. another

11 Then they _____ the _____ and _____ it later.

   A. up   B. return   C. pick   D. item

12 Jasmine: _____ _____ , _____

   A. 2019   B. 12   C. December

13 I _____ _____ a board game and got one in _____ _____ 30 minutes.

   A. less   B. for   C. than   D. asked

14 I love _____ money _____ _____ things that I don't often _____.

   A. borrowing   B. saving   C. by   D. need

15 _____, I think it's _____ _____ .

   A. friendly   B. also   C. environmentally

16 The _____ we buy, the _____ we save.

   A. more   B. fewer   C. resources   D. products

---

1 공유 경제 속 삶

2 아들: 아빠, 우리 이번 주말에 뭐 할 거예요?

3 아빠: 캠핑 가는 건 어떠니?

4 아들: 그런데 우리 텐트가 없잖아요.

5 하나 사야 할까요?

6 게다가 우리 개는 누가 돌봐요?

7 아빠: 걱정하지 마. 내가 우리를 도와줄 수 있는 몇 개의 앱들을 알고 있지.

8 당신의 이웃들로부터 빌려라!

9 Ask Your Neighbors는 사람들이 다른 사람들로부터 빌릴 수 있는 물건을 쉽게 찾도록 돕는다.

10 우선, 사용자들은 그 앱을 내려받고 그들이 필요한 물건을 가지고 있는 또 다른 사용자를 찾는다.

11 그리고 나서 그들은 그 물건을 받아서 나중에 반납한다.

12 Jasmine / 2019년 12월 12일

13 저는 보드게임을 요청했고 30분도 안 되어 하나를 구했어요.

14 저는 제가 자주 필요하지 않은 것들을 빌림으로써 돈을 아낄 수 있다는 것이 마음에 들어요.

15 게다가 이것이 환경친화적이라고 생각해요.

16 우리가 제품들을 더 적게 구매할수록, 우리는 더 많은 자원들을 아끼는 거예요.

17 Cassandra: _____ _____, _____
　　A. 7　　　　　　B. 2020　　　　C. March

18 _____ a lot of _____ _____, I decided to _____ a bike helmet.
　　A. reviews　　B. borrow　　C. seeing　　D. positive

19 When I _____ it, _____, it _____ _____.
　　A. broken　　B. got　　C. however　　D. was

20 I was _____ _____!
　　A. upset　　B. so

21 Ask Your Neighbors: _____ _____, _____
　　A. March　　B. 2020　　C. 9

22 We're sorry that you had _____ _____ _____ _____.
　　A. negative　　B. a　　C. experience　　D. such

23 To _____ this issue, we are asking _____ to _____ the pictures of their items _____.
　　A. update　　B. regularly　　C. fix　　D. lenders

24 This will _____ other users _____ the _____ condition of the _____.
　　A. product　　B. let　　C. exact　　D. know

25 **I _____ _____ _____ your pet!**
　　A. can　　B. after　　C. look

26 Pet Sitter Finder is the _____ _____ for pet _____ and pet _____.
　　A. owners　　B. perfect　　C. lovers　　D. app

27 It helps pet _____ find _____ people to _____ _____ their pets.
　　A. after　　B. reliable　　C. owners　　D. look

28 When a pet _____ is _____ for pet sitters, he or she a _____.
　　A. post　　B. looking　　C. uploads　　D. owner

29 Pet sitters or dog _____ can then _____ _____ to the _____.
　　A. send　　B. walkers　　C. owner　　D. messages

30 The owner _____ their _____ and _____ the best _____.
　　A. chooses　　B. checks　　C. person　　D. reviews

31 George: _____ _____, _____
　　A. 2019　　B. 12　　C. November

32 I _____ this app _____ I'm going _____ _____ town.
　　A. out　　B. use　　C. of　　D. whenever

17 Cassandra / 2020년 3월 7일

18 많은 긍정적인 후기들을 보고 나서, 저는 자전거 헬멧을 빌리기로 결심했어요.

19 그러나 제가 그것을 얻었을 때, 그것은 망가져 있었어요.

20 저는 몹시 기분이 상했어요!

21 Ask Your Neighbors / 2020년 3월 9일

22 고객님이 그런 부정적인 경험을 겪게 해 드려 죄송합니다.

23 이 문제를 바로잡기 위해서, 저희는 빌려주는 사람들에게 그들의 물건 사진을 정기적으로 업데이트해 줄 것을 요구하고 있습니다.

24 이것이 다른 사용자들에게 그 제품의 정확한 상태를 알 수 있도록 해 줄 것입니다.

25 제가 당신의 반려동물을 돌볼 수 있어요!

26 Pet Sitter Finder는 반려동물을 좋아하는 사람들과 반려동물 주인들을 위한 완벽한 앱이다.

27 그것은 반려동물 주인들이 그들의 반려동물을 돌보는 데 신뢰할 만한 사람들을 찾도록 돕는다.

28 반려동물 주인이 반려동물을 돌보는 사람들을 찾을 때, 그 또는 그녀는 게시물을 올린다.

29 그리고 나서 반려동물을 돌보는 사람들이나 개를 산책시키는 사람들이 주인에게 메시지를 보낼 수 있다.

30 주인은 그들의 후기들을 확인하고 최고의 사람을 선택한다.

31 George / 2019년 11월 12일

32 저는 교외로 나갈 때마다 이 앱을 사용해요.

33 I have some _____ about my _____ _____ _____.

    A. personal   B. concerns   C. though   D. information

34 _____ _____ people use my phone number for _____ _____?

    A. if   B. other   C. what   D. purposes

35 Pet Sitter Finder: _____ _____, _____

    A. 14   B. November   C. 2019

36 We're _____ _____ this _____.

    A. of   B. aware   C. issue

37 We're now developing a system that _____ users to freely _____ _____ their personal information.

    A. allows   B. showing   C. communicate   D. without

38 Samantha: _____ _____, _____

    A. 22   B. February   C. 2020

39 Animals _____ _____ in my apartment, so I don't _____ _____ pets.

    A. allowed   B. have   C. aren't   D. any

40 However, _____ _____ Pet Sitter Finder, I can _____ the joy of _____ a dog.

    A. using   B. experience   C. walking   D. by

41 Son: _____ _____ _____!

    A. great   B. what   C. apps

42 We can _____ a tent and find someone to _____ _____ _____ our dog.

    A. borrow   B. care   C. take   D. of

43 Dad: _____ _____.

    A. right   B. that's

44 These _____ of _____ are _____ of the "_____ economy."

    A. services   B. kinds   C. part   D. sharing

45 People can _____ their items _____ others and _____ services to them at a small _____ or for free.

    A. with   B. fee   C. share   D. provide

46 Son: But these _____ do _____ some _____.

    A. weaknesses   B. services   C. have

47 Some people _____ _____ _____ about the _____.

    A. services   B. negative   C. left   D. reviews

48 Dad: Well, I think the _____ people _____ the _____, the more they will _____.

    A. improve   B. use   C. more   D. services

---

33 하지만 저의 개인 정보에 대한 몇 가지 걱정이 있어요.

34 만약 다른 사람들이 제 전화번호를 다른 목적으로 사용하면 어쩌죠?

35 Pet Sitter Finder / 2019년 11월 14일

36 저희는 이 문제를 알고 있습니다.

37 저희는 현재 사용자들이 자신의 개인 정보를 보여주지 않으면서 자유롭게 소통할 수 있는 시스템을 개발하는 중입니다.

38 Samantha / 2020년 2월 22일

39 동물들이 제 아파트에서는 허락되지 않아서, 저는 반려동물을 키울 수 없어요.

40 그런데 Pet Sitter Finder를 이용하면서, 저는 개를 산책시키는 즐거움을 경험할 수 있어요.

41 아들: 정말 좋은 앱들이네요!

42 우리는 텐트를 빌리고 우리 개를 돌볼 누군가를 찾을 수 있어요.

43 아빠: 그렇지.

44 이런 종류의 서비스가 '공유 경제'의 일부란다.

45 사람들은 자신의 물건을 다른 사람들과 공유할 수 있고 적은 비용이나 무료로 그들에게 서비스를 제공할 수 있어.

46 아들: 하지만 사실 이런 서비스들은 몇 가지 약점들을 가지고 있어요.

47 몇몇 사람들이 서비스에 대해 부정적인 후기들을 남겼잖아요.

48 아빠: 글쎄, 나는 사람들이 그 서비스들을 더 많이 사용할수록, 그것들이 더 개선될 것이라고 생각해.

※ 다음 우리말과 일치하도록 빈칸에 알맞은 것을 골라 쓰시오.

1 _____ in the _____ _____

2 Son: _____ _____ _____ _____ this weekend, Dad?

3 Dad: _____ _____ _____ go camping?

4 Son: But we _____ _____ a tent.

5 Should we buy _____?

6 Also, who will _____ _____ _____ our dog?

7 Dad: _____ _____. I know _____ _____ that can help us.

8 _____ **from your** _____!

9 Ask Your Neighbors _____ _____ _____ _____ items that they can _____ _____ others.

10 First, users download the app and _____ _____ another user that has _____ _____ _____ _____.

11 Then they pick up the item and _____ _____ _____.

12 Jasmine: _____ _____, 2019

13 I _____ _____ a board game and got _____ in _____ _____ 30 minutes.

14 I love saving money _____ _____ things that I don't often need.

15 _____, I think it's _____ _____.

16 _____ _____ _____ we buy, _____ _____ _____ we _____.

1	공유 경제 속 삶
2	아들: 아빠, 우리 이번 주말에 뭐 할 거예요?
3	아빠: 캠핑 가는 건 어떠니?
4	아들: 그런데 우리 텐트가 없잖아요.
5	하나 사야 할까요?
6	게다가 우리 개는 누가 돌봐요?
7	아빠: 걱정하지 마. 내가 우리를 도와줄 수 있는 몇 개의 앱들을 알고 있지.
8	당신의 이웃들로부터 빌려라!
9	Ask Your Neighbors는 사람들이 다른 사람들로부터 빌릴 수 있는 물건을 쉽게 찾도록 돕는다.
10	우선, 사용자들은 그 앱을 내려받고 그들이 필요한 물건을 가지고 있는 또 다른 사용자를 찾는다.
11	그리고 나서 그들은 그 물건을 받아서 나중에 반납한다.
12	Jasmine / 2019년 12월 12일
13	저는 보드게임을 요청했고 30분도 안 되어 하나를 구했어요.
14	저는 제가 자주 필요하지 않은 것들을 빌림으로써 돈을 아낄 수 있다는 것이 마음에 들어요.
15	게다가 이것이 환경친화적이라고 생각해요.
16	우리가 제품들을 더 적게 구매할수록, 우리는 더 많은 자원들을 아끼는 거예요.

17 Cassandra: _____ 7, 2020

18 _____ a lot of _____ _____, I decided _____ _____ a bike helmet.

19 When I got it, _____, it _____ _____.

20 I was _____ _____!

21 Ask Your Neighbors: _____ _____, 2020

22 We're sorry that you had _____ _____ _____ _____.

23 _____ _____ this issue, we are asking lenders _____ _____ _____ _____ _____ of their items _____.

24 This will _____ other users _____ the _____ _____ of the product.

25 **I can _____ _____ your pet!**

26 Pet Sitter Finder is _____ _____ _____ for pet _____ and pet _____.

27 It helps pet owners find _____ _____ _____ _____ _____ their pets.

28 When a pet owner _____ _____ _____ pet sitters, he or she uploads _____ _____.

29 Pet sitters or dog walkers can then _____ _____ _____ the owner.

30 The owner _____ their _____ and _____ the best person.

31 George: _____ 12, 2019

32 I use this app _____ I'm going _____ _____.

---

17 Cassandra / 2020년 3월 7일

18 많은 긍정적인 후기들을 보고 나서, 저는 자전거 헬멧을 빌리기로 결심했어요.

19 그러나 제가 그것을 얻었을 때, 그것은 망가져 있었어요.

20 저는 몹시 기분이 상했어요!

21 Ask Your Neighbors / 2020년 3월 9일

22 고객님이 그런 부정적인 경험을 겪게 해 드려 죄송합니다.

23 이 문제를 바로잡기 위해서, 저희는 빌려주는 사람들에게 그들의 물건 사진을 정기적으로 업데이트해 줄 것을 요구하고 있습니다.

24 이것이 다른 사용자들에게 그 제품의 정확한 상태를 알 수 있도록 해 줄 것입니다.

25 제가 당신의 반려동물을 돌볼 수 있어요!

26 Pet Sitter Finder는 반려동물을 좋아하는 사람들과 반려동물 주인들을 위한 완벽한 앱이다.

27 그것은 반려동물 주인들이 그들의 반려동물을 돌보는 데 신뢰할 만한 사람들을 찾도록 돕는다.

28 반려동물 주인이 반려동물을 돌보는 사람들을 찾을 때, 그 또는 그녀는 게시물을 올린다.

29 그리고 나서 반려동물을 돌보는 사람들이나 개를 산책시키는 사람들이 주인에게 메시지를 보낼 수 있다.

30 주인은 그들의 후기들을 확인하고 최고의 사람을 선택한다.

31 George / 2019년 11월 12일

32 저는 교외로 나갈 때마다 이 앱을 사용해요.

33 I have some _____ about my _____ _____ though.

34 _____ _____ people use my phone number _____ _____ _____?

35 Pet Sitter Finder: _____ _____, _____

36 We're _____ _____ this issue.

37 We're now developing a system that _____ users _____ _____ freely _____ _____ their personal information.

38 Samantha: _____ 22, 2020

39 Animals _____ _____ in my apartment, _____ I don't have any pets.

40 However, _____ _____ Pet Sitter Finder, I _____ _____ the joy of _____ a dog.

41 Son: _____ great apps!

42 We can _____ a tent and find someone _____ _____ _____ _____ our dog.

43 Dad: That's _____.

44 These _____ of services are part of the "_____ _____."

45 People can _____ their items _____ others and _____ services to them _____ _____ _____ _____ or _____ _____.

46 Son: But these services _____ have some _____.

47 Some people _____ _____ _____ about the services.

48 Dad: Well, I think _____ people use _____, the more they _____ _____.

33 하지만 저의 개인 정보에 대한 몇 가지 걱정이 있어요.

34 만약 다른 사람들이 제 전화번호를 다른 목적으로 사용하면 어쩌죠?

35 Pet Sitter Finder / 2019년 11월 14일

36 저희는 이 문제를 알고 있습니다.

37 저희는 현재 사용자들이 자신의 개인 정보를 보여주지 않으면서 자유롭게 소통할 수 있는 시스템을 개발하는 중입니다.

38 Samantha / 2020년 2월 22일

39 동물들이 제 아파트에서는 허락되지 않아서, 저는 반려동물을 키울 수 없어요.

40 그런데 Pet Sitter Finder를 이용하면서, 저는 개를 산책시키는 즐거움을 경험할 수 있어요.

41 아들: 정말 좋은 앱들이네요!

42 우리는 텐트를 빌리고 우리 개를 돌볼 누군가를 찾을 수 있어요.

43 아빠: 그렇지,

44 이런 종류의 서비스가 '공유 경제'의 일부란다.

45 사람들은 자신의 물건을 다른 사람들과 공유할 수 있고 적은 비용이나 무료로 그들에게 서비스를 제공할 수 있어.

46 아들: 하지만 사실 이런 서비스들은 몇 가지 약점들을 가지고 있어요.

47 몇몇 사람들이 서비스에 대해 부정적인 후기들을 남겼잖아요.

48 아빠: 글쎄, 나는 사람들이 그 서비스들을 더 많이 사용할수록, 그것들이 더 개선될 것이라고 생각해.

※ 다음 문장을 우리말로 쓰시오.

1 Life in the Sharing Economy
➡ _____

2 Son: What should we do this weekend, Dad?
➡ _____

3 Dad: Why don't we go camping?
➡ _____

4 Son: But we don't have a tent.
➡ _____

5 Should we buy one?
➡ _____

6 Also, who will take care of our dog?
➡ _____

7 Dad: Don't worry. I know some apps that can help us.
➡ _____

8 Borrow from your neighbors!
➡ _____

9 Ask Your Neighbors helps people easily find items that they can borrow from others.
➡ _____

10 First, users download the app and search for another user that has the item they need.
➡ _____

11 Then they pick up the item and return it later.
➡ _____

12 Jasmine: December 12, 2019
➡ _____

13 I asked for a board game and got one in less than 30 minutes.
➡ _____

14 I love saving money by borrowing things that I don't often need.
➡ _____

15 Also, I think it's environmentally friendly.
➡ _____

16 The fewer products we buy, the more resources we save.
➡ _____

17 Cassandra: March 7, 2020

➡ _____

18 Seeing a lot of positive reviews, I decided to borrow a bike helmet.

➡ _____

19 When I got it, however, it was broken.

➡ _____

20 I was so upset!

➡ _____

21 Ask Your Neighbors: March 9, 2020

➡ _____

22 We're sorry that you had such a negative experience.

➡ _____

23 To fix this issue, we are asking lenders to update the pictures of their items regularly.

➡ _____
   _____

24 This will let other users know the exact condition of the product.

➡ _____

25 I can look after your pet!

➡ _____

26 Pet Sitter Finder is the perfect app for pet lovers and pet owners.

➡ _____

27 It helps pet owners find reliable people to look after their pets.

➡ _____

28 When a pet owner is looking for pet sitters, he or she uploads a post.

➡ _____

29 Pet sitters or dog walkers can then send messages to the owner.

➡ _____

30 The owner checks their reviews and chooses the best person.

➡ _____

31 George: November 12, 2019

➡ _____

32 I use this app whenever I'm going out of town.

➡ _____

33 I have some concerns about my personal information though.

➡ _____

34 What if people use my phone number for other purposes?

➡ _____

35 Pet Sitter Finder: November 14, 2019

➡ _____

36 We're aware of this issue.

➡ _____

37 We're now developing a system that allows users to communicate freely without showing their personal information.

➡ _____

38 Samantha: February 22, 2020

➡ _____

39 Animals aren't allowed in my apartment, so I don't have any pets.

➡ _____

40 However, by using Pet Sitter Finder, I can experience the joy of walking a dog.

➡ _____

41 Son: What great apps!

➡ _____

42 We can borrow a tent and find someone to take care of our dog.

➡ _____

43 Dad: That's right.

➡ _____

44 These kinds of services are part of the "sharing economy."

➡ _____

45 People can share their items with others and provide services to them at a small fee or for free.

➡ _____

46 Son: But these services do have some weaknesses.

➡ _____

47 Some people left negative reviews about the services.

➡ _____

48 Dad: Well, I think the more people use the services, the more they will improve.

➡ _____

※ 다음 괄호 안의 단어들을 우리말에 맞도록 바르게 배열하시오.

1 (in / Life / the / Economy / Sharing)
➡ _____

2 (Son: / should / what / do / we / weekend, / this / Dad?)
➡ _____

3 (Dad: / don't / why / go / we / camping?)
➡ _____

4 (Son: / we / but / have / don't / tent. / a)
➡ _____

5 (we / should / one? / buy)
➡ _____

6 (who / also, / take / will / of / care / dog? / our)
➡ _____

7 (Dad: / worry. / don't // know / I / apps / some / can / that / us. / help)
➡ _____

8 (from / borrow / neighbors! / your)
➡ _____

9 (people / Ask Your Neighbors / helps / easily / items / find / they / that / borrow / can / others. / from)
➡ _____

10 (users / first, / the / download / app / search / and / another / for / user / has / that / item / the / need. / they)
➡ _____

11 (they / then / up / pick / item / the / and / it / return / later.)
➡ _____

12 (Jasmine: / 12, / December / 2019)
➡ _____

13 (asked / I / a / for / game / board / and / one / got / less / in / 30 / than / minutes.)
➡ _____

14 (love / I / money / saving / by / things / borrowing / I / that / often / don't / need.)
➡ _____

15 (I / also, / it's / think / friendly. / environmentally)
➡ _____

16 (fewer / the / we / products / buy, / more / the / we / resources / save.)
➡ _____

1 공유 경제 속 삶

2 아들: 아빠, 우리 이번 수말에 뭐 할 거예요?

3 아빠: 캠핑 가는 건 어떠니?

4 아들: 그런데 우리 텐트가 없잖아요.

5 하나 사야 할까요?

6 게다가 우리 개는 누가 돌봐요?

7 아빠: 걱정하지 마. 내가 우리를 도와줄 수 있는 몇 개의 앱들을 알고 있지.

8 당신의 이웃들로부터 빌려라!

9 Ask Your Neighbors는 사람들이 다른 사람들로부터 빌릴 수 있는 물건을 쉽게 찾도록 돕는다.

10 우선. 사용자들은 그 앱을 내려받고 그들이 필요한 물건을 가지고 있는 또 다른 사용자를 찾는다.

11 그리고 나서 그들은 그 물건을 받아서 나중에 반납한다.

12 Jasmine / 2019년 12월 12일

13 저는 보드게임을 요청했고 30분도 안 되어 하나를 구했어요.

14 저는 제가 자주 필요하지 않은 것들을 빌림으로써 돈을 아낄 수 있다는 것이 마음에 들어요.

15 게다가 이것이 환경친화적이라고 생각해요.

16 우리가 제품들을 더 적게 구매할수록, 우리는 더 많은 자원들을 아끼는 거예요.

17 (Cassandra: / 7, / March / 2020)

➡ _____

18 (a / seeing / lot / positive / of / reviews, / decided / I / borrow / to / bike / a / helmet.)

➡ _____

19 (I / when / it, / got / however, / was / it / broken.)

➡ _____

20 (was / I / upset! / so)

➡ _____

21 (Ask Your Neighbors: / 2020 / 9, / March)

➡ _____

22 (sorry / we're / you / that / such / had / negative / a / experience.)

➡ _____

23 (fix / to / issue, / this / are / we / lenders / asking / update / to / the / of / pictures / their / regularly. / items)

➡ _____

24 (will / this / other / let / know / users / the / condition / exact / of / product. / the)

➡ _____

25 (can / I / after / look / pet! / your)

➡ _____

26 (is / Pet Sitter Finder / the / app / perfect / pet / for / and / lovers / owners. / pet)

➡ _____

27 (helps / it / owners / pet / reliable / find / to / people / after / look / pets. / their)

➡ _____

28 (a / when / owner / pet / looking / is / pet / for / sitters, / she / or / he / a / uploads / post.)

➡ _____

29 (sitters / pet / dog / or / can / walkers / then / messages / send / the / to / owner.)

➡ _____

30 (owner / the / their / checks / reviews / and / the / chooses / person. / best)

➡ _____

31 (George: / 12, / November / 2019)

➡ _____

32 (use / I / app / this / I'm / whenever / out / going / town. / of)

➡ _____

17 Cassandra / 2020년 3월 7일

18 많은 긍정적인 후기들을 보고 나서, 저는 자전거 헬멧을 빌리기로 결심했어요.

19 그러나 제가 그것을 얻었을 때, 그것은 망가져 있었어요.

20 저는 몹시 기분이 상했어요!

21 Ask Your Neighbors / 2020년 3월 9일

22 고객님이 그런 부정적인 경험을 겪게 해 드려 죄송합니다.

23 이 문제를 바로잡기 위해서, 저희는 빌려주는 사람들에게 그들의 물건 사진을 정기적으로 업데이트해 줄 것을 요구하고 있습니다.

24 이것이 다른 사용자들에게 그 제품의 정확한 상태를 알 수 있도록 해 줄 것입니다.

25 제가 당신의 반려동물을 돌볼 수 있어요!

26 Pet Sitter Finder는 반려동물을 좋아하는 사람들과 반려동물 주인들을 위한 완벽한 앱이다.

27 그것은 반려동물 주인들이 그들의 반려동물을 돌보는 데 신뢰할 만한 사람들을 찾도록 돕는다.

28 반려동물 주인이 반려동물을 돌보는 사람들을 찾을 때, 그 또는 그녀는 게시물을 올린다.

29 그리고 나서 반려동물을 돌보는 사람들이나 개를 산책시키는 사람들이 주인에게 메시지를 보낼 수 있다.

30 주인은 그들의 후기들을 확인하고 최고의 사람을 선택한다.

31 George / 2019년 11월 12일

32 저는 교외로 나갈 때마다 이 앱을 사용해요.

33 (have / I / concerns / some / my / about / personal / though. / information)

➡ _____

34 (if / what / use / people / phone / my / for / number / purposes? / other)

➡ _____

35 (Pet Sitter Finder: / 2019 / 14, / November)

➡ _____

36 (aware / we're / this / of / issue.)

➡ _____

37 (now / we're / a / developing / system / allows / that / users / communicate / to / without / freely / their / showing / information. / personal)

➡ _____

38 (Samantha: / 22, / February / 2020)

➡ _____

39 (aren't / animals / allowed / my / in / so / apartment, / don't / I / any / have / pets.)

➡ _____

40 (by / however, / Pet Sitter Finder, / using / can / I / the / experience / joy / the / walking / of / dog. / a)

➡ _____

_____

41 (Son: / great / what / apps!)

➡ _____

42 (can / we / a / borrow / tent / and / someone / find / take / to / of / care / dog. / our)

➡ _____

43 (Dad: / right. / that's)

➡ _____

44 (kinds / these / services / of / part / are / the / of / economy." / "sharing)

➡ _____

45 (can / people / their / share / with / items / others / and / services / provide / them / to / a / at / fee / small / for / or / free.)

➡ _____

_____

46 (Son: / these / but / do / services / some / have / weaknesses.)

➡ _____

47 (people / some / negative / left / about / reviews / services. / the)

➡ _____

48 (Dad: / I / well, / the / think / people / more / the / use / the / services, / they / more / improve. / will)

➡ _____

_____

---

33 하지만 저의 개인 정보에 대한 몇 가지 걱정이 있어요.

34 만약 다른 사람들이 제 전화번호를 다른 목적으로 사용하면 어쩌죠?

35 Pet Sitter Finder / 2019년 11월 14일

36 저희는 이 문제를 알고 있습니다.

37 저희는 현재 사용자들이 자신의 개인 정보를 보여주지 않으면서 자유롭게 소통할 수 있는 시스템을 개발하는 중입니다.

38 Samantha / 2020년 2월 22일

39 동물들이 제 아파트에서는 허락되지 않아서, 저는 반려동물을 키울 수 없어요.

40 그런데 Pet Sitter Finder를 이용하면서, 저는 개를 산책시키는 즐거움을 경험할 수 있어요.

41 아들: 정말 좋은 앱들이네요!

42 우리는 텐트를 빌리고 우리 개를 돌볼 누군가를 찾을 수 있어요.

43 아빠: 그렇지.

44 이런 종류의 서비스가 '공유 경제'의 일부란다.

45 사람들은 자신의 물건을 다른 사람들과 공유할 수 있고 적은 비용이나 무료로 그들에게 서비스를 제공할 수 있어.

46 아들: 하지만 사실 이런 서비스들은 몇 가지 약점들을 가지고 있어요.

47 몇몇 사람들이 서비스에 대해 부정적인 후기들을 남겼잖아요.

48 아빠: 글쎄, 나는 사람들이 그 서비스들을 더 많이 사용할수록, 그것들이 더 개선될 것이라고 생각해.

※ **다음 우리말을 영어로 쓰시오.**

1 공유 경제 속 삶
➡ _____

2 아들: 아빠, 우리 이번 주말에 뭐 할 거예요?
➡ _____

3 아빠: 캠핑 가는 건 어떠니?
➡ _____

4 아들: 그런데 우리 텐트가 없잖아요.
➡ _____

5 하나 사야 할까요?
➡ _____

6 게다가 우리 개는 누가 돌봐요?
➡ _____

7 아빠: 걱정하지 마. 내가 우리를 도와줄 수 있는 몇 개의 앱들을 알고 있지.
➡ _____

8 당신의 이웃들로부터 빌려라!
➡ _____

9 Ask Your Neighbors는 사람들이 다른 사람들로부터 빌릴 수 있는 물건을 쉽게 찾도록 돕는다.
➡ _____

10 우선, 사용자들은 그 앱을 내려받고 그들이 필요한 물건을 가지고 있는 또 다른 사용자를 찾는다.
➡ _____

11 그러고 나서 그들은 그 물건을 받아서 나중에 반납한다.
➡ _____

12 Jasmine / 2019년 12월 12일
➡ _____

13 저는 보드게임을 요청했고 30분도 안 되어 하나를 구했어요.
➡ _____

14 저는 제가 자주 필요하지 않은 것들을 빌림으로써 돈을 아낄 수 있다는 것이 마음에 들어요.
➡ _____

15 게다가 이것이 환경친화적이라고 생각해요.
➡ _____

16 우리가 제품들을 더 적게 구매할수록, 우리는 더 많은 자원들을 아끼는 거예요.
➡ _____

17 Cassandra / 2020년 3월 7일

➡ _____

18 많은 긍정적인 후기들을 보고 나서, 저는 자전거 헬멧을 빌리기로 결심했어요.

➡ _____

19 그러나 제가 그것을 얻었을 때, 그것은 망가져 있었어요.

➡ _____

20 저는 몹시 기분이 상했어요!

➡ _____

21 Ask Your Neighbors / 2020년 3월 9일

➡ _____

22 고객님이 그런 부정적인 경험을 겪게 해 드려 죄송합니다.

➡ _____

23 이 문제를 바로잡기 위해서, 저희는 빌려주는 사람들에게 그들의 물건 사진을 정기적으로 업데이트해 줄 것을 요구하고 있습니다.

➡ _____

24 이것이 다른 사용자들에게 그 제품의 정확한 상태를 알 수 있도록 해 줄 것입니다.

➡ _____

25 제가 당신의 반려동물을 돌볼 수 있어요!

➡ _____

26 Pet Sitter Finder는 반려동물을 좋아하는 사람들과 반려동물 주인들을 위한 완벽한 앱이다.

➡ _____

27 그것은 반려동물 주인들이 그들의 반려동물을 돌보는 데 신뢰할 만한 사람들을 찾도록 돕는다.

➡ _____

28 반려동물 주인이 반려동물을 돌보는 사람들을 찾을 때, 그 또는 그녀는 게시물을 올린다.

➡ _____

29 그리고 나서 반려동물을 돌보는 사람들이나 개를 산책시키는 사람들이 주인에게 메시지를 보낼 수 있다.

➡ _____

30 주인은 그들의 후기들을 확인하고 최고의 사람을 선택한다.

➡ _____

31 George / 2019년 11월 12일

➡ _____

32 저는 교외로 나갈 때마다 이 앱을 사용해요.

➡ _____

33 하지만 저의 개인 정보에 대한 몇 가지 걱정이 있어요.
➡ _____

34 만약 다른 사람들이 제 전화번호를 다른 목적으로 사용하면 어쩌죠?
➡ _____

35 Pet Sitter Finder / 2019년 11월 14일
➡ _____

36 저희는 이 문제를 알고 있습니다.
➡ _____

37 저희는 현재 사용자들이 자신의 개인 정보를 보여주지 않으면서 자유롭게 소통할 수 있는
시스템을 개발하는 중입니다.
➡ _____

_____

38 Samantha / 2020년 2월 22일
➡ _____

39 동물들이 제 아파트에서는 허락되지 않아서, 저는 반려동물을 키울 수 없어요.
➡ _____

40 그런데 Pet Sitter Finder를 이용하면서, 저는 개를 산책시키는 즐거움을 경험할 수 있어요.
➡ _____

41 아들: 정말 좋은 앱들이네요!
➡ _____

42 우리는 텐트를 빌리고 우리 개를 돌볼 누군가를 찾을 수 있어요.
➡ _____

43 아빠: 그렇지.
➡ _____

44 이런 종류의 서비스가 '공유 경제'의 일부란다.
➡ _____

45 사람들은 자신의 물건을 다른 사람들과 공유할 수 있고 적은 비용이나 무료로 그들에게
서비스를 제공할 수 있어.
➡ _____

46 아들: 하지만 사실 이런 서비스들은 몇 가지 약점들을 가지고 있어요.
➡ _____

47 몇몇 사람들이 서비스에 대해 부정적인 후기들을 남겼잖아요.
➡ _____

48 아빠: 글쎄, 나는 사람들이 그 서비스들을 더 많이 사용할수록, 그것들이 더 개선될 것이라고
생각해.
➡ _____

※ 다음 우리말과 일치하도록 빈칸에 알맞은 말을 쓰시오.

Do It Yourself

1. _____ _____, my family _____ _____ _____ a baseball game.

2. _____ _____ our team, we _____ a really _____ _____.

3. _____, our team _____ _____ _____.

4. _____ _____ about the win, we _____ _____ _____.

5. _____ _____ _____ _____, we _____ _____ the game.

1. 지난 일요일, 우리 가족은 야구 경기를 보러 갔다,
2. 우리 팀을 응원하면서, 우리는 함께 정말 좋은 시간을 가졌다.
3. 행복하게도, 우리 팀이 경기를 이겼다.
4. 승리에 대해 기쁨을 느껴서, 우리는 축하하기로 결정했다.
5. 함께 프라이드치킨을 먹으면서, 우리는 그 경기에 대해 얘기했다.

After You Read C Get the BIG Picture

1. _____ _____

2. where people _____ _____ their items _____ or _____ services _____ _____

Ask Your Neighbors

3. ⊕ _____ people _____ items _____ _____ _____

4. ⊕ _____ _____ _____ money and _____

5. ⊖ needs _____ _____ on _____ _____ _____

6. <⊕ _____, ⊖ _____>

1. 공유 경제
2. 사람들은 자신의 물건을 다른 사람들과 공유하거나 그들에게 서비스를 제공할 수 있는 곳
Ask Your Neighbors
3. ⊕ 사람들이 다른 사람들로부터 빌릴 수 있는 물건을 찾도록 돕는다
4. ⊕ 사람들이 돈과 자원들을 아끼도록 돕는다
5. ⊖ 각 제품의 상태에 관해 정기적인 업데이트가 필요하다
6. <⊕ 이점, ⊖ 약점>

Culture Link

1. _____ Economies _____ the World

2. I sometimes _____ other people _____ _____ _____ _____ _____ _____.

3. They can _____ _____ their destinations _____ _____ _____, and I can make some money.

4. _____ _____ also _____ _____ _____ _____ _____ cars on the road, _____ is _____ _____.

1. 세계의 공유 경제
2. 나는 때때로 출근길에 다른 사람들을 태워준다.
3. 그들은 적은 요금을 내고 목적지에 도착할 수 있고, 나는 약간의 돈을 벌 수 있다.
4. 출근 공유는 또한 도로 위의 차들의 수를 줄여 주는데, 그것은 환경친화적이다.

※ 다음 우리말을 영어로 쓰시오.

Do It Yourself

1. 지난 일요일, 우리 가족은 야구 경기를 보러 갔다.
   ➡ _____

2. 우리 팀을 응원하면서, 우리는 함께 정말 좋은 시간을 가졌다.
   ➡ _____

3. 행복하게도, 우리 팀이 경기에서 이겼다.
   ➡ _____

4. 승리에 대해 기쁨을 느껴서, 우리는 축하하기로 결정했다.
   ➡ _____

5. 함께 프라이드치킨을 먹으면서, 우리는 그 경기에 대해 얘기했다.
   ➡ _____

After You Read C Get the BIG Picture

1. 공유 경제
   ➡ _____

2. 사람들은 자신의 물건을 다른 사람들과 공유하거나 그들에게 서비스를 제공할 수 있는 곳
   ➡ _____

Ask Your Neighbors

3. ⊕ 사람들이 다른 사람들로부터 빌릴 수 있는 물건을 찾도록 돕는다
   ➡ _____

4. ⊕ 사람들이 돈과 자원들을 아끼도록 돕는다
   ➡ _____

5. ⊖ 각 제품의 상태에 관해 정기적인 업데이트가 필요하다
   ➡ _____

6. 〈⊕ 이점, ⊖ 약점〉
   ➡ _____

Culture Link

1. 세계의 공유 경제
   ➡ _____

2. 나는 때때로 출근길에 다른 사람들을 태워준다.
   ➡ _____

3. 그들은 적은 요금을 내고 목적지에 도착할 수 있고, 나는 약간의 돈을 벌 수 있다.
   ➡ _____

4. 출근 공유는 또한 도로 위의 차들의 수를 줄여 주는데, 그것은 환경친화적이다.
   ➡ _____

※ 다음 영어를 우리말로 쓰시오.

01 tool	_____	22 swarm	_____
02 threat	_____	23 praise	_____
03 cashier	_____	24 reality	_____
04 recipe	_____	25 intelligence	_____
05 common	_____	26 disaster	_____
06 navigate	_____	27 survivor	_____
07 forecast	_____	28 ensure	_____
08 perceive	_____	29 escape	_____
09 resource	_____	30 solution	_____
10 delivery	_____	31 present	_____
11 artificial	_____	32 route	_____
12 awesome	_____	33 safety	_____
13 destination	_____	34 invention	_____
14 recognize	_____	35 deal with	_____
15 sense	_____	36 work on	_____
16 bright	_____	37 keep track of	_____
17 difference	_____	38 such as	_____
18 self-driving	_____	39 a variety of	_____
19 perform	_____	40 with the help of	_____
20 nutrient	_____	41 so that ~	_____
21 equip	_____	42 make decisions	_____
		43 look toward	_____

※ 다음 우리말을 영어로 쓰시오.

01 지능, 정보 _____

02 출납원 _____

03 현재의, 존재하는 _____

04 기술, 기계 _____

05 칭찬 _____

06 요리법 _____

07 목적지, 도착지 _____

08 떼, 군중, 벌 떼 _____

09 인공적인, 인위적인 _____

10 인지하다, 감지하다 _____

11 위협, 협박 _____

12 해법, 해답, 해결책 _____

13 차이, 차이점 _____

14 공연하다, 실행하다 _____

15 안전, 안전한 곳 _____

16 굉장한, 아주 멋진 _____

17 생존자, 살아남은 사람 _____

18 밝은, 희망적인 _____

19 재해, 참사, 재난 _____

20 길을 찾다, 항해하다 _____

21 탈출하다, 달아나다,
   벗어나다 _____

22 영양소, 영양분 _____

23 자율 주행하는 _____

24 보장하다 _____

25 인식하다 _____

26 배달, 전달 _____

27 길, 경로 _____

28 ～에 (필요한 것을) 갖추다 _____

29 자원, 재원 _____

30 감지하다 _____

31 흔한 _____

32 예측, 예보 _____

33 편리한 _____

34 발명, 발명품 _____

35 ～의 도움으로 _____

36 처리하다, 다루다 _____

37 ～와 같은 _____

38 다양한 _____

39 앞날을 생각하다 _____

40 결정을 하다 _____

41 ～하기 위하여 _____

42 하루 종일 _____

43 ～에 노력을 들이다, 애쓰다 _____

※ 다음 영영풀이에 알맞은 단어를 <보기>에서 골라 쓴 후, 우리말 뜻을 쓰시오.

1 _____ : a risk or danger: _____

2 _____ : to be fully aware of: _____

3 _____ : to complete an action or activity: _____

4 _____ : the answer to a problem: _____

5 _____ : a person who remains alive: _____

6 _____ : made by humans: _____

7 _____ : a way to go from one place to another: _____

8 _____ : to be aware of something without seeing or hearing it: _____

9 _____ : a piece of work that must be done: _____

10 _____ : the ability to learn or understand things well: _____

11 _____ : something that humans have thought of and made: _____

12 _____ : to make one's way through an area: _____

13 _____ : to notice something with the senses: _____

14 _____ : a chemical or food that provides what is needed to live and grow:
_____

15 _____ : the action of taking things such as letters, parcels or goods to a person or
place: _____

16 _____ : an unfortunate event that damages a large area and may harm many
people: _____

보기

delivery	survivor	nutrient	sense
task	recognize	navigate	threat
disaster	perform	perceive	route
invention	artificial	intelligence	solution

※ 다음 우리말과 일치하도록 빈칸에 알맞은 말을 쓰시오.

Listen & Talk 1 A

G: Hey, _____ you _____ _____ a smart umbrella?

B: No, I _____. _____ _____ _____ _____ _____ _____?

G: Sure. It's an umbrella _____ gives you the _____ _____ for the day. If it _____ _____ _____ _____, the umbrella _____ a _____.

B: That's very _____.

여: 있잖아, 스마트 우산에 대해 들어 본 적 있니?

남: 아니, 들어 본 적 없어. 그게 무엇인지 설명해 줄 수 있니?

여: 물론이지. 그것은 그날의 일기 예보를 알려주는 우산이야. 만약 비가 올 예정이면, 우산에서 소리가 나.

남: 그거 참 편리하구나.

Listen & Talk 1 B

G: Look at these. They are the new _____ of the month!

B: They all look _____. What is the _____ on the first page?

G: It's a new smart refrigerator. It _____ the items inside _____ and _____ _____.

B: That sounds _____.

G: It _____. What do you _____ _____ this _____ camera? I want to buy it.

B: A flying camera? Could you explain _____ _____ _____?

G: Of course. This machine flies to a _____ _____ we have already _____. _____ _____ _____, it can take pictures from 500 meters above the location.

B: That sounds _____. _____ do you want to take pictures _____?

G: I want to _____ _____ _____ _____ birds!

여: 이것들을 봐. 이달의 새로운 발명품들이야!

남: 모두 멋져 보인다. 첫 번째 쪽에 있는 발명품은 뭐지?

여: 이건 새로 나온 스마트 냉장고야. 이 냉장고는 냉장고 내부의 음식들을 감지해서 요리법을 제시해 줘.

남: 유용하겠다.

여: 맞아. 이 플라잉 카메라에 대해서는 어떻게 생각해? 나는 이 카메라가 사고 싶어.

남: 플라잉 카메라? 이게 어떻게 작동하는 건지 설명해 줄 수 있니?

여: 물론이지. 이 기기는 우리가 미리 설정해 둔 목적지로 날아가. 비행하는 동안 이 기기는 그 지점의 500미터 상공에서 사진을 찍을 수 있어.

남: 정말 멋지다. 너는 무슨 사진을 찍고 싶니?

여: 나는 날고 있는 새들의 사진을 찍고 싶어!

Listen & Talk 1 C

B: What are you _____?

G: It's a show about a man _____ lost _____ _____ his _____ in an accident. _____, he can play _____ _____ very well.

B: _____ can he play the drums _____ only one arm?

G: _____ he uses two arms. One is a robot arm _____ by his _____.

B: That's _____. Could you _____ _____ _____ _____ _____ _____?

G: Sure. First, he thinks _____ he wants to do _____ his arm. Then those thoughts _____ _____ _____ electronic signals. The signals _____ _____ his brain _____ his robot arm and move it.

B: That's amazing! I think this _____ can help many people.

남: 무엇을 보고 있니?

여: 이건 사고로 한쪽 팔을 잃은 한 남자에 관한 프로야. 놀랍게도 그는 드럼을 매우 잘 쳐.

남: 그는 어떻게 한쪽 팔만으로 드럼을 칠 수 있는 거지?

여: 사실 그는 두 팔을 사용해. 한쪽 팔은 그의 뇌가 제어하는 로봇 팔이야.

남: 그거 정말 멋지다. 좀 더 구체적으로 설명해 줄 수 있니?

여: 물론이지. 먼저, 그는 자신의 팔로 하고 싶은 것을 생각해. 그런 다음 그 생각들이 전기 신호로 바뀌지. 그 신호들은 그의 뇌에서 로봇 팔로 이동해서 그 팔을 움직여.

남: 놀라운데! 이 기술이 많은 사람들에게 도움을 줄 수 있을 것 같다.

Listen & Talk 2 B

M: _____ climate change is going to make farming _____, there _____ _____ _____ enough _____ for the _____ number of people on Earth. _____ _____ _____, _____ _____ _____ _____ we will have to change _____ _____ _____ our food. For example, we won't kill animals for food. _____, meat _____ _____ _____ _____ in a lab _____ animal cells. This will require _____ _____, water, and _____ _____. Also, bugs _____ _____ ants will become part of our daily meals. You might not want to eat them, but they are actually very _____ in _____!

Listen & Talk 2 C

G: I _____ _____ wait _____ _____ at the store _____ _____ _____ _____ _____.

B: That's too bad. Maybe in the future _____ _____ _____ _____ _____ _____ _____.

G: What _____ _____ _____?

B: I read about a store _____ _____. You take _____ you want to buy and just _____ _____.

G: That's it? _____ do you pay _____ it?

B: There are cameras and _____ in the store. They _____ _____ _____ the items you choose and _____ _____ _____ to an app on your smartphone.

G: Then the app pays for _____ when you leave the store?

B: Exactly. _____ _____ _____ these _____ _____ stores will be more _____ in the future.

Do It Yourself A

B: Hey, _____ you _____ this game? It's really _____.

G: Yes, I _____. That game is pretty _____ these days.

B: The developers used AI technology in _____. The game characters _____ _____ _____ AI.

G: Oh, really? Could you _____ _____ _____ _____ _____?

B: Sure. The AI characters in the game learn from _____ _____ _____ and _____ _____ _____ _____.

G: Oh! That's _____ I sometimes _____ _____ they already knew my moves!

B: They're very smart. _____ _____ _____ _____ _____ the AI in games will _____ _____ _____ _____ _____.

남: 기후 변화가 농업을 더 어렵게 만들 것이기 때문에, 지구상의 점점 더 늘어나는 사람들을 위한 자원이 충분하지 않게 될지도 모른다. 이러한 이유로, 우리는 식량을 얻는 방법을 바꾸어야 할 가능성이 높다. 예를 들어, 우리는 식량을 얻기 위해 동물을 죽이지 않게 될 것이다. 대신, 동물 세포를 이용하여 실험실에서 고기가 배양될 것이다. 이는 더 적은 땅과 물, 그리고 다른 자원들을 필요로 할 것이다. 또한, 개미와 같은 곤충들이 우리 끼니의 일부가 될 것이다. 여러분은 먹고 싶지 않을 수도 있지만, 사실 곤충들은 영양분이 매우 풍부하다!

여: 매장에서 거의 20분 동안 줄을 서서 기다려야 했어.
남: 그것 참 안됐다. 어쩌면 미래에는 줄을 서서 기다릴 필요가 전혀 없을지도 몰라.
여: 그게 무슨 말이야?
남: 계산원이 없는 매장에 관한 글을 읽었거든. 사고 싶은 것을 가지고 그냥 걸어나가면 돼.
여: 그게 다야? 지불은 어떻게 해?
남: 매장 내에 카메라와 감지기가 있어. 그것들이 네가 고른 물건들을 계속 파악하면서 그 정보를 네 스마트폰에 있는 앱으로 보내.
여: 그러면 네가 매장을 나갈 때 앱이 물건 값을 지불하는 거고?
남: 바로 그거야. 미래에는 이런 종류의 매장이 더 흔해질 것 같아.

남: 저기, 이 게임 해봤니? 이거 정말 흥미진진해.
여: 응, 해봤어. 그 게임은 요즘 꽤 인기가 있어.
남: 개발자들이 이 게임에 인공지능 기술을 사용했어. 게임 캐릭터들에 인공지능이 탑재되어 있지.
여: 아, 정말? 좀 더 구체적으로 설명해 줄 수 있니?
남: 물론이지. 게임 속 인공지능 캐릭터들은 인간 플레이어가 하는 행동을 통해 배우고 자신의 기술을 발전시켜.
여: 아! 그래서 이따금씩 캐릭터들이 이미 내 움직임을 알고 있는 것처럼 느껴졌던 거구나!
남: 그들은 매우 똑똑해. 게임 속 인공지능은 점점 더 강화될 가능성이 높아.

※ 다음 우리말에 맞도록 대화를 영어로 쓰시오.

Listen & Talk 1 A

G: _____

B: _____

G: _____

_____

B: _____

여: 있잖아, 스마트 우산에 대해 들어 본 적 있니?

남: 아니, 들어 본 적 없어. 그게 무엇인지 설명해 줄 수 있니?

여: 물론이지. 그것은 그날의 일기 예보를 알려주는 우산이야. 만약 비가 올 예정이면, 우산에서 소리가 나.

남: 그거 참 편리하구나.

Listen & Talk 1 B

G: _____

B: _____

G: _____

B: _____

G: _____

B: _____

G: _____

_____

B: _____

G: _____

여: 이것들을 봐. 이달의 새로운 발명품들이야!

남: 모두 멋져 보인다. 첫 번째 쪽에 있는 발명품은 뭐지?

여: 이건 새로 나온 스마트 냉장고야. 이 냉장고는 냉장고 내부의 음식들을 감지해서 요리법을 제시해 줘.

남: 유용하겠다.

여: 맞아. 이 플라잉 카메라에 대해서는 어떻게 생각해? 나는 이 카메라가 사고 싶어.

남: 플라잉 카메라? 이게 어떻게 작동하는 건지 설명해 줄 수 있니?

여: 물론이지. 이 기기는 우리가 미리 설정해 둔 목적지로 날아가. 비행하는 동안 이 기기는 그 지점의 500미터 상공에서 사진을 찍을 수 있어.

남: 정말 멋지다. 너는 무슨 사진을 찍고 싶니?

여: 나는 날고 있는 새들의 사진을 찍고 싶어!

Listen & Talk 1 C

B: _____

G: _____

_____

B: _____

G: _____

B: _____

G: _____

_____

_____

B: _____

남: 무엇을 보고 있니?

여: 이건 사고로 한쪽 팔을 잃은 한 남자에 관한 프로야. 놀랍게도 그는 드럼을 매우 잘 쳐.

남: 그는 어떻게 한쪽 팔만으로 드럼을 칠 수 있는 거지?

여: 사실 그는 두 팔을 사용해. 한쪽 팔은 그의 뇌가 제어하는 로봇 팔이야.

남: 그거 정말 멋지다. 좀 더 구체적으로 설명해 줄 수 있니?

여: 물론이지. 먼저, 그는 자신의 팔로 하고 싶은 것을 생각해. 그런 다음 그 생각들이 전기 신호로 바뀌지. 그 신호들은 그의 뇌에서 로봇 팔로 이동해서 그 팔을 움직여.

남: 놀라운데! 이 기술이 많은 사람들에게 도움을 줄 수 있을 것 같아.

Listen & Talk 2 B

M: _____

_____

_____

_____

_____

_____

남: 기후 변화가 농업을 더 어렵게 만들 것이기 때문에, 지구상의 점점 더 늘어나는 사람들을 위한 자원이 충분하지 않게 될지도 모른다. 이러한 이유로, 우리는 식량을 얻는 방법을 바꾸어야 할 가능성이 높다. 예를 들어, 우리는 식량을 얻기 위해 동물을 죽이지 않게 될 것이다. 대신, 동물 세포를 이용하여 실험실에서 고기가 배양될 것이다. 이는 더 적은 땅과 물, 그리고 다른 자원들을 필요로 할 것이다. 또한, 개미와 같은 곤충들이 우리 끼니의 일부가 될 것이다. 여러분은 먹고 싶지 않을 수도 있지만, 사실 곤충들은 영양분이 매우 풍부하다!

Listen & Talk 2 C

G: _____
B: _____
G: _____
B: _____

G: _____
B: _____

G: _____
B: _____

여: 매장에서 거의 20분 동안 줄을 서서 기다려야 했어.
남: 그것 참 안됐다. 어쩌면 미래에는 줄을 서서 기다릴 필요가 전혀 없을지도 몰라.
여: 그게 무슨 말이야?
남: 계산원이 없는 매장에 관한 글을 읽었거든. 사고 싶은 것을 가지고 그냥 걸어나가면 돼.
여: 그게 다야? 지불은 어떻게 해?
남: 매장 내에 카메라와 감지기가 있어. 그것들이 네가 고른 물건들을 계속 파악하면서 그 정보를 네 스마트폰에 있는 앱으로 보내.
여: 그러면 네가 매장을 나갈 때 앱이 물건 값을 지불하는 거고?
남: 바로 그거야. 미래에는 이런 종류의 매장이 더 흔해질 것 같아.

Do It Yourself A

B: _____
G: _____
B: _____

G: _____
B: _____

G: _____
B: _____

남: 저기, 이 게임 해봤니? 이거 정말 흥미진진해.
여: 응, 해봤어. 그 게임은 요즘 꽤 인기가 있어.
남: 개발자들이 이 게임에 인공지능 기술을 사용했어. 게임 캐릭터들에 인공지능이 탑재되어 있지.
여: 아, 정말? 좀 더 구체적으로 설명해 줄 수 있니?
남: 물론이지. 게임 속 인공지능 캐릭터들은 인간 플레이어가 하는 행동을 통해 배우고 자신의 기술을 발전시켜.
여: 아! 그래서 이따금씩 캐릭터들이 이미 내 움직임을 알고 있는 것처럼 느껴졌던 거구나!
남: 그들은 매우 똑똑해. 게임 속 인공지능은 점점 더 강화될 가능성이 높아.

※ 다음 우리말과 일치하도록 빈칸에 알맞은 것을 골라 쓰시오.

1 _____ _____ Robots
   A. with   B. Life

2 _____ _____ **We** _____ **Robots?**
   A. See   B. Where   C. Do

3 Robots are _____ _____ in _____ and books _____.
   A. anymore   B. only   C. not   D. movies

4 _____ the world, robots are doing a _____ _____ _____.
   A. variety   B. around   C. tasks   D. of

5 There are _____ robots _____ in the sky, robot arms in factories, and service robots in _____ _____.
   A. flying   B. public   C. delivery   D. places

6 A _____ robot _____ the _____
   A. sky   B. delivery   C. in

7 Robot _____ _____ a _____
   A. factory   B. arms   C. in

8 A _____ _____ _____ the PyeongChang Olympics
   A. robot   B. service   C. at

9 **Robots** _____ _____ _____
   A. Becoming   B. Are   C. Smart

10 In the _____, robots _____ only easy _____ that humans _____ them to do.
   A. programmed   B. performed   C. tasks   D. past

11 However, robots are now _____ " _____," and soon they might be _____ to think like _____.
   A. getting   B. able   C. humans   D. smarter

12 _____ makes this _____ is _____ _____ (AI).
   A. artificial   B. what   C. intelligence   D. possible

13 Robots that have AI can _____ _____ and _____ _____.
   A. perceive   B. decisions   C. environments   D. make

14 They can also _____ _____, tell _____, and play games with _____.
   A. speech   B. jokes   C. humans   D. recognize

15 **AI Speakers:** They can _____ your _____, _____ in your home, and play music for you.
   A. control   B. answer   C. machines   D. questions

16 **AI Pets:** They _____ _____ _____ dogs.
   A. real   B. just   C. act   D. like

17 They _____ and play with their _____ and _____.
   A. recognize   B. walk   C. praise   D. owners

18 **Robots** _____ – _____ **and** _____
   A. Present   B. around   C. Future   D. Us

19 Robots are making _____ _____ and _____.
   A. faster   B. things   C. easier

1 로봇과 함께하는 삶

2 우리는 어디에서 로봇을 보는가?

3 로봇은 더는 영화와 책 속에만 있는 것은 아니다.

4 전 세계적으로 로봇은 다양한 임무를 수행하고 있다.

5 하늘에는 날아다니는 배달 로봇, 공장에는 로봇 팔, 그리고 공공장소에는 서비스 로봇이 있다.

6 하늘에서 날아다니는 배달 로봇

7 공장의 로봇 팔들

8 평창 올림픽의 서비스 로봇

9 로봇이 똑똑해지고 있다

10 과거에 로봇은 인간이 로봇에게 실행하도록 프로그램을 설정한 단순 업무만을 수행했다.

11 그러나 로봇은 이제 '더 똑똑'해지고 있으며, 곧 인간처럼 생각할 수 있을지도 모른다.

12 이러한 것을 가능하게 만드는 것은 인공 지능(AI)이다.

13 인공 지능을 가진 로봇은 환경을 인식하고 의사 결정을 할 수 있다.

14 그들은 또한 인간의 말을 인지하고, 농담을 건네며, 인간과 게임을 할 수 있다.

15 〈인공 지능 스피커〉 그들은 당신의 질문에 대답할 수 있고, 당신의 집에 있는 기계들을 조종할 수 있으며, 당신을 위해 음악을 재생할 수도 있다.

16 〈인공 지능 반려동물〉 그들은 마치 진짜 개처럼 행동한다.

17 그들은 그들의 주인과 함께 걷고 놀며 칭찬을 알아챈다.

18 우리 주변의 로봇들 – 현재와 미래

19 로봇은 일을 더 빠르고 더 쉽게 해 주고 있다.

20 They can help us _____ — in our homes, on roads, or _____ _____ _____.

    A. disaster   B. anywhere   C. areas   D. in

21 **Home Helper Robot:** This robot _____ your family _____ the _____.

    A. throughout   B. helps   C. day

22 Cooking and _____ _____ be _____ if you _____ one.

    A. easier   B. had   C. cleaning   D. would

23 It _____ talks _____ family members and can _____ _____.

    A. emotions   B. also   C. sense   D. with

24 **Self-Driving Car:** A _____ car _____ _____ a _____.

    A. driver   B. self-driving   C. need   D. doesn't

25 With cameras, _____, and software, it can _____ roads for you so that you can _____ and enjoy the _____.

    A. relax   B. sensors   C. ride   D. navitgate

26 **Robot Swarm:** A robot _____ is a _____ group of robots that can communicate with one _____, _____ ants or bees.

    A. like   B. swarm   C. another   D. large

27 They can be _____ in a _____ of places, _____ farms or building _____.

    A. including   B. used   C. sites   D. variety

28 They _____ on _____ and find _____ a group.

    A. as   B. work   C. solutions   D. tasks

29 **Search-and-Rescue Robot:** Search-and-rescue robots can go into _____ _____ that are _____ for _____.

    A. disaster   B. humans   C. areas   D. dangerous

30 They find _____, _____ with dangers, and clear _____ so that people can _____ to safety.

    A. survivors   B. escape   C. deal   D. routes

31 _____ _____ the _____

    A. toward   B. Looking   C. Future

32 Our _____ with robots _____ _____ but not _____.

    A. perfect   B. future   C. bright   D. looks

33 Some people _____ life to _____ more _____ with the _____ of robots.

    A. help   B. expect   C. convenient   D. become

34 However, other people _____ about problems they might _____, such as _____ to our jobs and _____.

    A. threats   B. worry   C. cause   D. safety

35 The important thing is to _____ possible _____ and to _____ that robots are only used for _____.

    A. ensure   B. good   C. find   D. solutions

20 그들은 어디에서나 우리를 도울 수 있다. 우리의 집에서, 길에서 또는 재난 지역에서 말이다.

21 〈집안일 도우미 로봇〉 이 로봇은 온종일 당신의 가족을 돕는다.

22 만약 당신이 이 로봇 하나를 가지고 있다면 요리와 청소가 더 쉬워질 것이다.

23 이 로봇은 또한 가족 모두와 이야기를 나누며 감정을 파악할 수 있다.

24 〈자율 주행 자동차〉 자율 주행 자동차는 운전자를 필요로 하지 않는다.

25 카메라, 감지기 그리고 소프트웨어를 갖춘 채, 이 자동차는 당신이 쉬면서 주행을 즐길 수 있도록 당신을 위해 길을 찾아갈 수 있다.

26 〈로봇 군집〉 로봇 군집은 개미나 벌처럼, 서로 의사소통할 수 있는 로봇의 대규모 집단을 말한다.

27 이 로봇들은 농장이나 건설 현장을 포함한 다양한 장소에서 사용될 수 있다.

28 그들은 하나의 집단으로서 임무를 완수하고 해결책을 찾는다.

29 〈수색 구조 로봇〉 수색 구조 로봇은 사람에게 위험한 재난 지역에 투입될 수 있다.

30 그들은 생존자를 찾고 위험한 상황을 처리하며, 사람들이 안전한 곳으로 대피할 수 있도록 길을 확보한다.

31 미래에 대한 전망

32 로봇과 함께하는 우리의 미래는 밝지만 완벽하지는 않다.

33 어떤 사람들은 로봇의 도움으로 삶이 더욱 편리해질 것을 기대한다.

34 그러나 다른 사람들은 우리의 일자리와 안전에 대한 위협과 같이, 로봇이 일으킬지 모르는 문제들에 대해 걱정한다.

35 중요한 것은 가능한 해결책을 찾아내는 것과 로봇이 오로지 좋은 일을 위해서만 쓰이게 됨을 확실히 하는 것이다.

※ 다음 우리말과 일치하도록 빈칸에 알맞은 것을 골라 쓰시오.

1 Life _____ _____

2 _____ _____ We _____ Robots?

3 Robots are _____ _____ in movies and books _____ .

4 Around the world, robots are doing _____ _____ _____ _____ .

5 There are delivery robots _____ in the sky, robot arms in factories, and service robots _____ _____ _____ .

6 A _____ robot in the sky

7 Robot _____ in a _____

8 _____ _____ _____ at the PyeongChang Olympics

9 **Robots Are** _____ _____

10 In the past, robots _____ only easy tasks that humans _____ _____ _____ _____ .

11 However, robots are now _____ "_____," and soon they might _____ _____ _____ think like humans.

12 _____ _____ _____ _____ is artificial intelligence (AI).

13 Robots that have AI can _____ _____ and make _____ .

14 They can also _____ _____ , tell jokes, and play games with humans.

15 **AI Speakers:** They can answer your questions, _____ _____ in your home, and play music for you.

16 **AI Pets:** They _____ _____ _____ real dogs.

17 They walk and play with their _____ and _____ _____ .

18 **Robots** _____ _____ – _____ **and Future**

19 Robots are making things _____ and _____ .

---

1 로봇과 함께하는 삶

2 우리는 어디에서 로봇을 보는가?

3 로봇은 더는 영화와 책 속에만 있는 것은 아니다.

4 전 세계적으로 로봇은 다양한 임무를 수행하고 있다.

5 하늘에는 날아다니는 배달 로봇, 공장에는 로봇 팔, 그리고 공공장소에는 서비스 로봇이 있다.

6 하늘에서 날아다니는 배달 로봇

7 공장의 로봇 팔들

8 평창 올림픽의 서비스 로봇

9 로봇이 똑똑해지고 있다

10 과거에 로봇은 인간이 로봇에게 실행하도록 프로그램을 설정한 단순 업무만을 수행했다.

11 그러나 로봇은 이제 '더 똑똑'해지고 있으며, 곧 인간처럼 생각할 수 있을지도 모른다.

12 이러한 것을 가능하게 만드는 것은 인공 지능(AI)이다.

13 인공 지능을 가진 로봇은 환경을 인식하고 의사 결정을 할 수 있다.

14 그들은 또한 인간의 말을 인지하고, 농담을 건네며, 인간과 게임을 할 수 있다.

15 〈인공 지능 스피커〉 그들은 당신의 질문에 대답할 수 있고, 당신의 집에 있는 기계들을 조종할 수 있으며, 당신을 위해 음악을 재생할 수도 있다.

16 〈인공 지능 반려동물〉 그들은 마치 진짜 개처럼 행동한다.

17 그들은 그들의 주인과 함께 걷고 놀며 칭찬을 알아챈다.

18 우리 주변의 로봇들 – 현재와 미래

19 로봇은 일을 더 빠르고 더 쉽게 해 주고 있다.

20 They can help us _____ — in our homes, on roads, or _____ _____ _____.

21 **Home Helper Robot:** This robot _____ your family _____ _____ _____.

22 Cooking and cleaning _____ _____ _____ if you _____ _____.

23 It also talks with family members and can _____ _____.

24 **Self-Driving Car:** A _____ _____ doesn't need _____ _____.

25 With cameras, sensors, and software, it _____ _____ roads for you _____ _____ you _____ relax and enjoy the ride.

26 **Robot Swarm:** A robot swarm is _____ _____ _____ _____ _____ that can _____ _____ _____ _____, like ants or bees.

27 They _____ _____ in a variety of places, _____ farms or _____ _____.

28 They _____ _____ tasks and find solutions _____ _____ _____.

29 **Search-and-Rescue Robot:** Search-and-rescue robots can go into _____ _____ that are _____ _____ _____.

30 They find survivors, deal with dangers, and clear routes _____ _____ people _____ _____ _____.

31 _____ _____ the Future

32 Our future with robots looks bright but _____ _____.

33 Some people expect life _____ _____ more convenient _____ _____ _____ robots.

34 However, other people worry about problems _____ _____ _____, _____ _____ threats to our jobs and safety.

35 The important thing is _____ _____ possible solutions and _____ _____ that robots are only used for _____.

20 그들은 어디에서나 우리를 도울 수 있다. 우리의 집에서, 길에서 또는 재난 지역에서 말이다.

21 〈집안일 도우미 로봇〉 이 로봇은 온종일 당신의 가족을 돕는다.

22 만약 당신이 이 로봇 하나를 가지고 있다면 요리와 청소가 더 쉬워질 것이다.

23 이 로봇은 또한 가족 모두와 이야기를 나누며 감정을 파악할 수 있다.

24 〈자율 주행 자동차〉 자율 주행 자동차는 운전자를 필요로 하지 않는다.

25 카메라, 감지기 그리고 소프트웨어를 갖춘 채, 이 자동차는 당신이 쉬면서 주행을 즐길 수 있도록 당신을 위해 길을 찾아갈 수 있다.

26 〈로봇 군집〉 로봇 군집은 개미나 벌처럼, 서로 의사소통할 수 있는 로봇의 대규모 집단을 말한다.

27 이 로봇들은 농장이나 건설 현장을 포함한 다양한 장소에서 사용될 수 있다.

28 그들은 하나의 집단으로서 임무를 완수하고 해결책을 찾는다.

29 〈수색 구조 로봇〉 수색 구조 로봇은 사람에게 위험한 재난 지역에 투입될 수 있다.

30 그들은 생존자를 찾고 위험한 상황을 처리하며, 사람들이 안전한 곳으로 대피할 수 있도록 길을 확보한다.

31 미래에 대한 전망

32 로봇과 함께하는 우리의 미래는 밝지만 완벽하지는 않다.

33 어떤 사람들은 로봇의 도움으로 삶이 더욱 편리해질 것을 기대한다.

34 그러나 다른 사람들은 우리의 일자리와 안전에 대한 위협과 같이, 로봇이 일으킬지 모르는 문제들에 대해 걱정한다.

35 중요한 것은 가능한 해결책을 찾아내는 것과 로봇이 오로지 좋은 일을 위해서만 쓰이게 됨을 확실히 하는 것이다.

※ 다음 문장을 우리말로 쓰시오.

1 ▶ Life with Robots

➡ _____

2 ▶ Where Do We See Robots?

➡ _____

3 ▶ Robots are not only in movies and books anymore.

➡ _____

4 ▶ Around the world, robots are doing a variety of tasks.

➡ _____

5 ▶ There are delivery robots flying in the sky, robot arms in factories, and service robots in public places.

➡ _____

6 ▶ A delivery robot in the sky

➡ _____

7 ▶ Robot arms in a factory

➡ _____

8 ▶ A service robot at the PyeongChang Olympics

➡ _____

9 ▶ Robots Are Becoming Smart

➡ _____

10 ▶ In the past, robots performed only easy tasks that humans programmed them to do.

➡ _____

11 ▶ However, robots are now getting "smarter," and soon they might be able to think like humans.

➡ _____

12 ▶ What makes this possible is artificial intelligence (AI).

➡ _____

13 ▶ Robots that have AI can perceive environments and make decisions.

➡ _____

14 ▶ They can also recognize speech, tell jokes, and play games with humans.

➡ _____

15 ▶ AI Speakers: They can answer your questions, control machines in your home, and play music for you.

➡ _____

_____

16 ▶ AI Pets: They act just like real dogs.

➡ _____

17 ▶ They walk and play with their owners and recognize praise.

➡ _____

18 ▶ Robots around Us – Present and Future

➡ _____

19 Robots are making things faster and easier.
➡ _____

20 They can help us anywhere — in our homes, on roads, or in disaster areas.
➡ _____

21 Home Helper Robot: This robot helps your family throughout the day.
➡ _____

22 Cooking and cleaning would be easier if you had one.
➡ _____

23 It also talks with family members and can sense emotions.
➡ _____

24 Self-Driving Car: A self-driving car doesn't need a driver.
➡ _____

25 With cameras, sensors, and software, it can navigate roads for you so that you can relax and enjoy the ride.
➡ _____
_____

26 Robot Swarm: A robot swarm is a large group of robots that can communicate with one another, like ants or bees.
➡ _____

27 They can be used in a variety of places, including farms or building sites.
➡ _____

28 They work on tasks and find solutions as a group.
➡ _____

29 Search-and-Rescue Robot: Search-and-rescue robots can go into disaster areas that are dangerous for humans.
➡ _____

30 They find survivors, deal with dangers, and clear routes so that people can escape to safety.
➡ _____

31 Looking toward the Future
➡ _____

32 Our future with robots looks bright but not perfect.
➡ _____

33 Some people expect life to become more convenient with the help of robots.
➡ _____

34 However, other people worry about problems they might cause, such as threats to our jobs and safety.
➡ _____

35 The important thing is to find possible solutions and to ensure that robots are only used for good.
➡ _____

※ 다음 괄호 안의 단어들을 우리말에 맞도록 바르게 배열하시오.

1 (with / Robots / Life)
➡ _____

2 (Do / Where / See / We / Robots?)
➡ _____

3 (are / Robots / only / not / movies / in / books / and / anymore.)
➡ _____

4 (the / around / world, / are / robots / a / doing / of / variety / tasks.)
➡ _____

5 (are / there / robots / delivery / in / flying / sky, / the / arms / robot / factories, / in / and / robots / service / public / in / places.)
➡ _____

6 (delivery / a / in / robot / sky / the)
➡ _____

7 (arms / robot / a / in / factory)
➡ _____

8 (service / a / at / robot / the / Olumpics / PyeongChang)
➡ _____

9 (Are / Robots / Smart / Becoming)
➡ _____

10 (the / in / past, / performed / robots / easy / only / that / tasks / programmed / humans / to / them / do.)
➡ _____

11 (robots / however, / now / are / getting / and / "smarter," / soon / might / they / able / be / think / to / humans. / like)
➡ _____

12 (makes / what / possible / this / artificial / is / (AI). / intelligence)
➡ _____

13 (that / robots / have / can / AI / perceive / and / environments / decisions. / make)
➡ _____

14 (can / they / recognize / also / speech, / jokes, / tell / play / and / with / games / humans.)
➡ _____

15 (AI Speakers: / can / they / your / answer / questions, / machines / control / your / in / home, / play / and / for / music / you.)
➡ _____

16 (AI Pets: / act / they / like / just / dogs. / real)
➡ _____

17 (walk / they / play / and / their / with / and / owners / praise. / recognize)
➡ _____

18 (around / Robots / Us / – / Future / and / Present)
➡ _____

19 (are / robots / things / making / easier. / and / faster)
➡ _____

1 로봇과 함께하는 삶

2 우리는 어디에서 로봇을 보는가?

3 로봇은 더는 영화와 책 속에만 있는 것은 아니다.

4 전 세계적으로 로봇은 다양한 임무를 수행하고 있다.

5 하늘에는 날아다니는 배달 로봇, 공장에는 로봇 팔, 그리고 공공장소에는 서비스 로봇이 있다.

6 하늘에서 날아다니는 배달 로봇

7 공장의 로봇 팔들

8 평창 올림픽의 서비스 로봇

9 로봇이 똑똑해지고 있다

10 과거에 로봇은 인간이 로봇에게 실행하도록 프로그램을 설정한 단순 업무만을 수행했다.

11 그러나 로봇은 이제 '더 똑똑'해지고 있으며, 곧 인간처럼 생각할 수 있을지도 모른다.

12 이러한 것을 가능하게 만드는 것은 인공 지능(AI)이다.

13 인공 지능을 가진 로봇은 환경을 인식하고 의사 결정을 할 수 있다.

14 그들은 또한 인간의 말을 인지하고, 농담을 건네며, 인간과 게임을 할 수 있다.

15 〈인공 지능 스피커〉 그들은 당신의 질문에 대답할 수 있고, 당신의 집에 있는 기계들을 조종할 수 있으며, 당신을 위해 음악을 재생할 수도 있다.

16 〈인공 지능 반려동물〉 그들은 마치 진짜 개처럼 행동한다.

17 그들은 그들의 주인과 함께 걷고 놀며 칭찬을 알아챈다.

18 우리 주변의 로봇들 – 현재와 미래

19 로봇은 일을 더 빠르고 더 쉽게 해 주고 있다.

20 (can / they / us / help / anywhere / — / our / in / homes, roads, / on / or / disaster / in / areas.)
➡ _____

21 (Home Helper Robot: / robot / this / your / helps / throughout / family / day. / the)
➡ _____

22 (cooking / cleaning / and / be / would / if / easier / had / you / one.)
➡ _____

23 (also / it / talks / family / with / members / and / sense / can / emotions.)
➡ _____

24 (Self-Driving Car: / self-driving / a / doesn't / car / need / driver. / a)
➡ _____

25 (cameras, / with / and / sensors, / it / software, / navigate / can / for / roads / so / you / that / can / you / relax / enjoy / and / ride. / the)
➡ _____

26 (Robot Swarm: / robot / a / swarm / a / is / group / large / robots / of / can / that / with / communicate / one / like / another, / or / bees. / ants)
➡ _____

27 (can / they / used / be / a / in / of / variety / places, / farms / including / or / sites. / building)
➡ _____

28 (work / they / tasks / on / and / solutions / find / a / as / group.)
➡ _____

29 (Search-and-Rescue Robot: / robots / search-and-rescue / can / into / go / areas / disaster / are / that / for / dangrous / humans.)
➡ _____

30 (find / they / deal / survivors, / dangers, / with / clear / and / so / routes / that / can / people / escape / safety. / to)
➡ _____

31 (toward / Looking / Future / the)
➡ _____

32 (future / our / robots / with / bright / looks / not / but / perfect.)
➡ _____

33 (people / some / life / expect / to / more / become / with / convenient / the / of / help / robots.)
➡ _____

34 (other / however, / worry / people / about / they / problems / might / such / cause, / as / to / threats / jobs / our / safety. / and)
➡ _____

35 (important / the / thing / to / is / possible / find / and / solutions / ensure / to / that / are / robots / only / for / used / good.)
➡ _____

20 그들은 어디에서나 우리를 도울 수 있다. 우리의 집에서, 길에서 또는 재난 지역에서 말이다.

21 〈집안일 도우미 로봇〉 이 로봇은 온종일 당신의 가족을 돕는다.

22 만약 당신이 이 로봇 하나를 가지고 있다면 요리와 청소가 더 쉬워질 것이다.

23 이 로봇은 또한 가족 모두와 이야기를 나누며 감정을 파악할 수 있다.

24 〈자율 주행 자동차〉 자율 주행 자동차는 운전자를 필요로 하지 않는다.

25 카메라, 감지기 그리고 소프트웨어를 갖춘 채, 이 자동차는 당신이 쉬면서 주행을 즐길 수 있도록 당신을 위해 길을 찾아갈 수 있다.

26 〈로봇 군집〉 로봇 군집은 개미나 벌처럼, 서로 의사소통할 수 있는 로봇의 대규모 집단을 말한다.

27 이 로봇들은 농장이나 건설 현장을 포함한 다양한 장소에서 사용될 수 있다.

28 그들은 하나의 집단으로서 임무를 완수하고 해결책을 찾는다.

29 〈수색 구조 로봇〉 수색 구조 로봇은 사람에게 위험한 재난 지역에 투입될 수 있다.

30 그들은 생존자를 찾고 위험한 상황을 처리하며, 사람들이 안전한 곳으로 대피할 수 있도록 길을 확보한다.

31 미래에 대한 전망

32 로봇과 함께하는 우리의 미래는 밝지만 완벽하지는 않다.

33 어떤 사람들은 로봇의 도움으로 삶이 더욱 편리해질 것을 기대한다.

34 그러나 다른 사람들은 우리의 일자리와 안전에 대한 위협과 같이, 로봇이 일으킬지 모르는 문제들에 대해 걱정한다.

35 중요한 것은 가능한 해결책을 찾아내는 것과 로봇이 오로지 좋은 일을 위해서만 쓰이게 됨을 확실히 하는 것이다.

※ 다음 우리말을 영어로 쓰시오.

1 로봇과 함께하는 삶

➡ _____

2 우리는 어디에서 로봇을 보는가?

➡ _____

3 로봇은 더는 영화와 책 속에만 있는 것은 아니다.

➡ _____

4 전 세계적으로 로봇은 다양한 임무를 수행하고 있다.

➡ _____

5 하늘에는 날아다니는 배달 로봇, 공장에는 로봇 팔, 그리고 공공장소에는 서비스 로봇이 있다.

➡ _____

6 하늘에서 날아다니는 배달 로봇

➡ _____

7 공장의 로봇 팔들

➡ _____

8 평창 올림픽의 서비스 로봇

➡ _____

9 로봇이 똑똑해지고 있다

➡ _____

10 과거에 로봇은 인간이 로봇에게 실행하도록 프로그램을 설정한 단순 업무만을 수행했다.

➡ _____

11 그러나 로봇은 이제 '더 똑똑'해지고 있으며, 곧 인간처럼 생각할 수 있을지도 모른다.

➡ _____

12 이러한 것을 가능하게 만드는 것은 인공 지능(AI)이다.

➡ _____

13 인공 지능을 가진 로봇은 환경을 인식하고 의사 결정을 할 수 있다.

➡ _____

14 그들은 또한 인간의 말을 인지하고, 농담을 건네며, 인간과 게임을 할 수 있다.

➡ _____

15 〈인공 지능 스피커〉 그들은 당신의 질문에 대답할 수 있고, 당신의 집에 있는 기계들을 조종할 수 있으며, 당신을 위해 음악을 재생할 수도 있다.

➡ _____

_____

16 〈인공 지능 반려동물〉 그들은 마치 진짜 개처럼 행동한다.

➡ _____

17 그들은 그들의 주인과 함께 걷고 놀며 칭찬을 알아챈다.

➡ _____

18 우리 주변의 로봇들 – 현재와 미래

➡ _____

19 로봇은 일을 더 빠르고 더 쉽게 해 주고 있다.
➡ _____

20 그들은 어디에서나 우리를 도울 수 있다. 우리의 집에서, 길에서 또는 재난 지역에서 말이다.
➡ _____

21 〈집안일 도우미 로봇〉 이 로봇은 온종일 당신의 가족을 돕는다.
➡ _____

22 만약 당신이 이 로봇 하나를 가지고 있다면 요리와 청소가 더 쉬워질 것이다.
➡ _____

23 이 로봇은 또한 가족 모두와 이야기를 나누며 감정을 파악할 수 있다.
➡ _____

24 〈자율 주행 자동차〉 자율 주행 자동차는 운전자를 필요로 하지 않는다.
➡ _____

25 카메라, 감지기 그리고 소프트웨어를 갖춘 채, 이 자동차는 당신이 쉬면서 주행을 즐길 수 있도록 당신을 위해 길을 찾아갈 수 있다.
➡ _____

26 〈로봇 군집〉 로봇 군집은 개미나 벌처럼, 서로 의사소통할 수 있는 로봇의 대규모 집단을 말한다.
➡ _____

27 이 로봇들은 농장이나 건설 현장을 포함한 다양한 장소에서 사용될 수 있다.
➡ _____

28 그들은 하나의 집단으로서 임무를 완수하고 해결책을 찾는다.
➡ _____

29 〈수색 구조 로봇〉 수색 구조 로봇은 사람에게 위험한 재난 지역에 투입될 수 있다.
➡ _____

30 그들은 생존자를 찾고 위험한 상황을 처리하며, 사람들이 안전한 곳으로 대피할 수 있도록 길을 확보한다.
➡ _____

31 미래에 대한 전망
➡ _____

32 로봇과 함께하는 우리의 미래는 밝지만 완벽하지는 않다.
➡ _____

33 어떤 사람들은 로봇의 도움으로 삶이 더욱 편리해질 것을 기대한다.
➡ _____

34 그러나 다른 사람들은 우리의 일자리와 안전에 대한 위협과 같이, 로봇이 일으킬지 모르는 문제들에 대해 걱정한다.
➡ _____

35 중요한 것은 가능한 해결책을 찾아내는 것과 로봇이 오로지 좋은 일을 위해서만 쓰이게 됨을 확실히 하는 것이다.
➡ _____

※ 다음 우리말과 일치하도록 빈칸에 알맞은 말을 쓰시오.

Presentation Time Step 3

1. _____ _____ _____ _____ this painting shows?

2. I think it shows a machine _____ _____ _____ _____ _____.

3. The machine _____ _____ _____ today's robot _____ _____, but they _____ _____ _____.

4. For example, _____ _____ _____ _____ _____ _____, the machine in the painting _____ _____ _____ a human.

After You Read B

1. home helper robot: I _____ _____ _____ _____ a child of the family I _____ _____.

2. He felt sad _____ _____ his _____ _____.

3. search-and-rescue robot: Last week, after a storm _____, I cleared a route to _____ _____ _____ _____ _____.

4. robot swarm: We _____ _____ _____ _____ _____ and built a tower _____ _____ _____.

Think and Write Step 3

1. School Life _____ 30 Years

2. In 30 years, school life _____ _____ very _____ _____ now.

3. _____ _____ _____ _____ _____ there will be _____ _____ _____ _____ _____.

4. Students _____ _____ _____ go to school.

5. _____, they will study at home _____ _____ _____ _____.

6. One _____ _____ of such a change _____ _____ that students could save time _____ they would _____ _____ _____ to school and _____ _____.

7. However, there _____ _____ some _____ _____ too.

8. For example, students _____ _____ _____ _____ meet their friends _____ often.

9. We don't know exactly _____ _____ _____ _____ _____ _____ in the future, but I hope it will be _____ fun and meaningful _____ _____ _____ _____.

1. 여러분은 이 그림이 무엇을 보여준다고 생각하나요?
2. 저는 이것이 사람들이 집을 청소하는 것을 도와주는 기계를 보여준다고 생각합니다.
3. 그 기계는 오늘날의 로봇 진공청소기와 비슷하게 보이지만 약간의 차이가 있습니다.
4. 예를 들어, 오늘날의 로봇 진공청소기와는 다르게 그림에 있는 기계는 인간에 의해 조종됩니다.

1. 집안일 도우미 로봇: 나는 내가 일하는 가족의 한 아이의 기운을 북돋워주려고 했다.
2. 그는 나쁜 점수 때문에 슬픔을 느꼈다.
3. 수색 구조 로봇: 지난주에 나는 폭풍이 강타한 뒤에 한 소년이 탈출하는 것을 돕기 위해 길을 청소했다.
4. 로봇 군집: 우리는 서로 의사소통하고, 함께 일함으로써 탑을 지었다.

1. 30년 후의 학교 생활
2. 30년 후에, 학교 생활은 지금과 많이 달라질 것이다.
3. 장소에 큰 변화가 있을 것이다.
4. 학생들은 학교에 갈 필요가 없게 될 것이다.
5. 대신, 그들은 집에서 다양한 앱을 이용하여 공부할 것이다.
6. 그러한 변화의 한 가지 긍정적인 효과는 학생들이 학교에 다녀올 필요가 없기 때문에 시간을 절약할 수 있다는 것이다.
7. 하지만, 부정적인 효과 또한 있을 수 있다.
8. 예를 들어, 학생들이 전과 같이 자주 친구들을 만날 수 없을 것이다.
9. 우리는 미래에 학교 생활이 어떻게 될지 정확하게 알 수는 없다. 그렇지만, 나는 오늘날과 마찬가지로 재미있고, 의미 있기를 희망한다.

※ 다음 우리말을 영어로 쓰시오.

Presentation Time Step 3

1. 여러분은 이 그림이 무엇을 보여준다고 생각하나요?
   ➡ _____

2. 저는 이것이 사람들이 집을 청소하는 것을 도와주는 기계를 보여준다고 생각합니다.
   ➡ _____

3. 그 기계는 오늘날의 로봇 진공청소기와 비슷하게 보이지만 약간의 차이가 있습니다.
   ➡ _____

4. 예를 들어, 오늘날의 로봇 진공청소기와는 다르게 그림에 있는 기계는 인간에 의해 조종됩니다.
   ➡ _____

After You Read B

1. 집안일 도우미 로봇: 나는 내가 일하는 가족의 한 아이의 기운을 북돋워주려고 했다.
   ➡ _____

2. 그는 나쁜 점수 때문에 슬픔을 느꼈다.
   ➡ _____

3. 수색 구조 로봇: 지난주에 나는 폭풍이 강타한 뒤에 한 소년이 탈출하는 것을 돕기 위해 길을 청소했다.
   ➡ _____

4. 로봇 군집: 우리는 서로 의사소통하고, 함께 일함으로써 탑을 지었다.
   ➡ _____

Think and Write Step 3

1. 30년 후의 학교 생활
   ➡ _____

2. 30년 후에, 학교 생활은 지금과 많이 달라질 것이다.
   ➡ _____

3. 장소에 큰 변화가 있을 것이다.
   ➡ _____

4. 학생들은 학교에 갈 필요가 없게 될 것이다.
   ➡ _____

5. 대신, 그들은 집에서 다양한 앱을 이용하여 공부할 것이다.
   ➡ _____

6. 그러한 변화의 한 가지 긍정적인 효과는 학생들이 학교에 다녀올 필요가 없기 때문에 시간을 절약할 수 있다는 것이다.
   ➡ _____
   _____

7. 하지만, 부정적인 효과 또한 있을 수 있다.
   ➡ _____

8. 예를 들어, 학생들이 전과 같이 자주 친구들을 만날 수 없을 것이다.
   ➡ _____

9. 우리는 미래에 학교 생활이 어떻게 될지 정확하게 알 수는 없다. 그렇지만, 나는 오늘날과 마찬가지로 재미있고, 의미 있기를 희망한다.
   ➡ _____
   _____

※ 다음 영어를 우리말로 쓰시오.

01 thief _____

02 climb _____

03 kindness _____

04 path _____

05 survival _____

06 travel _____

07 whole _____

08 compare _____

09 pioneer _____

10 strongly _____

11 attack _____

12 bottom _____

13 separate _____

14 destination _____

15 correct _____

16 wise _____

17 realize _____

18 further _____

19 gone _____

20 create _____

21 hurry _____

22 someday _____

23 pioneer _____

24 hunger _____

25 thick _____

26 wisdom _____

27 protect _____

28 reach _____

29 disagree _____

30 guide _____

31 straight _____

32 take _____

33 move _____

34 solve _____

35 thanks to _____

36 in the end _____

37 act on _____

38 make one's way to ~ _____

39 become lost _____

40 the way out _____

41 on the way _____

42 die of _____

43 without ~ing _____

※ 다음 우리말을 영어로 쓰시오.

01 굶주림

02 친절

03 보호하다

04 동의하다, 찬성하다

05 지혜로운, 현명한

06 서두르다, 서둘러 가다

07 생존

08 두꺼운, (나무가) 울창한

09 비교하다

10 도둑

11 지혜, 슬기

12 옳은

13 깨닫다, 자각하다

14 선구자, 개척자

15 분리된, 서로 다른

16 공격하다

17 (문제, 곤경을) 해결하다, 풀다

18 목적지, 도착지

19 똑바로

20 창조하다

21 길

22 안내인, 가이드

23 강경히, 강하게

24 동의하지 않다, 의견이 다르다

25 더 멀리; 더 먼

26 전체의, 모든

27 (시간이) 걸리다

28 가버린, 떠난

29 움직이다, 감동시키다

30 밑, 바닥

31 오르다, 올라가다

32 ~에 이르다[닿다], 도착하다

33 (미래의) 언젠가, 훗날

34 여행; 여행하다

35 나가는 길, 출구

36 ~에 따라 행동하다

37 마침내, 결국

38 길을 잃다

39 가는 길에

40 ~ 덕분에

41 ~으로 죽다

42 ~하지 않고

43 ~로 나아가다

※ 다음 영영풀이에 알맞은 단어를 <보기>에서 골라 쓴 후, 우리말 뜻을 쓰시오.

1 _____ : to try to hurt or damage: _____

2 _____ : to go up something towards the top: _____

3 _____ : the feeling of needing food: _____

4 _____ : not together or the same: _____

5 _____ : to cause someone to feel strong emotions: _____

6 _____ : to have a different opinion: _____

7 _____ : to accept an idea suggested by someone else: _____

8 _____ : the state of continuing to live, after despite difficult conditions: _____

9 _____ : a way or track that is built or is made by the action of people walking: _____

10 _____ : the place where somebody or something is going or being sent: _____

11 _____ : the quality of behaving in a thoughtful, helpful, or friendly way: _____

12 _____ : one of the first people to do something or to travel to a new area: _____

13 _____ : to know and understand that something is true or has happened: _____

14 _____ : to examine people or things to see how they are similar and how they are different: _____

15 _____ : to make sure that somebody/something is not harmed, injured, damaged, etc.: _____

16 _____ : the ability to make sensible decisions and give good advice because of the experience and knowledge that you have: _____

보기			
pioneer	survival	kindness	agree
wisdom	attack	compare	climb
path	disagree	destination	move
protect	separate	realize	hunger

※ 다음 우리말과 일치하도록 빈칸에 알맞은 것을 골라 쓰시오.

1 The _____ _____ _____
   A. Wise   B. Five   C. Men

2 _____ day, five _____ men _____ _____ the road.
   A. on   B. one   C. met   D. wise

3 They _____ _____ _____ _____ .
   A. together   B. to   C. agreed   D. travel

4 On the _____ , however, they _____ _____ in a _____ forest.
   A. thick   B. way   C. lost   D. became

5 Before walking _____ _____ , they decided to stop and find the best _____ _____ .
   A. way   B. further   C. out   D. any

6 After _____ for a _____ , the first man said, "I _____ feel that we should go _____ ."
   A. strongly   B. while   C. left   D. thinking

7 The _____ man said, "We should go _____ , _____ *right* also means '_____ .'"
   A. because   B. correct   C. right   D. second

8 Then the _____ man said, "Let's _____ _____ .
   A. back   B. third   C. walk

9 We came that _____ , _____ we can _____ _____ way.
   A. so   B. way   C. leave   D. that

10 Then we can _____ the _____ ."
   A. forest   B. around   C. walk

11 The fourth man _____ and said, "I think we should _____ _____ _____ .
   A. walking   B. disagreed   C. keep   D. straight

12 The _____ cannot _____ _____ _____ .
   A. on   B. forest   C. forever   D. go

13 A _____ _____ will _____ ."
   A. path   B. new   C. open

14 _____ at them all, the _____ man _____ his head and said, "I know how to _____ this. Just wait."
   A. fifth   B. looking   C. solve   D. shook

15 He started to _____ the _____ tree he _____ .
   A. tallest   B. climb   C. find   D. could

16 As he _____ , everyone else _____ to go their _____ .
   A. separate   B. climbed   C. ways   D. decided

---

1 5명의 지혜로운 사람들

2 어느 날 5명의 지혜로운 사람들이 길에서 만났다.

3 그들은 여행을 함께 하기로 했다.

4 그러나 도중에 그들은 울창한 숲속에서 길을 잃게 되었다.

5 더 멀리 가기 전에 그들은 멈추고 빠져나갈 최선의 방법을 찾기로 결정했다.

6 잠시 동안 생각한 후, 첫 번째 남자는 "우리가 왼쪽으로 가야 한다는 생각이 강하게 들어요." 라고 말했다.

7 두 번째 남자가 "우리는 오른쪽으로 가야 해요. 왜냐하면 '오른쪽'은 또한 '옳은'이라는 의미이기 때문이죠."라고 말했다.

8 그러자 세 번째 남자가 "뒤로 돌아갑시다.

9 우리가 그 길로 왔으니 그 길로 나갈 수 있을 겁니다.

10 그러면 우리는 숲을 한 바퀴 돌 수 있고요."라고 말했다.

11 네 번째 남자가 이의를 제기하며 "나는 우리가 똑바로 계속 걸어 나가야 한다고 생각해요.

12 숲이 영원히 계속될 수는 없으니까요.

13 새로운 길이 열릴 것입니다."라고 말했다.

14 모두를 바라보면서 다섯 번째 남자가 고개를 저으며 "나는 이것을 해결하는 방법을 알아요. 잠깐 기다려 보세요."라고 말했다.

15 그는 그가 찾을 수 있는 가장 높은 나무를 오르기 시작했다.

16 그가 올라가자 다른 모든 사람들은 각자 서로 다른 길을 가기로 결정했다.

17 When the fifth man _____ the _____, he could see the _____ _____.

  A. top   B. forest   C. reached   D. whole

18 Looking at all the _____, he found the _____ _____ _____.

  A. paths   B. way   C. shortest   D. out

19 He _____ _____ to tell the _____.

  A. others   B. down   C. hurried

20 However, when he _____ to the _____, everyone _____ _____.

  A. bottom   B. gone   C. got   D. was

21 He _____ to _____, *Where did they go? I* _____ *the best way* _____.

  A. himself   B. thought   C. out   D. found

22 He _____ they were all _____ and he was the _____ _____ man.

  A. wrong   B. wise   C. thought   D. only

23 _____, he was _____.

  A. wrong   B. however

24 _____ was _____.

  A. wise   B. everyone

25 Each man had _____ his _____ and _____ his _____.

  A. created   B. chosen   C. future   D. path

26 The man who went to the left _____ _____ _____ the _____.

  A. deeper   B. walked   C. forest   D. into

27 He was _____ by wild animals and almost _____ _____.

  A. died   B. hunger   C. attacked   D. of

28 Soon he _____ _____ to _____ _____ and find food.

  A. himself   B. learned   C. protect   D. how

29 In the _____, he made his way out of the _____ and taught others _____ _____.

  A. survival   B. end   C. skills   D. forest

30 The man who went to the _____ met a _____ _____ _____.

  A. thieves   B. right   C. of   D. group

31 They _____ everything _____ him and _____ him _____ them.

  A. made   B. join   C. took   D. from

32 _____ he was _____ them, he showed them _____ _____.

  A. kindness   B. while   C. with   D. great

17 다섯 번째 남자가 꼭대기에 이르자 그는 전체 숲을 볼 수 있었다.

18 모든 길을 바라보며 그는 빠져나갈 가장 짧은 길을 찾았다.

19 그는 다른 사람들에게 알리기 위해 급히 내려갔다.

20 하지만 그가 밑으로 내려왔을 때, 모든 사람들은 이미 가 버리고 없었다.

21 그는 '다들 어디 간 거야? 내가 빠져나갈 최선의 길을 찾았는데.'라고 마음속으로 생각했다.

22 그는 그들이 모두 틀렸고 자신이 유일하게 현명한 사람이라고 생각했다.

23 그러나 그가 틀렸다.

24 모두가 지혜로웠다.

25 각자 자신의 길을 선택했고 자신의 미래를 만들었다.

26 왼쪽으로 간 남자는 숲속으로 더 깊이 걸어 들어갔다.

27 그는 야생 동물들의 습격을 받았고 거의 굶어 죽을 뻔했다.

28 머지않아 그는 자신을 지키고 먹을 것을 찾는 방법을 터득했다.

29 결국 그는 숲 밖으로 빠져나왔고 다른 사람들에게 생존 기술을 가르쳤다.

30 오른쪽으로 간 남자는 도둑 무리를 만났다.

31 그들은 그에게서 모든 것을 가져갔고 그를 그들과 합류시켰다.

32 그는 그들과 함께 있는 동안 그들에게 많은 친절을 베풀었다.

33 The _____ were _____ by his _____ and learned from his _____.

    A. wisdom   B. moved   C. kindness   D. thieves

34 _____, they also _____ _____ _____.

    A. wise   B. became   C. later   D. men

35 The man who _____ _____ created a _____ _____ around the forest.

    A. safe   B. back   C. path   D. walked

36 Using this path, people could get where they were going _____ _____ _____, even though the trip took a little _____.

    A. without   B. longer   C. lost   D. getting

37 The man who _____ _____ _____ a _____.

    A. straight   B. went   C. pioneer   D. became

38 He left the _____ and discovered _____ no one else _____ _____ before.

    A. been   B. forest   C. had   D. places

39 _____ _____ _____ him, people could _____ these new beautiful _____.

    A. lands   B. to   C. enjoy   D. thanks

40 The man _____ _____ the tree _____ a _____.

    A. climbed   B. became   C. who   D. guide

41 _____ he had found many different paths, he was _____ to teach people how to find the quickest _____ to their _____.

    A. able   B. destinations   C. ways   D. since

42 This is _____ the five men _____ their _____ _____.

    A. paths   B. found   C. how   D. own

43 _____ them, we are each on our own journey in life, and we cannot _____ one _____ to _____.

    A. journey   B. another   C. like   D. compare

44 You _____ to create _____ _____ _____.

    A. own   B. have   C. path   D. your

45 Listen to yourself, _____ a _____, and _____ _____ it.

    A. decision   B. make   C. on   D. act

46 Then, someday, you will _____ that you have _____ _____ the life that is _____ for you.

    A. right   B. realize   C. living   D. been

33 그 도둑들은 그의 친절에 감동을 받았고 그의 지혜에서 배우게 되었디.

34 나중에 그들 또한 지혜로운 사람들이 되었다.

35 뒤돌아 간 남자는 숲 주변에 안전한 길을 만들었다.

36 사람들은 이 길을 이용할 때 길을 잃지 않고 자신이 가고자 하는 길에 다다를 수 있었다. 비록 이동 시간이 약간 더 오래 걸려도 말이다.

37 똑바로 간 남자는 개척자가 되었다.

38 그는 숲을 벗어나 아무도 이전에 가 본 적이 없는 곳을 발견했다.

39 그 남자 덕분에, 사람들은 이 새롭고 아름다운 지역을 즐길 수 있었다.

40 나무 위로 올라간 남자는 가이드가 되었다.

41 그는 여러 다양한 길을 발견했었기 때문에, 사람들에게 자신의 목적지에 이르는 가장 빠른 길을 찾는 법을 가르쳐 줄 수 있었다.

42 이런 식으로 다섯 남자는 자신만의 길을 찾아냈다.

43 그들처럼 우리는 각각 인생에서 자기 자신만의 여행을 하고 있고, 우리는 한 여정을 다른 것과 비교할 수 없다.

44 당신은 당신 자신만의 길을 만들어가야 한다.

45 자신의 목소리를 듣고, 결정하고, 그 결정에 따라 행동하라.

46 그러면 언젠가 당신은 당신에게 맞는 삶을 살아가고 있다는 것을 깨닫게 될 것이다.

Step2

※ 다음 우리말과 일치하도록 빈칸에 알맞은 것을 골라 쓰시오.

1 The Five _____ _____

2 _____ _____, five wise men _____ on the road.

3 They _____ _____ _____ together.

4 On the way, however, they _____ _____ in a _____ _____.

5 Before walking _____ _____, they decided to stop and find the best _____ _____.

6 After thinking _____ _____ _____, the first man said, "I _____ _____ that we should go left."

7 The second man said, "We should go right, _____ *right* also means '_____.'"

8 Then the third man said, "_____ _____ _____.

9 We came that way, _____ we can _____ _____ _____.

10 Then we can _____ _____ the forest."

11 The fourth man _____ and said, "I think we should _____ _____ _____.

12 The forest cannot _____ _____ _____.

13 A _____ _____ will _____."

14 Looking at them all, the fifth man _____ _____ _____ and said, "I know _____ _____ _____ this. Just wait."

15 He started _____ _____ the tallest tree he _____ _____.

16 As he climbed, everyone else decided to go their _____ ways.

1 5명의 지혜로운 사람들

2 어느 날 5명의 지혜로운 사람들이 길에서 만났다.

3 그들은 여행을 함께 하기로 했다.

4 그러나 도중에 그들은 울창한 숲속에서 길을 잃게 되었다.

5 더 멀리 가기 전에 그들은 멈추고 빠져나갈 최선의 방법을 찾기로 결정했다.

6 잠시 동안 생각한 후, 첫 번째 남자는 "우리가 왼쪽으로 가야 한다는 생각이 강하게 들어요." 라고 말했다.

7 두 번째 남자가 "우리는 오른쪽으로 가야 해요. 왜냐하면 '오른쪽'은 또한 '옳은'이라는 의미이기 때문이죠."라고 말했다.

8 그러자 세 번째 남자가 "뒤로 돌아갑시다.

9 우리가 그 길로 왔으니 그 길로 나갈 수 있을 겁니다.

10 그러면 우리는 숲을 한 바퀴 돌수 있고요."라고 말했다.

11 네 번째 남자가 이의를 제기하며 "나는 우리가 똑바로 계속 걸어 나가야 한다고 생각해요.

12 숲이 영원히 계속될 수는 없으니까요.

13 새로운 길이 열릴 것입니다."라고 말했다.

14 모두를 바라보면서 다섯 번째 남자가 고개를 저으며 "나는 이것을 해결하는 방법을 알아요. 잠깐 기다려 보세요."라고 말했다.

15 그는 그가 찾을 수 있는 가장 높은 나무를 오르기 시작했다.

16 그가 올라가자 다른 모든 사람들은 각자 서로 다른 길을 가기로 결정했다.

17 When the fifth man _____ the top, he could see the _____ _____.

18 _____ _____ all the paths, he found the _____ _____ _____.

19 He _____ _____ to tell _____ _____.

20 However, when he got to the bottom, everyone _____ _____.

21 He _____ _____ _____, *Where did they go? I found the* _____ _____ _____.

22 He thought they were all _____ and he was _____ _____ man.

23 _____, he was _____.

24 _____ was _____.

25 Each man _____ _____ his path and _____ _____ _____.

26 The man who went to the left _____ _____ _____ the forest.

27 He _____ _____ by wild animals and almost _____ _____ _____.

28 Soon he learned _____ _____ _____ _____ and find food.

29 In the end, he _____ _____ _____ _____ _____ the forest and taught others _____ _____.

30 The man who went to the right met _____ _____ _____.

31 They took everything from him and made him _____ _____.

32 _____ he was with them, he showed them _____ _____.

17 다섯 번째 남자가 꼭대기에 이르자 그는 전체 숲을 볼 수 있었나.

18 모든 길을 바라보며 그는 빠져나갈 가장 짧은 길을 찾았다.

19 그는 다른 사람들에게 알리기 위해 급히 내려갔다.

20 하지만 그가 밑으로 내려왔을 때, 모든 사람들은 이미 가 버리고 없었다.

21 그는 '다들 어디 간 거야? 내가 빠져나갈 최선의 길을 찾았는데.'라고 마음속으로 생각했다.

22 그는 그들이 모두 틀렸고 자신이 유일하게 현명한 사람이라고 생각했다.

23 그러나 그가 틀렸다.

24 모두가 지혜로웠다.

25 각자 자신의 길을 선택했고 자신의 미래를 만들었다.

26 왼쪽으로 간 남자는 숲속으로 더 깊이 걸어 들어갔다.

27 그는 야생 동물들의 습격을 받았고 거의 굶어 죽을 뻔했다.

28 머지않아 그는 자신을 지키고 먹을 것을 찾는 방법을 터득했다.

29 결국 그는 숲 밖으로 빠져나왔고 다른 사람들에게 생존 기술을 가르쳤다.

30 오른쪽으로 간 남자는 도둑 무리를 만났다.

31 그들은 그에게서 모든 것을 가져갔고 그를 그들과 합류시켰다.

32 그는 그들과 함께 있는 동안 그들에게 많은 친절을 베풀었다.

33 The thieves _____ _____ _____ his _____ and learned from his wisdom.

34 _____, they also _____ _____ _____.

35 The man who _____ _____ created _____ _____ _____ around the forest.

36 Using this path, people could get where they were going _____ _____ _____, _____ _____ the trip took a little longer.

37 The man who _____ _____ became a _____.

38 He left the forest and discovered places no one else _____ _____ before.

39 _____ _____ him, people could enjoy these new beautiful lands.

40 The man _____ _____ the tree became a guide.

41 Since he had found many _____ _____, he was able to teach people how to find _____ _____ _____ to _____ _____.

42 _____ _____ _____ the five men found _____ _____.

43 _____ them, we are each on our own journey in life, and we cannot compare _____ _____ to _____.

44 You _____ _____ create _____ _____ _____.

45 Listen to yourself, _____ a _____, and _____ _____.

46 Then, someday, you will realize that you _____ _____ _____ the life that is _____ _____ you.

33 그 도둑들은 그의 친절에 감동을 받았고 그의 지혜에서 배우게 되었다.

34 나중에 그들 또한 지혜로운 사람들이 되었다.

35 뒤돌아 간 남자는 숲 주변에 안전한 길을 만들었다.

36 사람들은 이 길을 이용할 때 길을 잃지 않고 자신이 가고자 하는 길에 다다를 수 있었다. 비록 이동 시간이 약간 더 오래 걸려도 말이다.

37 똑바로 간 남자는 개척자가 되었다.

38 그는 숲을 벗어나 아무도 이전에 가 본 적이 없는 곳을 발견했다.

39 그 남자 덕분에, 사람들은 이 새롭고 아름다운 지역을 즐길 수 있었다.

40 나무 위로 올라간 남자는 가이드가 되었다.

41 그는 여러 다양한 길을 발견했었기 때문에, 사람들에게 자신의 목적지에 이르는 가장 빠른 길을 찾는 법을 가르쳐 줄 수 있었다.

42 이런 식으로 다섯 남자는 자신만의 길을 찾아냈다.

43 그들처럼 우리는 각각 인생에서 자기 자신만의 여행을 하고 있고, 우리는 한 여정을 다른 것과 비교할 수 없다.

44 당신은 당신 자신만의 길을 만들어가야 한다.

45 자신의 목소리를 듣고, 결정하고, 그 결정에 따라 행동하라.

46 그러면 언젠가 당신은 당신에게 맞는 삶을 살아가고 있다는 것을 깨닫게 될 것이다.

※ 다음 문장을 우리말로 쓰시오.

1 The Five Wise Men

➡ _____

2 One day, five wise men met on the road.

➡ _____

3 They agreed to travel together.

➡ _____

4 On the way, however, they became lost in a thick forest.

➡ _____

5 Before walking any further, they decided to stop and find the best way out.

➡ _____

6 After thinking for a while, the first man said, "I strongly feel that we should go left."

➡ _____

7 The second man said, "We should go right, because *right* also means 'correct.'"

➡ _____

8 Then the third man said, "Let's walk back.

➡ _____

9 We came that way, so we can leave that way.

➡ _____

10 Then we can walk around the forest."

➡ _____

11 The fourth man disagreed and said, "I think we should keep walking straight.

➡ _____

12 The forest cannot go on forever.

➡ _____

13 A new path will open."

➡ _____

14 Looking at them all, the fifth man shook his head and said, "I know how to solve this. Just wait."

➡ _____

15 He started to climb the tallest tree he could find.

➡ _____

16 As he climbed, everyone else decided to go their separate ways.

➡ _____

17 When the fifth man reached the top, he could see the whole forest.

➡ _____

18 Looking at all the paths, he found the shortest way out.

➡ _____

19 He hurried down to tell the others.

➡ _____

20 However, when he got to the bottom, everyone was gone.

➡ _____

21 He thought to himself, *Where did they go? I found the best way out.*

➡ _____

22 He thought they were all wrong and he was the only wise man.

➡ _____

23 However, he was wrong.

➡ _____

24 Everyone was wise.

➡ _____

25 Each man had chosen his path and created his future.

➡ _____

26 The man who went to the left walked deeper into the forest.

➡ _____

27 He was attacked by wild animals and almost died of hunger.

➡ _____

28 Soon he learned how to protect himself and find food.

➡ _____

29 In the end, he made his way out of the forest and taught others survival skills.

➡ _____

30 The man who went to the right met a group of thieves.

➡ _____

31 They took everything from him and made him join them.

➡ _____

32 While he was with them, he showed them great kindness.

➡ _____

33 The thieves were moved by his kindness and learned from his wisdom.

➡ _____

34 Later, they also became wise men.

➡ _____

35 The man who walked back created a safe path around the forest.

➡ _____

36 Using this path, people could get where they were going without getting lost, even though the trip took a little longer.

➡ _____

_____

37 The man who went straight became a pioneer.

➡ _____

38 He left the forest and discovered places no one else had been before.

➡ _____

39 Thanks to him, people could enjoy these new beautiful lands.

➡ _____

40 The man who climbed the tree became a guide.

➡ _____

41 Since he had found many different paths, he was able to teach people how to find the quickest ways to their destinations.

➡ _____

42 This is how the five men found their own paths.

➡ _____

43 Like them, we are each on our own journey in life, and we cannot compare one journey to another.

➡ _____

44 You have to create your own path.

➡ _____

45 Listen to yourself, make a decision, and act on it.

➡ _____

46 Then, someday, you will realize that you have been living the life that is right for you.

➡ _____

Step4

※ 다음 괄호 안의 단어들을 우리말에 맞도록 바르게 배열하시오.

1 (Five / The / Men / Wise)
➡ _____

2 (day, / one / wise / five / met / men / the / on / road.)
➡ _____

3 (agreed / they / to / togehter. / travel)
➡ _____

4 (the / on / way, / they / however, / became / in / lost / a / forest. / thick)
➡ _____

5 (walking / before / further, / any / decided / they / stop / to / and / the / find / best / out. / way)
➡ _____

6 (thinking / after / a / for / while, / first / the / said, / man / strongly / "I / that / feel / should / we / left." / go)
➡ _____

7 (second / the / said, / man / should / "we / right, / go / *right* / because / also / 'correct.'" / means)
➡ _____

8 (the / then / man / third / said, / walk / "let's / back.)
➡ _____

9 (came / we / way, / that / we / so / leave / can / way. / that)
➡ _____

10 (we / then / walk / can / the / around / forest.")
➡ _____

11 (fourth / the / disagreed / man / said, / and / think / "I / should / we / walking / keep / straight.)
➡ _____

12 (forest / the / go / cannot / forever. / on)
➡ _____

13 (new / a / will / path / open.")
➡ _____

14 (at / looking / all, / them / fifth / the / shook / man / head / his / said, / and / know / "I / to / how / this. // solve / wait." / just)
➡ _____

15 (started / he / climb / to / tallest / the / he / tree / find. / could)
➡ _____

16 (he / as / climbed, / else / everyone / to / decided / go / separate / their / ways.)
➡ _____

1 5명의 지혜로운 사람들
2 어느 날 5명의 지혜로운 사람들이 길에서 만났다.
3 그들은 여행을 함께 하기로 했다.
4 그러나 도중에 그들은 울창한 숲속에서 길을 잃게 되었다.
5 더 멀리 가기 전에 그들은 멈추고 빠져나갈 최선의 방법을 찾기로 결정했다.
6 잠시 동안 생각한 후. 첫 번째 남자는 "우리가 왼쪽으로 가야 한다는 생각이 강하게 들어요."라고 말했다.
7 두 번째 남자가 "우리는 오른쪽으로 가야 해요. 왜냐하면 '오른쪽'은 또한 '옳은'이라는 의미이기 때문이죠."라고 말했다.
8 그러자 세 번째 남자가 "뒤로 돌아갑시다.
9 우리가 그 길로 왔으니 그 길로 나갈 수 있을 겁니다.
10 그러면 우리는 숲을 한 바퀴 돌 수 있고요."라고 말했다.
11 네 번째 남자가 이의를 제기하며 "나는 우리가 똑바로 계속 걸어 나가야 한다고 생각해요.
12 숲이 영원히 계속될 수는 없으니까요.
13 새로운 길이 열릴 것입니다."라고 말했다.
14 모두를 바라보면서 다섯 번째 남자가 고개를 저으며 "나는 이것을 해결하는 방법을 알아요. 잠깐 기다려 보세요."라고 말했다.
15 그는 그가 찾을 수 있는 가장 높은 나무를 오르기 시작했다.
16 그가 올라가자 다른 모든 사람들은 각자 서로 다른 길을 가기로 결정했다.

17 (the / when / man / fifth / the / reached / top, / could / he / the / see / forest. / whole)

➡ _____

18 (at / looking / the / all / paths, / found / he / shortest / the / out. / way)

➡ _____

19 (hurried / he / to / down / tell / others. / the)

➡ _____

20 (when / however, / he / to / got / bottom, / the / was / everyone / gone.)

➡ _____

21 (thought / he / himself, / to / *did* / *where* / *they* / *go*? / *they* // *found* / *I* / *best* / *the* / *out.* / *way*)

➡ _____

22 (thought / he / were / they / wrong / all / and / was / he / only / the / man. / wise)

➡ _____

23 (he / however, / wrong. / was)

➡ _____

24 (was / everyone / wise.)

➡ _____

25 (man / each / chosen / had / path / his / and / his / created / future.)

➡ _____

26 (man / the / went / who / the / to / left / deeper / walked / the / into / forest.)

➡ _____

27 (was / he / by / attacked / wild / and / animals / died / almost / hunger. / of)

➡ _____

28 (he / soon / how / learned / protect / to / himself / and / food. / find)

➡ _____

29 (the / in / end, / made / he / way / his / of / out / forest / the / and / others / taught / skills. / survival)

➡ _____

➡ _____

30 (man / the / went / who / the / to / right / a / met / of / group / thieves.)

➡ _____

31 (took / they / from / everything / him / made / and / join / him / them.)

➡ _____

32 (he / while / with / was / them, / showed / he / great / them / kindness.)

➡ _____

17 다섯 번째 남자가 꼭대기에 이르자 그는 전체 숲을 볼 수 있었다.

18 모든 길을 바라보며 그는 빠져나갈 가장 짧은 길을 찾았다.

19 그는 다른 사람들에게 알리기 위해 급히 내려갔다.

20 하지만 그가 밑으로 내려왔을 때, 모든 사람들은 이미 가 버리고 없었다.

21 그는 '다들 어디 간 거야? 내가 빠져나갈 최선의 길을 찾았는데.'라고 마음속으로 생각했다.

22 그는 그들이 모두 틀렸고 자신이 유일하게 현명한 사람이라고 생각했다.

23 그러나 그가 틀렸다.

24 모두가 지혜로웠다.

25 각자 자신의 길을 선택했고 자신의 미래를 만들었다.

26 왼쪽으로 간 남자는 숲속으로 더 깊이 걸어 들어갔다.

27 그는 야생 동물들의 습격을 받았고 거의 굶어 죽을 뻔했다.

28 머지않아 그는 자신을 지키고 먹을 것을 찾는 방법을 터득했다.

29 결국 그는 숲 밖으로 빠져나왔고 다른 사람들에게 생존 기술을 가르쳤다.

30 오른쪽으로 간 남자는 도둑 무리를 만났다.

31 그들은 그에게서 모든 것을 가져갔고 그를 그들과 합류시켰다

32 그는 그들과 함께 있는 동안 그들에게 많은 친절을 베풀었다.

33 (thieves / the / moved / were / his / by / kindness / and / from / learned / wisdom. / his)

➡ _____

34 (they / later, / became / also / men. / wise)

➡ _____

35 (man / the / walked / who / created / back / safe / a / path / the / around / forest.)

➡ _____

36 (this / using / path, / could / people / where / get / they / going / were / getting / without / lost, / though / even / trip / the / a / took / longer. little)

➡ _____

_____

37 (man / the / went / who / became / straight / pioneer. / a)

➡ _____

38 (left / he / forest / the / and / places / discovered / one / no / else / been / had / before.)

➡ _____

39 (to / thanks / him, / could / people / these / enjoy / beautiful / new / lands.)

➡ _____

40 (man / the / climbed / who / tree / the / a / became / guide.)

➡ _____

41 (he / since / found / had / different / many / paths, / was / he / to / able / people / teach / how / find / to / quickest / the / to / ways / destinations. / their)

➡ _____

_____

42 (is / this / the / how / five / men / their / found / paths. / own)

➡ _____

43 (them, / like / are / we / each / our / on / journey / own / life, / in / and / cannot / we / one / compare / to / journey / another.)

➡ _____

_____

44 (have / you / create / to / own / your / path.)

➡ _____

45 (to / listen / yourself, / a / make / decision, / act / and / it. / on)

➡ _____

46 (someday, / then, / will / you / that / realize / have / you / living / been / life / the / is / that / for / right / you.)

➡ _____

_____

33 그 도둑들은 그의 친절에 감동을 받았고 그의 지혜에서 배우게 되었다.

34 나중에 그들 또한 지혜로운 사람들이 되었다.

35 뒤돌아 간 남자는 숲 주변에 안전한 길을 만들었다.

36 사람들은 이 길을 이용할 때 길을 잃지 않고 자신이 가고자 하는 길에 다다를 수 있었다. 비록 이동 시간이 약간 더 오래 걸려도 말이다.

37 똑바로 간 남자는 개척자가 되었다.

38 그는 숲을 벗어나 아무도 이전에 가 본 적이 없는 곳을 발견했다.

39 그 남자 덕분에, 사람들은 이 새롭고 아름다운 지역을 즐길 수 있었다.

40 나무 위로 올라간 남자는 가이드가 되었다.

41 그는 여러 다양한 길을 발견했기 때문에, 사람들에게 자신의 목적지에 이르는 가장 빠른 길을 찾는 법을 가르쳐 줄 수 있었다.

42 이런 식으로 다섯 남자는 자신만의 길을 찾아냈다.

43 그들처럼 우리는 각각 인생에서 자기 자신만의 여행을 하고 있고, 우리는 한 여정을 다른 것과 비교할 수 없다.

44 당신은 당신 자신만의 길을 만들어가야 한다.

45 자신의 목소리를 듣고, 결정하고, 그 결정에 따라 행동하라.

46 그러면 언젠가 당신은 당신에게 맞는 삶을 살아가고 있다는 것을 깨닫게 될 것이다.

※ **다음 우리말을 영어로 쓰시오.**

1 5명의 지혜로운 사람들

➡ _____

2 어느 날 5명의 지혜로운 사람들이 길에서 만났다.

➡ _____

3 그들은 여행을 함께 하기로 했다.

➡ _____

4 그러나 도중에 그들은 울창한 숲속에서 길을 잃게 되었다.

➡ _____

5 더 멀리 가기 전에 그들은 멈추고 빠져나갈 최선의 방법을 찾기로 결정했다.

➡ _____

6 잠시 동안 생각한 후, 첫 번째 남자는 "우리가 왼쪽으로 가야 한다는 생각이 강하게 들어요." 라고 말했다.

➡ _____

7 두 번째 남자가 "우리는 오른쪽으로 가야 해요. 왜냐하면 '오른쪽'은 또한 '옳은'이라는 의미이기 때문이죠."라고 말했다.

➡ _____

8 그러자 세 번째 남자가 "뒤로 돌아갑시다.

➡ _____

9 우리가 그 길로 왔으니 그 길로 나갈 수 있을 겁니다.

➡ _____

10 그러면 우리는 숲을 한 바퀴 돌 수 있고요."라고 말했다.

➡ _____

11 네 번째 남자가 이의를 제기하며 "나는 우리가 똑바로 계속 걸어 나가야 한다고 생각해요.

➡ _____

12 숲이 영원히 계속될 수는 없으니까요.

➡ _____

13 새로운 길이 열릴 것입니다."라고 말했다.

➡ _____

14 모두를 바라보면서 다섯 번째 남자가 고개를 저으며 "나는 이것을 해결하는 방법을 알아요. 잠깐 기다려 보세요."라고 말했다.

➡ _____

15 그는 그가 찾을 수 있는 가장 높은 나무를 오르기 시작했다.

➡ _____

16 그가 올라가자 다른 모든 사람들은 각자 서로 다른 길을 가기로 결정했다.

➡ _____

17 다섯 번째 남자가 꼭대기에 이르자 그는 전체 숲을 볼 수 있었다.

➡ _____

18 모든 길을 바라보며 그는 빠져나갈 가장 짧은 길을 찾았다.

➡ _____

19 그는 다른 사람들에게 알리기 위해 급히 내려갔다.

➡ _____

20 하지만 그가 밑으로 내려왔을 때, 모든 사람들은 이미 가 버리고 없었다.

➡ _____

21 그는 '다들 어디 간 거야? 내가 빠져나갈 최선의 길을 찾았는데.'라고 마음속으로 생각했다.

➡ _____

22 그는 그들이 모두 틀렸고 자신이 유일하게 현명한 사람이라고 생각했다.

➡ _____

23 그러나 그가 틀렸다.

➡ _____

24 모두가 지혜로웠다.

➡ _____

25 각자 자신의 길을 선택했고 자신의 미래를 만들었다.

➡ _____

26 왼쪽으로 간 남자는 숲속으로 더 깊이 걸어 들어갔다.

➡ _____

27 그는 야생 동물들의 습격을 받았고 거의 굶어 죽을 뻔했다.

➡ _____

28 머지않아 그는 자신을 지키고 먹을 것을 찾는 방법을 터득했다.

➡ _____

29 결국 그는 숲 밖으로 빠져나왔고 다른 사람들에게 생존 기술을 가르쳤다.

➡ _____

30 오른쪽으로 간 남자는 도둑 무리를 만났다.

➡ _____

31 그들은 그에게서 모든 것을 가져갔고 그를 그들과 합류시켰다.

➡ _____

32 그는 그들과 함께 있는 동안 그들에게 많은 친절을 베풀었다.

➡ _____

33 그 도둑들은 그의 친절에 감동을 받았고 그의 지혜에서 배우게 되었다.

➡ _____

34 나중에 그들 또한 지혜로운 사람들이 되었다.

➡ _____

35 뒤돌아 간 남자는 숲 주변에 안전한 길을 만들었다.

➡ _____

36 사람들은 이 길을 이용할 때 길을 잃지 않고 자신이 가고자 하는 길에 다다를 수 있었다. 비록 이동 시간이 약간 더 오래 걸려도 말이다.

➡ _____

_____

37 똑바로 간 남자는 개척자가 되었다.

➡ _____

38 그는 숲을 벗어나 아무도 이전에 가 본 적이 없는 곳을 발견했다.

➡ _____

39 그 남자 덕분에, 사람들은 이 새롭고 아름다운 지역을 즐길 수 있었다.

➡ _____

40 나무 위로 올라간 남자는 가이드가 되었다.

➡ _____

41 그는 여러 다양한 길을 발견했었기 때문에, 사람들에게 자신의 목적지에 이르는 가장 빠른 길을 찾는 법을 가르쳐 줄 수 있었다.

➡ _____

_____

42 이런 식으로 다섯 남자는 자신만의 길을 찾아냈다.

➡ _____

43 그들처럼 우리는 각각 인생에서 자기 자신만의 여행을 하고 있고, 우리는 한 여정을 다른 것과 비교할 수 없다.

➡ _____

_____

44 당신은 당신 자신만의 길을 만들어가야 한다.

➡ _____

45 자신의 목소리를 듣고, 결정하고, 그 결정에 따라 행동하라.

➡ _____

46 그러면 언젠가 당신은 당신에게 맞는 삶을 살아가고 있다는 것을 깨닫게 될 것이다.

➡ _____

영어 기출 문제집

적중100

2학기

정답 및 해설

능률 | 김성곤

중 3

영어 기출 문제집

영어 기출 문제집

2학기

정답 및 해설

능률 | 김성곤

중 3

Take Part in the Economy

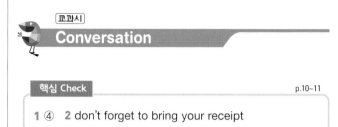

시험대비 실력평가   p.08

01 unreliable   02 ①   03 ①
04 (1) policy (2) product (3) allowance
05 (1) looked after (2) looked for
   (3) environmentally friendly (4) asked for
   (5) less than
06 ④

01 주어진 관계는 반의어 관계를 나타낸다. reliable: 믿을 수 있는,
   unreliable: 믿을 수 없는

02 '장점이 부족한 상태나 조건'을 나타내는 말은 weakness(약점)
   이다.

03 reasonable: 합리적인

04 policy: 정책, product: 상품, allowance: 용돈

05 environmentally friendly: 친환경적인, look for: ~을 찾
   다, look after: ~을 돌보다, less than: ~보다 적은, ~ 미만의,
   ask for: ~을 요청하다

06 주어진 문장에서 fix는 '고치다'를 의미하며 이와 같은 의미로 쓰
   인 것은 ④번이다. 나머지는 '박다, 고정시키다'를 의미한다.

서술형 시험대비   p.09

01 negative
02 (1) for free (2) focused on (3) aware of
03 (1) fee (2) weaknesses (3) improve (4) spend
   (5) discount
04 (1) He should register the birth of his son as soon
       as possible.
   (2) She doesn't want to open up about her
       weakness to anyone.
   (3) Wise consumers always try to save money.
05 (1) My sister prefers rock music to pop music.
   (2) The cashier gave the student a discount.
   (3) The salesperson didn't give me a refund.

01 주어진 관계는 반의어 관계를 나타낸다. positive: 긍정적인,
   negative: 부정적인

02 for free: 무료로, focus on: 초점을 맞추다. be aware of: ~
   을 알다, 알아차리다

03 weakness: 약점, spend: 쓰다, improve: 향상시키다,

discount: 할인, fee: 요금

04 register: 등록하다, weakness: 약점, consumer: 소비자

05 prefer A to B: A를 B보다 더 좋아하다, cashier: 계산원,
   discount: 할인, refund: 환불

[교과서]
Conversation

핵심 Check   p.10~11

1 ④ 2 don't forget to bring your receipt

교과서 대화문 익히기

Check(√) True or False   p.12

1 T 2 F 3 T 4 F

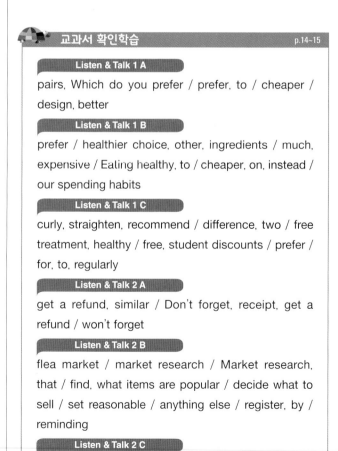

교과서 확인학습   p.14~15

Listen & Talk 1 A

pairs, Which do you prefer / prefer, to / cheaper /
design, better

Listen & Talk 1 B

prefer / healthier choice, other, ingredients / much,
expensive / Eating healthy, to / cheaper, on, instead /
our spending habits

Listen & Talk 1 C

curly, straighten, recommend / difference, two / free
treatment, healthy / free, student discounts / prefer /
for, to, regularly

Listen & Talk 2 A

get a refund, similar / Don't forget, receipt, get a
refund / won't forget

Listen & Talk 2 B

flea market / market research / Market research,
that / find, what items are popular / decide what to
sell / set reasonable / anything else / register, by /
reminding

Listen & Talk 2 C

review / How, review / focus on / to talk, bad points
/ balanced review / it easier for, to choose better
products / useful information

시험대비 기본평가 p.16

01 ① 02 to 03 the receipt 04 ③

02 prefer A to B: B보다 A를 더 좋아하다 / be important to: ~에게 중요하다

03 영수증(receipt)을 가리킨다.

04 (A)는 clothes를 가리키는 ones, (B) forget to: ~할 것을 잊어버리다

시험대비 실력평가 p.17~18

01 (C) → (B) → (D) → (A) → (E)

02 ⓔ → to register 03 ④

04 ⑤ 05 ③

06 She is asking him to remember to bring his receipt.

07 It's because he found he has similar ones.

08 It was because he didn't bring the receipt.

09 (A) straighten (B) healthy (C) for 10 ⑤

01 (C) 두 군데 장소 추천 → (B) 두 장소의 차이점 질문 → (D) Styles Studio의 특징 설명 → (A) Hair Castle에 대한 특징 질문 → (E) Hair Castle의 특징 설명

02 forget to ~: ~할 것을 잊다

03 요즘 어떤 물건들이 인기 있는지는 대화를 통해 알 수 없다.

04 Sujin은 시장 조사 후에 벼룩시장에서 무엇을 판매할지 정할 수 있다고 생각한다.

05 (A)는 잊지 않을 것이라는 대답이므로 won't, (B) balanced: 균형 잡힌, (C) 선행사를 포함한 관계대명사 what이 적절하다.

06 엄마는 Jack에게 영수증을 가져갈 것을 기억하라고 요청하였다.

07 Jack은 비슷한 옷들을 갖고 있는 것을 발견하여 환불하고 싶어한다.

08 Jack은 영수증을 가져가지 않아 환불을 받지 못했었다.

09 (A) straight: 곧은, straighten: 곧게 펴다, (B) keep+목적어+목적격보어 형태로 '건강한'을 의미하는 healthy, (C) for free: 무료로

10 Gina는 스타일 스튜디오를 선호한다.

서술형 시험대비 p.19

01 (D) → (C) → (A) → (B)

02 It's made with lots of fresh vegetables and other healthy ingredients.

03 It's because eating healthy is important to him.

04 It's because she'll spend her money on books instead.

05 register

06 (A) what items are popular
   (B) set reasonable prices

01 (D) 선호하는 신발 묻기 → (C) 선호하는 신발 대답 → (A) 이유 질문 → (B) 이유 대답

02 스페셜 샌드위치는 신선한 야채들과 다른 건강한 재료들로 만들어졌다.

03 Brian에게 건강하게 먹는 것이 중요하기 때문에 스페셜 샌드위치를 더 선호한다.

04 수지는 돈을 책을 사는 데 쓸 것이므로 더 저렴한 샌드위치를 더 좋아한다.

05 '당신의, 누군가의, 무언가의 이름을 공식적인 목록에 기록하다'를 의미하는 말은 register(등록하다)이다.

06 시장 조사를 통해, Tom과 수진은 무슨 물건이 요즘 인기 있는지를 알아낼 수 있다. 게다가 그들은 물건에 합리적인 가격을 정할 수 있다.

교과서

Grammar

핵심 Check p.20~21

1 The more you give, the less you will lose.

2 (1) pouring (2) Left

시험대비 기본평가 p.22

01 ④ 02 ③

03 (1) The bigger, higher (2) louder, to focus
   (3) older, wiser (4) more, more familiar

04 (1) he took a shower (2) she was hungry
   (3) Though he felt scared

01 tired의 비교급은 more 또는 less를 앞에 붙인다. tired의 비교급으로 tireder도 있으나 잘 쓰지 않는다.

02 부사절을 분사구문으로 바꿀 때, 주어가 같으면 주어를 생략하고 분사를 쓴다. ④, ⑤는 수동태의 분사구문을 만들 때 사용한다.

03 'The+비교급 ~, the+비교급 …' 구문이다. 형용사 또는 부사

의 비교급에 대해 정확하게 공부해야 하며, big, high 등은 er을 뒤에 쓰지만, familiar는 more/less를 앞에 쓰고, much나 many는 아예 more가 된다. (2)번 문장은 내용상 가주어-진주어 구문이므로 동사 focus를 to부정사로 변형하는 것에 유의한다.

04 분사구문은 분사를 활용하여 부사절을 부사구로 줄인 표현이다. 대개 양보, 동시동작, 이유, 시간, 조건 등의 부사절이며, 절과 구의 전환시 동사의 시제 등에 유의해야 한다. (3)은 내용상 양보이므로 Though 외에도 Although, Even though 등의 접속사가 가능하다.

시험대비 실력평가   p.23~25

01 ④	02 ④	03 ③	04 ③
05 ④	06 ④	07 ①	08 ⑤
09 ④	10 ④	11 ④	12 ②
13 ③			

14 The more often you use the sharing economy services, the less resources

15 The higher the price of some products gets, the more people want to buy them.

16 ④

01 'Sally가 추위를 느껴서, 옷을 더 입었다.'는 문장이다. 접속사와 주어를 생략하고, -ing형의 분사구문으로 만든다.

02 'The+비교급 ~, the+비교급 …' 구문이다. '당신이 더 열심히 일할수록 결과가 더 좋아질 것이다.'

03 'The+비교급 ~, the+비교급 …' 구문이다. '그녀의 병이 더 악화될수록, 더 많은 고통을 느낄 것이다.'

04 접속사가 있는 부사절로 영작하면, 'While she played[was playing] the piano,'가 된다. 종속절과 주절의 주어가 같으므로, 접속사와 주어를 생략하고, 동사를 분사로 만든 ③이 적절하다.

05 부사절로 영작하면, 'As he used[was using] the sharing economy apps,'이다. 종속절과 주절의 주어가 같으므로 접속사와 주어를 생략하고, 알맞은 분사형으로 바꾼 ④가 적절하다.

06 '우리가 여러 종류의 제품들을 덜 구매할수록, 우리는 더욱 많은 자원을 아낄 수 있다.'라는 내용이다. 사회와 환경에 도움이 되고, 금전적으로도 절약인데, 판매자에게는 반갑지 않다. ①, ②, ③, ⑤는 의미가 반대가 되는 셈이어서 어색하다.

07 '당신이 더 많은 제품을 대여할수록, 공유 경제는 더 활성화될 것이다.'라는 내용이다. ② become이 있으므로 부사 actively를 형용사 active로 바꿔야 한다. 반대로 ③, ④는 do, work를 수식해야 하므로 actively가 더 적절하다. ⑤ active의 비교급은 more active

08 <보기>와 ⑤는 '이유'를 나타내는 분사구문이다. ① '양보' ②

'양보' ③ '조건' ④ '동시 동작, 부대상황'

09 <보기>와 ④는 '조건'을 나타내는 분사구문이다. ① '시간' ② '이유' ③ '이유' ⑤ '시간'

10 <보기>와 ④는 '양보' 의미의 분사구문이다. ① '조건' ② '이유' ③ '이유' ⑤ '이유'

11 부사절로 쓰면, 'As there were no seats available in the bus'가 된다. 주어가 다르므로, 유도부사 there는 생략할 수 없다. 'Being'을 'There being'으로 고쳐야 한다.

12 '보기'의 문장을 내용상 부사절을 이용해서 바꿔보면, 'As animals aren't allowed in my apartment'가 된다. 주절과 종속절의 주어가 다르므로, 독립분사구문을 써야 하고, 종속절 주어 Animals 뒤에 not (being) allowed를 쓰는 것이 적절하다.

13 <보기>는 '더 많은 사람들이 공유 경제 서비스를 이용함에 따라, 더 많이 개선될 것이다'라는 뜻이다. 'The+비교급 ~, the+비교급 …' 구문을 사용해서 정확하게 표현한 문장은 ③이다. '더 많은 사람들이 공유 경제 서비스를 이용할수록, 더 많이 개선될 것이다.' 나머지는 모두 어법상 옳지 않은 문장들이다.

14 'The+비교급 ~, the+비교급 …' 구문을 사용한 문장이다.

15 'The+비교급 ~, the+비교급 …' 구문을 사용한 문장이다. '더 많은 사람들'은 'the more people'로 나타낸다.

16 내용상 though의 역접관계가 아닌, and 또는 so와 같은 순접관계의 접속사가 적절하다. '공유경제가 빠르게 확장하여, 많은 자원들이 절약되도록 한다.'

서술형 시험대비   p.26~27

01 (1) The bigger money she makes, the more her family want.

(2) The more often we use the service, the faster we will promote the sharing economy.

(3) The harder she works, the brighter her future will be.

(4) The more closely we know the system, the stronger our trust in the sharing economy becomes.

(5) The more frequently the app is used, the greater the concern about the personal information gets.

02 (1) When he looked through the window of the restaurant,

(2) and it makes resources less used

(3) If you have trouble that you cannot talk to your loved ones,

(4) Because he did not want to disturb his daughter,

(5) While we use various kinds of apps,

(6) Though there are some weaknesses with the services,

03 The less we throw away, the cleaner

04 (1) Borrowing things that she doesn't often need

(2) Though having been built only two years ago

(3) Not having any tents, we borrowed one

(4) Though there being sharing economy service apps available

05 (1) The more, the wiser

(2) The farther, the healthier

(3) The older, the more

(4) The louder, the more confident

01 'The+비교급 ~, the+비교급 …' 구문 문장이다.

02 문제에 쓰인 분사구문은 다음과 같다. (1) 시간 '그가 식당 창문을 통해 봤을 때,' (2) 병렬 '그리고 그것은 자원들이 덜 사용되도록 한다.' (3) 조건 '만약 당신이 사랑하는 사람들에게 말할 수 없는 어려움이 있다면,' (4) 이유 '자신의 딸을 방해하고 싶지 않았기 때문에,' (5) 동시 동작 '우리가 다양한 종류의 앱을 사용하여,' (6) 양보 '비록 그 서비스에는 몇 가지 단점들이 있지만,'

03 'The+비교급 ~, the+비교급 …'이다. less에 유의한다.

04 (1) 'Because she borrows things that she doesn't often need,'의 부사절을 분사구문으로 만들었다. (2) 주절보다 종속절 시제가 앞서고, 수동태이므로 완료분사구문의 수동형인 'Having been p.p.'를 활용한다. 접속사의 의미를 명확히 하기 위해 분사구문 앞에 접속사를 쓸 수 있으며, 여기서는 though를 문두에 사용했다. *leak: 물이 새다 (3) 분사구문의 부정은 분사 앞에 not이나 never를 쓴다. 'As we didn't have any tents,'의 부사절을 분사구문으로 만들었다. (4) 주절과 종속절의 주어가 다른 독립분사구문 중에서 유도부사 there가 이끄는 부사절은 분사구문으로 전환할 때에도 there를 분사 앞에 쓴다. 원래의 부사절은 'Though there are sharing economy service apps available,'이다.

05 (1) 그 학생들이 더 많은 책을 읽을수록, 그들은 더 지혜로워질 것이다. (2) 그 할머니가 매일 더 멀리 걸을수록, 그녀는 더욱 건강해질 것이다. (3) 그 소녀가 나이를 먹을수록, 그녀의 할머니와 더 닮았다. (4) 그 소년이 더욱 크게 말하기를 연습할수록 더 많은 자신감을 느낀다.

교과서
Reading

확인문제   p.28

1 T   2 F   3 T   4 F   5 T   6 F

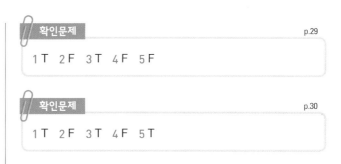

확인문제   p.29

1 T   2 F   3 T   4 F   5 F

확인문제   p.30

1 T   2 F   3 T   4 F   5 T

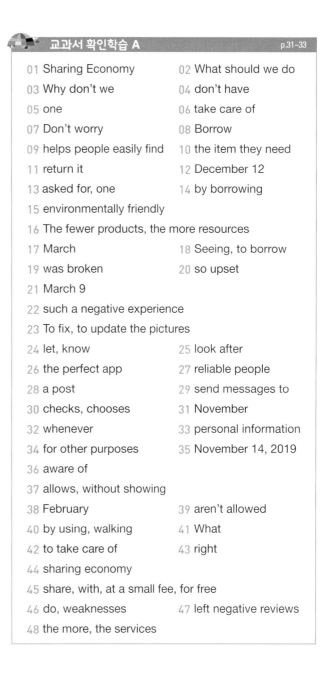

교과서 확인학습 A   p.31~33

01 Sharing Economy
02 What should we do
03 Why don't we
04 don't have
05 one
06 take care of
07 Don't worry
08 Borrow
09 helps people easily find
10 the item they need
11 return it
12 December 12
13 asked for, one
14 by borrowing
15 environmentally friendly
16 The fewer products, the more resources
17 March
18 Seeing, to borrow
19 was broken
20 so upset
21 March 9
22 such a negative experience
23 To fix, to update the pictures
24 let, know
25 look after
26 the perfect app
27 reliable people
28 a post
29 send messages to
30 checks, chooses
31 November
32 whenever
33 personal information
34 for other purposes
35 November 14, 2019
36 aware of
37 allows, without showing
38 February
39 aren't allowed
40 by using, walking
41 What
42 to take care of
43 right
44 sharing economy
45 share, with, at a small fee, for free
46 do, weaknesses
47 left negative reviews
48 the more, the services

교과서 확인학습 B   p.34~36

1 Life in the Sharing Economy

2 Son: What should we do this weekend, Dad?

3 Dad: Why don't we go camping?

4 Son: But we don't have a tent.

5 Should we buy one?

6 Also, who will take care of our dog?

7 Dad: Don't worry. I know some apps that can help us.

8 Borrow from your neighbors!

9 Ask Your Neighbors helps people easily find items that they can borrow from others.

10 First, users download the app and search for another user that has the item they need.

11 Then they pick up the item and return it later.

12 Jasmine: December 12, 2019

13 I asked for a board game and got one in less than 30 minutes.

14 I love saving money by borrowing things that I don't often need.

15 Also, I think it's environmentally friendly.

16 The fewer products we buy, the more resources we save.

17 Cassandra: March 7, 2020

18 Seeing a lot of positive reviews, I decided to borrow a bike helmet.

19 When I got it, however, it was broken.

20 I was so upset!

21 Ask Your Neighbors: March 9, 2020

22 We're sorry that you had such a negative experience.

23 To fix this issue, we are asking lenders to update the pictures of their items regularly.

24 This will let other users know the exact condition of the product.

25 I can look after your pet!

26 Pet Sitter Finder is the perfect app for pet lovers and pet owners.

27 It helps pet owners find reliable people to look after their pets.

28 When a pet owner is looking for pet sitters, he or she uploads a post.

29 Pet sitters or dog walkers can then send messages to the owner.

30 The owner checks their reviews and chooses the best person.

31 George: November 12, 2019

32 I use this app whenever I'm going out of town.

33 I have some concerns about my personal information though.

34 What if people use my phone number for other purposes?

35 Pet Sitter Finder: November 14, 2019

36 We're aware of this issue.

37 We're now developing a system that allows users to communicate freely without showing their personal information.

38 Samantha: February 22, 2020

39 Animals aren't allowed in my apartment, so I don't have any pets.

40 However, by using Pet Sitter Finder, I can experience the joy of walking a dog.

41 Son: What great apps!

42 We can borrow a tent and find someone to take care of our dog.

43 Dad: That's right.

44 These kinds of services are part of the "sharing economy."

45 People can share their items with others and provide services to them at a small fee or for free.

46 Son: But these services do have some weaknesses.

47 Some people left negative reviews about the services.

48 Dad: Well, I think the more people use the services, the more they will improve.

시험대비 실력평가
p.37~41

01 ③   02 a tent   03 ④   04 ②

05 (A) positive reviews   (B) condition

06 download → update   07 ②   08 ②

09 a board game   10 chooses

11 ②, ⑤   12 (A) reviews   (B) send messages

13 ②   14 ①, ④   15 ④

16 ①, ③, ④   17 ②   18 ③   19 ⑤

20 ②   21 ③   22 sharing   23 ③

24 ④   25 ④

26 such a negative experience   27 ①

01 ③은 '캠핑을 가라, 알겠니?'(명령문의 부가의문문), 나머지는 모두 '~하는 게 어때?'

02 '텐트'를 가리킨다.

03 아빠가 "걱정하지 마. 내가 우리를 도와줄 수 있는 몇 개의 앱들을 알고 있지."라고 말했기 때문에, 뒤에 올 내용으로는 '아들의 걱정을 해결하기 위한 몇 개의 앱들에 대한 소개'가 적절하다.

04 자전거 헬멧을 얻었을 때, 그것은 망가져 있었으므로, 몹시 '기분이 상했다'고 하는 것이 적절하다. upset: 속상한, ① excited: 흥분한, ③ 초조한, ④ 기쁜, ⑤ 부끄러운

05 사용자들이 많은 '긍정적인 후기들'을 보고 나서 빌리기로 결심한 물건을 얻었을 때, 물건의 '상태'가 좋지 않다는 것을 발견하

06 **Ask your Neighbors**는 빌려주는 사람들에게 그들의 물건 사진을 정기적으로 '업데이트'해 줄 것을 요구하고 있다고 해야 하므로, download를 update로 고치는 것이 적절하다. download: (데이터를) 다운로드하다[내려받다]

07 이 글의 첫 단락은 '앱을 사용하여 다른 사람들로부터 빌릴 수 있는 물건을 쉽게 찾고 그 물건을 받은 다음 나중에 반납하는 것'에 관한 글이므로, 제목으로는 ②번 '당신의 이웃들로부터 빌려라!'가 적절하다.

08 주어진 문장의 Then에 주목한다. ②번 앞 문장의 내용을 하고 난 다음을 가리키므로 ②번이 적절하다.

09 '보드게임'을 가리킨다.

10 동사 checks와 병렬구문을 이루도록 'chooses'로 쓰는 것이 적절하다.

11 look after = care for = take care of: ~을 보살피다[돌보다], ① ~을 알아차리다, 주의하다, ③ ~을 이용하다, ④ ~을 닮다

12 반려동물 주인이 게시물을 올리고 나서 그나 그녀에게 '메시지를 보낸' 반려동물을 돌보는 사람들이나 개를 산책시키는 사람들에 대한 '후기들'을 확인한다. 그러면 반려동물 주인은 그들 중에서 최고의 사람을 선택할 수 있다.

13 동물들이 아파트에 허락되지 않아서, 반려동물을 키울 수 없지만, Pet Sitter Finder를 이용하면서, '강아지를 산책시키는' 즐거움을 경험할 수 있다고 하는 것이 적절하다.

14 (A)와 ②, ③, ⑤: 동명사, ①, ④: 현재분사

15 ⓐ search for: ~를 찾다, ⓑ in: (시간의 경과를 나타내어) ~ 후에[~ 만에/~ 있으면]

16 ⓒ와 ①, ③, ④: 동명사, ②, ⑤: 현재분사

17 ② 우선, 사용자들은 그 앱을 내려받고 '그들이 필요한 물건을 가지고 있는' 또 다른 사용자를 찾을 필요가 있다.

18 앞에 나오는 내용과 상반되는 내용이 뒤에 이어지므로 However가 가장 적절하다. ① 다시 말해서, ② 게다가, 더욱이, ④ 똑같이, 비슷하게, ⑤ 그 결과

19 저희는 이 문제를 알고 있다고 한 다음에 사용자들이 자신의 개인 정보를 보여주지 않으면서 자유롭게 소통할 수 있는 시스템을 개발하는 중이라고 했으므로, 앞에 올 내용으로는 '개인 정보가 알려지는 문제'가 나왔을 것이라고 하는 것이 적절하다.

20 ⓐ와 ②: (문장 끝에 와서) 그렇지만[하지만](부사), ①, ③, ④, ⑤: ~이지만, ~에도 불구하고(접속사)

21 '반려동물 주인이 자신의 반려동물을 돌봐줄 신뢰할 만한 사람을 찾는 데 얼마나 오래 걸리는지'는 대답할 수 없다. ① It is the perfect app for pet lovers and pet owners. ② They send messages to the owner when he or she uploads a post. ④ He uses it whenever he's going out of town. ⑤ He has some concerns about his personal information.

22 앱들을 통해 텐트를 빌리고 개를 돌볼 누군가를 찾는 서비스는 '공유 경제'의 일부이다. sharing economy: 공유 경제

23 이 글은 '앱들을 사용하여 사람들은 자신의 물건을 다른 사람들과 공유할 수 있고 적은 비용이나 무료로 그들에게 서비스를 제공할 수 있지만, 이런 서비스들은 몇 가지 단점들을 가지고 있다'는 내용의 글이므로, 주제로는 ③번 '공유 경제의 혜택과 약점'이 적절하다. benefits: 혜택, weaknesses: 단점

24 ④ (C)의 It이 주어진 글의 Pet Sitter Finder를 가리키므로 제일 먼저 오고 (B)의 their가 (A)의 Pet sitters or dog walkers를 가리키므로 (A) 다음에 (B)가 와야 한다. 그러므로 (C)-(A)-(B)의 순서가 적절하다.

25 전반부의 'Seeing a lot of positive reviews, I decided to borrow a bike helmet.'을 통해 'expectant'를, 후반부의 'I was so upset!'을 통해 'disappointed'를 찾을 수 있다. expectant: (특히 좋거나 신나는 일을) 기대하는, disappointed: 실망한, ① bored: 지루한, ② puzzled: 어리둥절해하는, upset: 속상한, ③ amazed: 놀란, ⑤ nervous: 초조한, satisfied: 만족한

26 'such+a+형용사+명사'의 순서로 쓰는 것이 적절하다.

23 ⓑ와 ①: 바로잡다, 고치다, ②, ④: (움직이지 않게) 고정시키다[박다], ③ 결정하다, ⑤ <시선·주의 등을> (~에) 집중시키다, 모으다

🦉 서술형 시험대비
p.42~43

01 camping

02 (1) 그들은 텐트가 없으므로 텐트를 하나를 사야 하는 것일까?

   (2) 개는 누가 돌봐줄 것인가?

03 free of charge 또는 for nothing 또는 at no cost

04 the more people use the services, the more they will improve

05 (A) positive   (B) lenders   (C) users

06 빌려주는 사람들이 그들의 물건 사진을 정기적으로 업데이트하는 것

07 (A) Cassandra   (B) negative

08 I saw   09 (A) the pictures   (B) lenders

10 개인 정보에 대한 몇 가지 걱정이 있을 수 있다는 문제 또는 다른 사람들이 앱 사용자의 전화번호를 다른 목적으로 사용할 수도 있다는 문제

11 communicate

12 (A) pets   (B) by using Pet Sitter Finder

01 go ~ing: ~하러 가다

02 'Why don't we go camping?'이라는 아빠의 물음에 대한 아들의 대답을 쓰는 것이 적절하다.

03 for free = free of charge = for nothing = at no cost: 무

04 the+비교급 …, the+비교급 ~: …하면 할수록 더 ~하다

05 (A) 많은 '긍정적인' 후기들을 보고 나서 빌리기로 결심했고 해야 하므로 positive가 적절하다. positive: 긍정적인, negative: 부정적인, (B) '빌려주는 사람들'에게 그들의 물건 사진을 정기적으로 업데이트해 줄 것을 요구한다고 해야 하므로 lenders가 적절하다. lenders: 빌려주는 사람들, users: 사용자들, (C) 다른 '사용자들'에게 그 제품의 정확한 상태를 알 수 있도록 해준다고 해야 하므로 users가 적절하다.

06 앞 문장에서 Ask Your Neighbors가 빌려주는 사람들에게 요구하는 내용을 가리킨다.

07 Ask Your Neighbors는 'Cassandra'에게 매우 '부정적인' 경험을 준 것에 대해 사과한다. apologize to A for B: B에 대해 A에게 사과하다, Cassandra에게 사과하는 것보다 부정적인 경험을 준 것이 더 먼저 일어난 일이므로, for having given으로 쓰는 것이 적절하다.

08 Seeing은 시간을 나타내는 분사구문으로, '~한 후에'라는 의미로 해석한다.

09 '빌려주는 사람들'에 의해 물건 '사진'이 정기적으로 업데이트된다면, 다른 사용자들은 그 제품의 정확한 상태를 알 수 있을 것이다.

10 George가 말한 'I have some concerns about my personal information.' 또는 'What if people use my phone number for other purposes?'을 가리킨다.

11 allow+목적어+to부정사 = let+목적어+원형부정사

12 Samantha는 '반려동물'을 키울 수 없지만 'Pet Sitter Finder를 이용하면서' 개를 산책시키는 즐거움을 경험할 수 있다.

영역별 핵심문제
p.45~49

01 upload   02 ⑤   03 ①   04 ⑤
05 (B) → (C) → (A)
06 Styles Studio provides free treatment to keep their hair healthy.
07 Students can get discounts.
08 She likes it more because it's important for her to get hair treatment regularly.
09 don't forget to talk about their bad points too
10 ⑤   11 (D) → (B) → (E) → (C) → (A)
12 ④   13 ④   14 ⑤   15 ⑤
16 ④   17 ③   18 ④   19 ④
20 another user that has the item they need
21 fewer products, more resources
22 ④   23 to know → know 또는 let → allow
24 ②   25 ③   26 ④   27 ⑤
28 a week → up to two days

01 주어진 관계는 반의어 관계를 나타낸다. download: 다운로드하다, upload: 업로드하다

02 '누군가가 필요로 하거나 원하는 무언가를 주거나 이용할 수 있게 하다'를 가리키는 말은 provide(제공하다)이다.

03 wherever: 어디든지

04 on sale: 할인 중인, out of town: 도시를 떠나, 다른 곳으로 떠나, search for: ~를 찾다

05 (B) 계획 설명 → (C) 영수증 지참을 상기시키기 → (A) 대답 및 반응

06 Styles Studio는 손님들에게 머리카락을 건강하게 유지해주는 트리트먼트를 무료로 제공해 준다.

07 학생들이 Hair Castle로부터 할인을 받을 수 있다.

08 Gina는 헤어 트리트먼트를 정기적으로 받는 게 중요하기 때문에 Styles Studio를 더 좋아한다.

10 Jane은 상품에 대해 더 유용한 정보를 사람들에게 주고 싶어 한다.

11 (D) 선호하는 샌드위치 선택 및 이유 설명 → (B) 상대방이 선택한 샌드위치의 비싼 가격을 설명 → (E) 비싸지만 선택한 이유 설명 → (C) 가격과 관련하여 선호하는 샌드위치 선택 및 이유 설명 → (A) 소비 습관이 다르다는 것을 설명

12 '인터넷으로 수많은 부정적인 후기들을 보고서, 그 연구원은 그 제품들을 사지 않기로 결심했다.'라는 문장이다. '이유' 의미의 접속사 As를 이용하는 부사절이 적절하다.

13 There가 있는 '독립분사구문'이다. 해석을 하면 '그녀의 친구들이 만든 Pet Sitter Finder앱이 있음에도, 그녀는 그 서비스를 이용하지 않았다.'라는 문장으로, '양보'의 부사절이다. '양보'의 접속사 Even though가 쓰인 문장이 적절하다.

14 ⑤ '더 높이 올라갈수록, 당신은 숨 쉬는 것이 더 어려워진다.'는 문장이다. 'the more it is difficult'가 아니라, 'the more difficult it is'의 어순이 적절하다.

15 분사구문의 부정은 분사 앞에 not을 쓴다. 접속사를 앞에 쓸 경우, 접속사 뒤에 주어를 쓰면, 분사구문이 아니라 절을 만들어야 한다.

16 ① the more faster → the faster ② More → The more, more → the more ③ do → are 또는 will be ⑤ the more they will be careful → the more careful they will be

17 분사구문의 능동과 수동을 구분하는 문제이다. ① '감기에 걸리다'를 수동으로 착각하지 않도록 유의한다. Caught → Catching ② Turned → Turning ④ Interesting → Interested ⑤ Educating → Educated

18 'Anne과 시간을 보낼 때마다, 그는 전보다 더 좋게 느낀다.'라는 문장은 'Anne과 더 많은 시간을 보낼수록, 그는 더 행복해진다.'와 가장 유사하며, 'The+비교급, the+비교급' 구문을 통해 표현한다. ①, ②, ③은 그가 아닌 다른 주어가 행복을 느끼는 것이며, ⑤는 does가 어법상 부적절하다.

19 Ask Your Neighbors는 사람들이 다른 사람들로부터 '빌릴

20 주격 관계대명사 that을 사용하고, 목적격 관계대명사는 생략하여 8단어로 영작하는 것이 적절하다.

21 'the+비교급 …, the+비교급 ~' 구문을 접속사 As를 사용하여 고칠 때는, 비교급 앞의 the를 생략한 다음에 As 뒤로 적절한 자리를 찾아 옮겨 쓰는 것이 적절하다. the+비교급 …, the+비교급 ~: …하면 할수록, 더 ~하다

22 ④번 다음 문장의 This에 주목한다. 주어진 문장에서 'Ask Your Neighbors가 빌려주는 사람들에게 요구하는 내용'을 받고 있으므로 ④번이 적절하다.

23 let+목적어+원형부정사, allow+목적어+to부정사

24 이 글은 '사용자들이 쓴 많은 긍정적인 후기들을 보고 나서 물건을 빌리기로 결심했는데, 상태가 좋지 않은 물건을 얻게 되어 기분이 상하게 되는 문제를 해결하기 위한 Ask Your Neighbors의 해결책'에 관한 글이므로, 주제로는 ②번 '앱을 사용하여 물건을 빌릴 때의 문제점과 해결책'이 적절하다. ③ unreliable: 믿을[신뢰할] 수 없는

25 ⓐ와 ③: 강조의 조동사, ① 의문문의 조동사, ② (어떤 동작이나 행위를) 하다(본동사), ④ 부정문의 조동사, ⑤ 대동사(문장의 동사를 반복하지 않기 위해 그 대신에 씀.)

26 이런 종류의 서비스들은 '몇 가지 약점들을 가지고 있다.

27 위 글은 '안내문'이다. notice: (보통 공공장소에 붙이는) 공고문[안내문], ① 수필, ② (신문·잡지의) 글, 기사, ③ (특히 기계 등을 사면 따라 나오는) 설명서, ④ (책·연극·영화 등에 대한) 논평[비평], 감상문

28 사용자들은 '이틀까지' 줄넘기를 빌릴 수 있다.

단원별 예상문제
p.50~53

01 ②   02 ②

03 (1) The coat was on sale last week.

　(2) She took care of her friend's pet during vacation.

　(3) These pancakes were made with organic eggs.

04 ③   05 ④   06 ②, ③

07 (A) Hair Castle   (B) student discounts

08 (A) cheaper   (B) design   09 ⓒ → to

10 ⑤   11 ④   12 ①   13 ⑤

14 ②

15 (1) Wanting to protect the environment we live in

　(2) Though not knowing what the students wanted

16 the item

17 The less products → The fewer products /
the less resources → the more resources

18 (1) **사용자들은 Ask Your Neighbors 앱을 내려받고 그들이 필요한 물건을 가지고 있는 또 다른 사용자를 찾는다.**

　(2) 그러고 나서 그들은 그 물건을 받아서 나중에 반납한다.

19 ③   20 ②   21 ③

01 '한 나라나 지역의 화폐, 산업 및 무역이 구조화되는 체제'는 economy(경제)이다.

02 주어진 문장에서 condition은 '상태'를 의미하며 이와 같은 의미로 쓰인 것은 ②번이다. 나머지는 모두 '조건'을 뜻한다.

03 on sale: 할인 중인, take care of: 돌보다, be made with: ~로 만들어지다 organic: 유기 비료의

06 A와 B 두 가지 중에서 어떤 것을 선호하는지 물을 때 'Which (one) do you prefer?'로 표현한다. 같은 표현으로 'Which (one) do you like better[more]?'를 쓸 수 있다.

09 prefer A to B: B보다 A를 더 선호하다

10 소녀가 신발을 구매하겠다는 내용은 없다.

11 종속절이 주절보다 앞선 시제이므로, 완료분사구문이 필요하다. 준동사의 부정은 not을 앞에 쓴다.

12 부사절과 종속절의 주어가 같으므로, 접속사와 주어를 생략하고 동사를 현재분사로 바꾼다. ②, ③, ④ 접속사와 주어를 쓰면 분사구문을 만들 수 없다. ⑤ 능동/수동도 맞지 않고, 독립분사구문으로 표현하려면 the sharing economy가 문두로 와야 한다.

13 The+비교급 ~, the+비교급 …' 구문과 특수한 경우를 제외하고는 비교급 앞에 the를 쓰지 않는다. 접속사 As와 When이 있는 ①, ② 문장에서 the 비교급은 맞지 않고, ④는 어법상 불가능한 구조이다. ③ less 앞에 more가 부적절하다.

14 'The+비교급 ~, the+비교급 …' 구문이다. 형용사 hot은 ①과 ④처럼 more hotter 또는 more hot으로 비교급을 쓰지 않는다. ③은 are needed가 틀렸다, ⑤는 내용상 better보다 more를 쓰는 것이 적절하다.

15 주어진 어휘에 접속사들이 없으므로, 분사구문을 배열하는 문제이다. 각각 (1) '이유', (2) '양보'의 부사절을 분사구문으로 만든 것이다.

16 '그 물건'을 가리킨다.

17 우리가 제품들을 더 '적게' 구매할수록, 우리는 '더 많은' 자원들을 아끼는 것이다. products는 셀 수 있는 명사이기 때문에 fewer로 고치고, 더 많은 자원들을 아끼는 것이라고 해야 하므로 the more resources로 고치는 것이 적절하다.

18 첫 번째 단락의 First, 다음 부분을 쓰는 것이 적절하다.

19 이 글의 첫 단락은 '반려동물을 좋아하는 사람들과 반려동물 주인들을 위한 완벽한 앱인 Pet Sitter Finder를 통해 반려동물 주인들이 그들의 반려동물을 돌보는 데 신뢰할 만한 사람들을 찾는 것'에 관한 글이므로, 제목으로는 ③번 '제가 당신의 반려동물을 돌볼 수 있어요!'가 적절하다.

20 whenever = every time: ~할 때는 언제든지, ① ~하는 동안, ③ 곧, ④ ~하는 바로 그 순간[~하자마자], ⑤ ~하자마자

21 반려동물 주인은 반려동물을 돌보는 사람들이나 개를 산책시키는 사람들의 '후기들을 확인하고' 최고의 사람을 선택한다.

01 He wants to do some market research.

02 She should remember to register their names by this Friday.

03 It is going to be held next month.

04 (1) older, wiser　(2) smaller, shorter

(3) sooner, better　(4) harder, better

(5) fewer, happier

05 (1) Not having a car,　(2) Frankly speaking,

(3) It having snowed the day before,

(4) Being a little tired,

(5) Finding the purse Jenny had lost,

06 Pet sitters or dog walkers

07 What if people use my phone number for other purposes?

08 (A) look after their pets　(B) personal information

09 (A) find　(B) download　(C) save

10 (A) borrow　(B) app

01 Tom은 요즘 인기 있는 물품을 알아내기 위해 시장 조사를 하고 싶어 한다.

02 수진은 이번 주 금요일까지 그들의 이름을 등록하는 것을 기억해야 한다.

03 벼룩시장은 다음 달에 열릴 것이다.

04 (1) 그 청년은 나이를 먹을수록, 더 지혜로워졌다. (2) 동영상의 크기가 더 작을수록, 게시하는데 더 짧게 걸릴 것이다. (3) 그녀가 최종 보고서를 일찍 마무리할수록, 협상에서 더 유리한 위치를 차지할 수 있다. (4) 더 열심히 공부할수록, 당신은 더 좋은 성적을 받을 것이다. (5) 중간고사 직후에 수업이 더 적을수록, 학생들은 더 행복하게 느낀다.

05 (1) 분사구문의 부정은 Not을 분사 앞에 쓴다. (2) 비인칭 독립분사구문이므로, We를 쓸 필요가 없다. (3) 원래의 부사절에서 비인칭주어 it이 있으므로, 'It having snowed'와 같이 독립분사구문 형태로 표현하는 것이 적절하다. (4) 내용상 부사 a little은 tired를 수식하기 때문에, 분사 being 앞에 쓰지 않는다. (5) 능동이므로 Found → Finding이 적절하다.

06 '반려동물을 돌보는 사람들이나 개를 산책시키는 사람들'을 가리킨다.

07 'if'를 보충하면 된다. What if ~?: ~라면 어쩌지?

08 'Pet Sitter Finder'라는 앱의 장점은 그것이 반려동물 주인들이 '그들의 반려동물을 돌보는 데' 신뢰할 만한 사람들을 찾도록 돕는다는 것이고, 단점은 '개인 정보'에 대한 몇 가지 걱정이 있다는 것이다. advantage: 장점, disadvantage: 단점

09 (A) 'help+목적어+원형부정사'이므로 find가 적절하다. (B) 사용자들은 그 앱을 '내려받고' 그들이 필요한 물건을 가지고 있는 또 다른 사용자를 찾는다고 해야 하므로 download가 적절하다. download: (데이터를) 다운로드하다[내려받다],

upload: 업로드하다(더 큰 컴퓨터 시스템으로 데이터를 보내는 것), (C) 우리가 제품들을 더 적게 구매할수록, 우리는 더 많은 자원들을 '아끼는 것'이라고 해야 하므로 save가 적절하다. waste: 낭비하다

10 Ask Your Neighbors라는 '앱' 덕분에 사람들은 그들이 다른 사람들로부터 '빌릴 수' 있는 것을 쉽게 찾을 수 있다.

|모범답안|

01 (A) the Special Sandwich

(B) the Classic Sandwich　(C) eating healthy

(D) cheaper　(E) books　(F) spending

02 (1) The more she sees, the more she wants.

(2) The less the baby eats, the more worried her mom becomes.

(3) The slower the student answers, the angrier his teacher gets.

02 표의 단어들을 적절히 조합하여 어법에 맞게 영작한 답이면 된다.

01 (1) download　(2) natural resources

(3) negative reviews　(4) exact meaning

02 (1) owner　(2) reliable　(3) concerns　(4) personal

(5) provide

03 (1) What if it rains tomorrow?

(2) I'll search for the recipe on the Internet.

(3) How can we send messages to other children?

04 ①　　05 ③　　06 ①, ③　　07 ⑤

08 ingredient　　　　09 ②　　10 ⑤

11 ④, ⑤　　12 ②　　13 ①　　14 ②

15 ③

16 (1) The more people understand the sharing economy, the fewer resources will be used on Earth.

(2) The more it rained, the more pleased she felt.

(3) The more popular the singer becomes, the more crowded the concert will be.

17 borrowing things that I don't often need

18 The fewer products we buy, the more resources we save.

19 ④　　　20 ③　　　21 upload　　22 ④

23 Because animals aren't allowed in her apartment.

24 ⑤　　　25 ⑤　　　26 ③

30 (1) 일주일에 한 번 빌릴 수 있다.

　　(2) 잃어버리거나 망가뜨리면 물건 값을 지불해야 한다.

01 resource: 자원, review: 비평, 서평, negative: 부정적인, exact: 정확한

02 personal: 개인적인, provide: 제공하다, owner: 주인, reliable: 믿을 수 있는, concern: 근심

03 What if ~?: ~하면 어쩌지?, ~라면 어떻게 될까?, search for ~: ~를 찾다, send messages to ~: ~에게 메시지를 보내다

04 이어지는 대화에서 추천하는 장소를 설명하고 있는 (A)가 적절하다.

05 위 대화에서 Judy가 선호하는 곳은 알 수 없다.

06 be sure to: 확실히 ~하다

07 Jack은 영수증을 갖고 가는 것을 잊지 않을 것이다.

08 '무언가를 구성하는 것들 중 하나로 특히 특정한 요리를 만들기 위해 함께 사용하는 음식의 하나'를 가리키는 말은 ingredient(재료)이다.

09 (A) prefer A to B: B보다 A를 선호하다, (B) 주어 역할을 하는 동명사 Eating, (C) 주어가 habits이므로 are가 적절하다.

10 위 대화를 통해 건강하게 먹는 것이 Brain에게 왜 중요한지 알 수 없다.

11 ④ '논문을 제시간에 제출하기 위해 열심히 일해서 곯아 떨어졌다.'는 내용이므로, 능동의 분사구문이 되어야 한다. 'Worked → Working' ⑤ 'look'이 자동사로 쓰였으므로 수동태로 쓸 수 없다. 'Being looked → Looking'

12 주절과 종속절의 주어가 같으므로, 보통의 분사구문을 만들면 되는데, 종속절에 명확히 주어의 정체성이 나타나 있으므로, 주절의 he or she 대신 종속절의 a pet owner를 주절에 쓰는 것이 적절하다.

13 '땅속으로 더 깊이 들어갈수록, 온도가 더 뜨거워진다.'라는 문장이다. '조건'을 나타내는 부사절로 바꿀 수 있다. ① '당신이 계속 땅 속으로 들어간다면, 온도가 더 뜨거워진다.'

14 '날씨가 너무 추웠다.'는 내용과, '해변에 수영과 놀이를 하러 나가지 못했다.'는 내용은 '양보'가 아니라 '이유'로 표현하는 것이 맞다. Although → Because 또는 As/Since

15 ①, ④는 주절과 종속절의 주어가 다르므로, 분사구문의 주어를 쓰는 것이 좋다. '독립분사구문' ① Eating → Samantha eating ④　Putting → We putting ②, ⑤는 주절과 종속절의 주어가 같기 때문에, 반대로 주어를 생략해야 한다. ④ Putting → We putting, ⑤ You borrowing → Borrowing

16 (1) many, few의 비교급과 수동태 표현 등에 유의한다. (2) please를 more pleased로 활용하는 것에 유의한다. (3) crowd를 crowded로 활용하는 것에 유의한다.

17 '제가 자주 필요하지 않은 것들을 빌리는 것'을 가리킨다.

18 the+비교급 …, the+비교급 ~: …하면 할수록, 더 ~하다

19 앞에 나오는 내용과 상반되는 내용이 뒤에 이어지므로 however가 가장 적절하다. ② 그러므로, ③ 즉[말하자면], ⑤ 게다가, 더욱이

20 ⓑ와 ②, ③, ⑤: 부사적 용법, ①: 형용사적 용법, ④: 명사적 용법

21 당신의 컴퓨터로 자료를 옮기거나 또는 당신의 컴퓨터로부터 다른 컴퓨터로 자료를 옮기다, upload: 올리다, 업로드하다

22 ④번 다음 문장의 their에 주목한다. 주어진 문장의 Pet sitters or dog walkers을 받고 있으므로 ④번이 적절하다.

23 동물들이 그녀의 아파트에서는 허락되지 않기 때문이다.

24 Samantha는 Pet Sitter Finder를 이용하면서 '개를 산책시키는 즐거움을 경험할 수 있다.'

25 ⓐ share A with B: A를 B와 공유하다, ⓑ at: [수량·값] ~으로, ~에

26 ③번 다음 문장의 Some people left negative reviews ~.에 주목한다. 주어진 문장의 some weaknesses에 해당하는 것이므로 ③번이 적절하다.

27 'the+비교급 …, the+비교급 ~' 구문을 접속사 as를 사용하여 고칠 때는, 비교급 앞의 the를 생략한 다음에 as 뒤의 적절한 자리를 찾아 옮겨 쓰는 것이 적절하다. the+비교급 …, the+비교급 ~: …하면 할수록, 더 ~하다

28 ⓐ와 ④: (특정한 수·정도 등)까지, 내 차에는 네 사람까지 태울 수 있다. ① 일을 감당하는, ② ~에게 달려 있는, ③ (특히 나쁜 짓을) 하고 있는, ⑤ (특정한 기준·수준)만큼, 그녀의 최신 책은 그녀의 평상시 수준만큼 안 된다[수준에 못 미친다].

29 feel free to: 자유롭게 ~하다

30 (1) You can borrow it once a week. (2) You must pay for the item if you lose or break it.

Future Changes through Technology

시험대비 실력평가
p.66

01 (c)riticism　　　02 ①　　　03 ②
04 (1) (e)quipped　(2) (s)ites　(3) (p)erceive
05 (1) keep track of　(2) be used in　(3) forecast
　　(4) destination　(5) deal with
06 ④

01 주어진 관계는 반의어 관계를 나타낸다. bright: 밝은, 희망적인
- dark: 어두운, 암울한, criticism: 비평, 비난 - praise: 칭찬
02 '쉽게 사용될 수 있는'을 나타내는 말은 convenient(편리한, 간
편한)이다.
03 signal: 신호, autograph: 사인, signature: 서명
04 equip: ~에 (필요한 것을) 갖추다, site: 위치, 장소, 용지, 부
지, 현장, perceive: 인지하다, 감지하다
05 deal with: 처리하다, 다루다, keep track of: ~을 놓치지 않
다, ~의 자국을 뒤밟다, destination: 목적지, 도착지, be used
in: ~으로 사용되다, forecast: 예측, 예보
06 주어진 문장과 ④: 현재의, ①, ② 있는, 참석[출석]한, ③ 수여
[증정]하다, ⑤ 선물

서술형 시험대비
p.67

01 (p)erceive
02 (1) a variety of　(2) With the help of　(3) such as
03 (1) This word is not common in casual
　　conversation.
　　(2) A microwave is a convenient cooking device.
　　(3) Which is the best route to take?
04 (s)ense / (n)avigate / (n)utrient
　　(1) navigated　(2) sensed　(3) nutrients
05 (1) These dogs are known for their high
　　intelligence.
　　(2) Natural disasters, such as floods and
　　earthquakes, affect thousands of people every
　　year.

01 주어진 관계는 동의어 관계를 나타낸다. go into: ~에 들어
가다 - enter: 들어가다, perceive: 인지하다, 감지하다 -

recognize: 인지하다, 알아보다
02 a variety of: 다양한, with the help of: ~의 도움으로, such
as: ~와 같은
03 common: 흔한, convenient: 편리한, 간편한, route: 경로,
길
04 (1) navigate: 길을 찾다, 항해하다 / 한 지역의 길을 찾다 / 예
전에는 여행자들이 대개 별을 보며 길을 찾았다. (2) sense: 감
지하다 / 보거나 듣지 않고도 어떤 것을 알다 / 그녀는 그때 누군
가가 자신을 지켜보고 있다는 걸 깨달았다. (3) nutrient: 영양
소, 영양분 / 살아가고 성장하기 위해 필요한 것을 제공하는 음
식이나 화학 물질 / 비타민은 우리에게 필수적인 영양소이다.
05 be known for: ~로 알려지다 intelligence: 지능,
disaster: 재해, 참사, 재난 such as: ~와 같은 floods: 홍
수, earthquake: 지진, affect: 영향을 미치다 thousands of
people: 수천 명

교과서 Conversation

핵심 Check
p.68~69

1 ③　2 it is likely that we will have to change how
　　　we get our food.

교과서 대화문 익히기

Check(√) True or False
p.70

1 F　2 T　3 T　4 F

교과서 확인학습
p.72~73

Listen & Talk 1 A
heard of / Could you explain what it is / that, weather
forecast, is going to, makes / convenient

Listen & Talk 1 B
inventions / great / senses, it, suggests / helpful /
does, think of, flying / how it works / that, set, While
it's flying / awesome, What, of / flying

Listen & Talk 1 C
who, one of, arms, the drums / How, with /
controlled / in, detail / what, with, are turned into,
travel / technology

Listen & Talk 2 B

As, harder, may not be, increasing, For this reason, it is likely that, how we get, Instead, will be grown, using, such as, rich, nutrients

Listen & Talk 2 C

had to, in line / we'll never have to / do you mean / what / How, for / keep track of, send the information / them / It's likely that, common

Do It Yourself A

exciting / have, popular / it, are equipped with / explain in more detail / what human players do / why, felt like / It is likely that

---

시험대비 기본평가　　　　　　　　p.74

01 ②　　　　　　02 ④

03 Could you tell me what it is?

04 만약 비가 올 예정이면, 우산에서 소리가 나는 것.

01 ②번 다음에 나오는 That이 주어진 문장의 내용을 받고 있으므로 ②번이 적절하다.

02 B는 플라잉 카메라의 작동법을 몰라서 G에게 묻고 있다.

03 'Could you explain what it is?'는 'Could you tell me what it is?'로 바꿔 쓸 수 있다.

04 밑줄 친 (B)의 That은 앞 문장의 내용을 받고 있다.

시험대비 실력평가　　　　　　　p.75~76

01 (C) → (B) → (A) → (D) → (E)

02 ①

03 ⓐ increased → ⓐ increasing, ⓒ will grow → ⓒ will be grown, ⓓ used → ⓓ using, ⓔ it → ⓔ them

04 ⑤

05 bugs such as ants will become part of our daily meals

06 ③

07 사고 싶은 것을 가지고 그냥 걸어나가면 매장을 나갈 때 스마트폰에 있는 앱이 물건 값을 지불한다.

08 It's likely that these kinds of stores will be more common in the future.

09 ④　　　　　　10 ②

11 It is possible that the AI in games will get stronger and stronger.

01 (C)에서 주어진 질문에 답하며 내용을 설명하고 (B)에서 궁금한 것을 묻고 (A)에서 질문에 답한다. (D)의 That이 (A)의 내용을 받고 있으므로 (D)가 다음에 나오고 마지막 That이 (E)

의 내용을 받고 있으므로 (E)가 마지막에 연결되는 것이 적절하다.

02 앞에 나온 내용의 예를 들고 있으므로 For example이 적절하다.

03 ⓐ 사람들이 계속 늘어나고 있는 것이므로 increased를 increasing으로 고쳐야 한다. ⓒ 고기가 배양되는 것이므로 수동태가 적절하다. ⓓ animal cells라는 목적어가 있으므로 using이 적절하다. ⓔ bugs를 받고 있으므로 them이 적절하다.

04 '여러분은 먹고 싶지 않을 수도 있지만, 사실 곤충들은 영양분이 매우 풍부하다!'라고 하고 있을 뿐이다.

05 such as: ~와 같은 (= like), A such as B: B와 같은 A

06 밑줄 친 (A)는 '그것 참 안됐다.'는 말이므로 ③번으로 대신하여 쓸 수 있다.

07 매장 내의 카메라와 감지기가 고객이 고른 물건들을 계속 파악하면서 그 정보를 스마트폰에 있는 앱으로 보내면 고객이 매장을 나갈 때 앱이 물건 값을 지불한다.

08 'It's likely that ~'은 자신이 생각하는 어떤 일에 대한 가능성의 정도를 나타낼 때 사용하는 표현이다.

09 (A) 현재완료로 물은 질문에 대한 답이므로 have, (B) from과 do의 목적어 역할을 할 수 있는 what, (C) 뒤에 '결과'가 이어지므로 why가 적절하다. That's because 뒤에는 '원인'이 이어진다. That's why ~.: 그것이 ~한 이유이다.

10 'Could you explain ~?'이라는 표현은 어떤 사실이나 대상에 대해 설명을 해달라고 요청할 때 쓸 수 있다.

11 'It's likely that ~'은 자신이 생각하는 어떤 일에 대한 가능성의 정도를 나타낼 때 사용하는 표현으로 'It's possible that ~'으로 쓸 수 있다.

서술형 시험대비　　　　　　　　p.77

01 (D) → (C) → (A) → (B)

02 It senses the items inside it and suggests recipes.

03 We can take pictures from 500 meters above the location.

04 Could you explain how it works?

05 weather forecast　　　　06 convenient

07 만약 비가 올 예정이면, 우산에서 소리가 난다.

01 (D) 미래에 우리 삶이 어떻게 변할지 묻고 (C) 식당들이 변할 것이라고 대답하고 (A) 식당들이 어떻게 변할지 질문하고 (B) 이에 대답하는 순서가 적절하다. (A)의 they가 (D)의 our lives가 아니라 (C)의 restaurants임에 유의한다.

02 스마트 냉장고는 냉장고 내부의 음식들을 감지해서 요리법을 제시해 준다.

03 플라잉 카메라는 미리 설정해 둔 목적지로 날아가서 비행하는

동안 그 지점의 500미터 상공에서 사진을 찍을 수 있다.

04 'how it works'를 explain의 목적어로 하는 간접의문문으로 영작한다.

05 뒤에서 '만약 비가 올 예정이면, 우산에서 소리가 나.'라고 하고 있으므로 weather forecast(일기 예보)가 적절하다.

06 '무언가를 하는 방법이 X라면, 그것은 쉽거나 매우 유용하거나 특정 목적에 적합하다'에 해당하는 것은 convenient(편리한, 간편한)이다.

07 'If it is going to rain, the umbrella makes a sound.'라고 하고 있다.

Grammar 교과서

핵심 Check
p.78~79

1 (1) were a robot, I would listen to her
  (2) would buy an apartment in Seoul if I had some money
2 (1) that (2) so that

시험대비 기본평가
p.80

01 (1) are → were (2) can → could (3) eats → ate
  (4) will → would
02 (1) that, could (2) so cold that (3) that they can
03 ④   04 ③

01 문제에서 모든 문장이 가정법 문장이라고 했고, 모든 문장들의 구조는 '가정법 과거' 형태로 볼 수 있으므로, 조건절의 동사를 과거로, 주절의 조동사도 과거형으로 고치는 것이 적절하다.

02 '목적'을 나타내는 'so that'과 '결과'를 나타내는 'so+수식어(형/부)+that'을 이해하고, 적용하는 문제이다. that을 기준으로 앞, 뒤 문장에 나타난 동사의 시제를 일치시키는 데 유의하여, so that을 활용하도록 한다.

03 주절에 조동사의 과거형이 나왔으므로, 가정법 문장이다. 가정법 과거에서 동사의 과거형 또는 조동사의 과거형을 사용하는 것이 적절하다.

04 'so that ~ 주어 can'은 '~하기 위해서', 'so 형용사 that 주어 V'는 '너무 ~해서 …하다'라는 의미이다.

시험대비 실력평가
p.81~83

01 ③   02 ④   03 ⑤   04 ④

---

05 donated their allowances so that people in need could get help
06 to get enough sleep in order that you can focus
07 it were sunny, we could go to the amusement park
08 raised a pet robot, she wouldn't be bored
09 ⑤   10 ②
11 ① are → were ② developed → developing
  ③ will → would ④ be designed → design
12 ②   13 ④   14 ④   15 ②

01 가정법 과거로서 '반대' 개념의 직설법 현재 시제와 적절하게 전환된 문장은 ③번뿐이다.

02 'so that+주어+조동사'가 적절히 사용된 것을 고른다. ⑤의 경우 so를 in으로 바꾸면 in order that이 되어 바르게 된다.

03 'so that+주어+조동사'가 적절히 사용된 것을 찾는다. ④의 so as는 절이 아닌, 'so as to V' 형태로 사용된다.

04 가정법 문장이라면 won't를 wouldn't로, 직설법 문장이라면 had를 has로 쓰는 것이 적절하다.

05 '목적'을 나타내는 'so that'을 활용하는 문제이다. '어려운 사람들'은 'people in need'로 표현한다. * allowance: 용돈

06 '목적'을 나타내는 'so that'과 같은 의미인 'in order that'을 활용하는 문제이다.

07 가정법 과거 시제의 문장이다. If 절에 과거동사 were가 오고, 주절에 조동사의 과거형 could를 쓰는 것에 유의하여 알맞게 배열한다.

08 가정법 과거 시제의 문장이다. If 절에 과거동사 raised가 오고, 주절에 조동사의 과거형 would와 not을 결합한 wouldn't를 쓰는 것에 유의하여 알맞게 배열한다.

09 ① follows → followed ② had been · could be ③ can → could ④ don't → didn't

10 ① has → had ③ will → would ④ had invented → invented, can → could ⑤ know → knew

11 '만약 당신이 로봇을 개발하는 과학자라면, 어떤 종류의 로봇을 설계할 것입니까?'라는 의미의 문장이다. 문제의 조건에서 가정법 과거 문장으로 제한했으므로, if절의 be동사를 were로 고치고, 주절의 will도 과거형 would로 고친다. 또한 a scientist를 후치 수식하는 develop은 현재분사를 쓰며, 로봇을 설계하는 것은 수동이 아닌, 능동의 원형동사 design이다.

12 다른 문장들은 모두 '목적'을 나타내는 표현 형태인데, ②의 두 번째 문장은 '결과'를 나타낸다. 보통, '결과'의 so (that)는 앞 문장의 끝에 콤마(쉼표)를 붙인다.

13 가정법 과거 형태의 문장들이다. If절에는 동사의 과거형을, 주절에는 조동사의 과거형을 쓰는 것이 적절하다.

14 '로봇들이 진짜 친구처럼 행동하도록, 인간의 감정을 인식할 수 있는 로봇을 과학자들이 만들려고 노력한다.'는 문장들로서 모두

'목적'을 나타내는데, ④만 '진짜 친구처럼 행동할 수 있을 경우에'라는 '조건'이다. 'in case that'은 '만약 ~가 …할 경우'라는 뜻이다.

15 ②는 '공손한 질문'을 위한 조동사 Could이다. 나머지 다른 문장들과, <보기>에 주어진 could는 가정법의 주절에 사용된 can의 과거시제형이다.

서술형 시험대비

p.84~85

01 (1) won't → wouldn't (2) is → were[was]
   (3) be → have been (4) make → made
   (5) can → could (6) will → would
   (7) can → could

02 (1) sensed human emotions, we could get along
   (2) were no search-and-rescue robots, humans would go into disaster areas
   (3) a pet robot so that he could help the lonely people

03 (1) If it were not for (2) If there were no
   (3) Were it not for
   (4) As there are cameras and the GPS system, the self-driving cars can

04 (1) Mom returned home in order that she could take the umbrella with her.
   (2) Abigail runs every day so that she can join his sports club.
   (3) Semi left for Italy in order that she could learn cooking.
   (4) Be sure to get enough sleep so that you can focus during class.
   (5) Sean ran fast so that he would not be late for the wedding.

05 (1) If the coronavirus were[was] in my town, we wouldn't feel relieved.
   (2) If Brian had not had an invitation, it would not have been easy for them to enter the castle.
   (3) If she were[was] rich enough, she would not sell her books on the street market.
   (4) If there were[was] money left, Mr. Robert would join the party.

06 the last leaf fell, it would be my last day

01 문제에서 각 문장이 가정법이라고 했으므로, 'if절' 또는 'I wish' 뒤의 동사를 과거형으로, be동사는 were 또는 was로 고친다. (3) 내용상 과거 시제이므로 '가정법 과거완료'로 표현한다. 가정법 과거완료의 주절에는 '조동사+have+p.p.'를 쓴다.

02 (1), (2) 가정법의 동사 구조에 유의하여, 주어진 단어들을 적절히 배열한다. (3) '목적'을 나타내는 부사절에 'so that 주어

could'를 사용한다.

03 '카메라와 GPS 시스템이 없으면, 자율 주행 자동차는 길을 찾아갈 수 없을 텐데.' 직설법은, '카메라와 GPS 시스템이 있어서, 자율 주행 자동차가 길을 찾아갈 수 있다.'가 된다. 가정법 표현, 'Without = If it were not for = Were it not for'를 기억하는 것이 좋다.

04 '목적'을 나타내는 to부정사 또는 'in order to', 'so as to' 등의 표현은 'so[in order]+that+주어+조동사'로 바꿔 쓸 수 있다.

05 가정법 과거는 직설법 현재의 반대, 가정법 과거완료는 직설법 과거의 반대를 나타낸다. (2)는 가정법 과거완료이다

06 그림의 문장은, '마지막 잎이 떨어지면, 나의 마지막 날이 될 것이다.'라는 의미의 직설법이다. 가정법 과거시제를 활용해서 falls를 fell로, will을 would로 변형하는 것에 유의하여 영작한다.

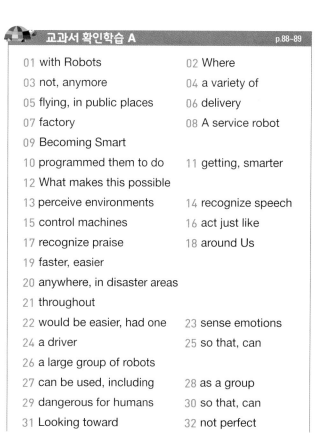

교과서
Reading

확인문제
p.86
1 T 2 F 3 T 4 F

확인문제
p.87
1 T 2 F 3 T 4 F 5 T 6 F

교과서 확인학습 A
p.88~89

01 with Robots   02 Where
03 not, anymore   04 a variety of
05 flying, in public places 06 delivery
07 factory   08 A service robot
09 Becoming Smart
10 programmed them to do 11 getting, smarter
12 What makes this possible
13 perceive environments 14 recognize speech
15 control machines   16 act just like
17 recognize praise   18 around Us
19 faster, easier
20 anywhere, in disaster areas
21 throughout
22 would be easier, had one 23 sense emotions
24 a driver   25 so that, can
26 a large group of robots
27 can be used, including 28 as a group
29 dangerous for humans   30 so that, can
31 Looking toward   32 not perfect

33 to become 34 they might cause

35 to find, to ensure, good

교과서 확인학습 B
p.90~91

1 Life with Robots

2 Where Do We See Robots?

3 Robots are not only in movies and books anymore.

4 Around the world, robots are doing a variety of tasks.

5 There are delivery robots flying in the sky, robot arms in factories, and service robots in public places.

6 A delivery robot in the sky

7 Robot arms in a factory

8 A service robot at the PyeongChang Olympics

9 Robots Are Becoming Smart

10 In the past, robots performed only easy tasks that humans programmed them to do.

11 However, robots are now getting "smarter," and soon they might be able to think like humans.

12 What makes this possible is artificial intelligence (AI)

13 Robots that have AI can perceive environments and make decisions.

14 They can also recognize speech, tell jokes, and play games with humans.

15 AI Speakers: They can answer your questions, control machines in your home, and play music for you.

16 AI Pets: They act just like real dogs.

17 They walk and play with their owners and recognize praise.

18 Robots around Us — Present and Future

19 Robots are making things faster and easier

20 They can help us anywhere — in our homes, on roads, or in disaster areas.

21 Home Helper Robot: This robot helps your family throughout the day.

22 Cooking and cleaning would be easier if you had one.

23 It also talks with family members and can sense emotions.

24 Self-Driving Car: A self-driving car doesn't need a driver.

25 With cameras, sensors, and software, it can navigate roads for you so that you can relax and enjoy the ride.

26 Robot Swarm: A robot swarm is a large group of robots that can communicate with one another, like ants or bees.

27 They can be used in a variety of places, including farms or building sites.

28 They work on tasks and find solutions as a group.

29 Search-and-Rescue Robot: Search-and-rescue robots can go into disaster areas that are dangerous for humans.

30 They find survivors, deal with dangers, and clear routes so that people can escape to safety.

31 Looking toward the Future

32 Our future with robots looks bright but not perfect.

33 Some people expect life to become more convenient with the help of robots.

34 However, other people worry about problems they might cause, such as threats to our jobs and safety.

35 The important thing is to find possible solutions and to ensure that robots are only used for good.

시험대비 실력평가
p.92~95

01 ③

02 (1) 하늘에서 날아다니는 배달 로봇 (2) 공장의 로봇 팔 (3) 공공장소의 서비스 로봇

03 ②, ④, ⑤ 04 ⑤

05 (A) robots, the past (C) Robots that have AI

06 ③ 07 safe → dangerous

08 to escape 09 ② 10 had

11 Robots are making things faster and easier.

12 ② 13 ①, ④

14 What makes this possible is artificial intelligence (AI).

15 ④ 16 A self-driving car 17 ②

18 ④ 19 ② 20 navigate

21 which include 22 ③

23 with the help of 24 robots 25 like

26 They are threats to our jobs and safety.

01 이 글은 '로봇이 하늘, 공장, 공공장소에서 다양한 임무를 수행하고 있다'는 내용의 글이므로, 제목으로는 ③번 '우리는 어디에서 로봇을 보는가?'가 적절하다.

02 (1) delivery robots flying in the sky, (2) robot arms in factories, (3) service robots in public places를 쓰는 것이 적절하다.

03 ⓒ와 ②, ④, ⑤: 현재분사, ①, ③: 동명사

04 앞에 나오는 내용과 상반되는 내용이 뒤에 이어지므로 However가 가장 적절하다. ① 게다가, 더욱이, ② 다시 말해서, ④ 그러므로

05 (A) '과거의 로봇' (C) '인공 지능을 가진 로봇'을 가리킨다.

06 (B)와 ③: 관계대명사, ①과 ④: 의문대명사, ②와 ⑤: 의문형용사

07 수색 구조 로봇은 사람에게 '위험한' 재난 지역에 투입될 수 있다고 하는 것이 적절하다.

08 목적을 나타내는 so that 부사절을 'to부정사'로 바꾸는 것이 적절하다.

09 로봇과 함께하는 우리의 미래는 밝지만 '완벽하지는 않다.'

10 가정법 과거 시제이므로, 'had'로 쓰는 것이 적절하다.

11 동사 'are making'의 목적어 'things'를 쓴 다음에 목적격보어 'faster and easier'를 쓰는 것이 적절하다.

12 로봇은 '어디에서나' 우리를 도울 수 있다.

13 ⓐ에는 목적격 관계대명사를, ⓑ에는 주격 관계대명사를 쓰는 것이 적절하다.

14 선행사를 포함하는 관계대명사 What을 주어로 하여 쓰는 것이 적절하다.

15 ④ '인공 지능을 가진 로봇'이 환경을 인식하고 의사 결정을 할 수 있다. 모든 로봇이 가능한 것은 아니다.

16 '자율 주행 자동차'를 가리킨다.

17 ⓑ와 ②: [역할·자격·기능·성질 따위를 나타내어] ~으로서(전치사), ① ~이기 때문에(접속사), ③ ~와 같이(접속사), ④ [보통 as ~ as ...로 형용사·부사 앞에서] …와 같은 정도로(as ~ as ...에서, 앞의 as가 지시부사, 뒤의 as는 접속사), ⑤ ~하고 있을 때(접속사)

18 로봇 군집은 '개미나 벌처럼, 서로 의사소통할 수 있는' 로봇의 대규모 집단을 말한다.

19 ⓐ With cameras, sensors, and software: 카메라, 감지기 그리고 소프트웨어를 '갖춘 채', ⓑ communicate with one another: 서로 의사소통하다

20 navigate: 길을 찾다, 항해하다, 그것은 종종 지도를 사용하여 바다나 육지의 지역을 가로지르거나 따라서 가는, 혹은 너머 가서 방향을 찾는 것을 의미한다.

21 'a variety of+복수 명사'는 복수 취급이므로, which include로 바꿔 쓰는 것이 적절하다.

22 로봇 군집 안에 몇 개의 로봇이 있는지는 대답할 수 없다. ① No, it doesn't. ② It is a large group of robots. ④ It can be used in a variety of places, including farms or building sites. ⑤ No, it doesn't. It works on tasks and finds solutions as a group.

23 with the help of: ~의 도움으로

24 '로봇'을 가리킨다.

25 such as = like: ~와 같은

26 로봇이 일으킬지 모르는 문제들에는 '우리의 일자리와 안전에 대한 위협'이 있다.

서술형 시험대비

01 What   02 sillier → smarter

03 (A) programmed   (B) performed

04 (A) AI   (B) AI

05 They act just like real dogs.

06 They can walk and play with their owners and recognize praise.

07 (A) your questions   (B) machines

08 survivors   09 safety   10 treat 또는 handle

11 (1) 가능한 해결책을 찾아내는 것

(2) 로봇이 오로지 좋은 일을 위해서만 쓰이게 됨을 확실히 하는 것

12 on   13 in order that

14 Because with cameras, sensors, and software, it can navigate roads for you (so that you can relax and enjoy the ride).

15 It can communicate with one another.

01 선행사를 포함하는 관계대명사 What을 쓰는 것이 적절하다.

02 앞에 나오는 내용과 상반되는 내용이 뒤에 이어지는 However로 문장이 시작하고 있으므로, 로봇은 이제 '더 똑똑해'지고 있으며, 곧 인간처럼 생각할 수 있을지도 모른다라고 고치는 것이 적절하다. sillier: 더 어리석은

03 과거에는 로봇이 실행할 단순 업무들을 인간이 '프로그램으로 짠' 다음에 로봇은 오직 그 업무들만을 '실행했다.'

04 환경을 인식하고 의사 결정을 할 수 있는 로봇은 '인공 지능'을 가지고 있다. '인공 지능' 덕분에 그들은 또한 인간의 말을 인지하고, 농담을 건네며, 인간과 게임을 할 수 있다.

05 like: …처럼(전치사)

06 그들은 그들의 주인과 함께 걷고 놀며 칭찬을 알아챘다.

07 그들은 '당신의 질문'에 대답할 수 있고, 당신의 집에 있는 '기계들'을 조종할 수 있으며, 당신을 위해 음악을 재생할 수도 있다. reply to = answer, manage: 다루다, 조종하다

08 survivor: 생존자, 살아남은 사람, 죽음 가까이 갔지만 계속 살아남은 사람들

09 전치사 to 다음이므로, safe의 명사 형태로 쓰는 것이 적절하다.

10 deal with = treat: ~을 다루다, 처리하다

11 중요한 것은 '가능한 해결책을 찾아내는 것'과 '로봇이 오로지 좋은 일을 위해서만 쓰이게 됨을 확실히 하는 것'이다.

12 work on: (해결·개선하기 위해) ~에 노력을 들이다, 착수하다

13 목적을 나타내는 부사절에서 so that 대신에 in order that을 쓸 수도 있다.

14 자율 주행 자동차는 '카메라, 감지기 그리고 소프트웨어를 갖춘 채, 당신이 쉬면서 주행을 즐길 수 있도록 당신을 위해 길을 찾아갈 수 있기 때문에' 운전자를 필요로 하지 않는다.

15 로봇 군집은 '서로' 의사소통할 수 있다.

01 (a)rtificial   02 ⑤   03 ①   04 escape

05 (1) deal with   (2) make decisions   (3) Look toward
    (4) work on   (5) find solutions

06 ④

07 스마트 냉장고가 냉장고 내부의 음식들을 감지해서
    요리법을 제시해 주는 것.

08 ②   09 ①   10 signal

11 what he wants to do, electronic signals, to his
    robot arm and move it

12 ④   13 order that, get ready for

14 (1) it rained hard, we could not go to the stadium
       to cheer
   (2) it doesn't rain hard, we can go to the stadium
       to cheer

15 (1) artificial intelligence had not been developed,
       computers couldn't have won over humans
   (2) artificial intelligence was developed, computers
       could win over humans

16 ①, ⑤   17 ②   18 ②

19 (1) in order that it can reduce the risks
   (2) so that they can work on tasks as a group

20 would

21 They can help us anywhere—in our homes, on
    roads, or in disaster areas.

22 ③   23 ①   24 ②   25 ③

26 학생들은 학교에 갈 필요가 없고 집에서 공부할 것이다.

27 ⑤

---

01 artificial: 인공적인, 인위적인, fake: 가짜의, 인조의 / 그는
    59살이고 인공 팔을 잘 사용한다.

02 '큰 지역에 손상을 가해 많은 사람들에게 해를 입힐 수도 있는
    불행한 사건'을 가리키는 말은 disaster(참사, 재난, 재해)이다.

03 여기서 perform은 '실행[수행]하다'의 뜻으로 쓰였다.

04 주어진 관계는 동의어 관계를 나타낸다. praise: 칭찬 -
    compliment: 칭찬, escape: 탈출하다, 달아나다, 벗어나다 -
    flee: 도망치다, 피하다

05 make decisions: 결정을 하다, work on: ~에 노력을 들이다,
    애쓰다, find solutions: 해결책을 찾다, look toward: 앞날을
    생각하다, deal with: 처리하다, 다루다

06 (D)의 That이 (D) 앞 문장의 내용을 받고 있으므로 제일 먼저
    나오고, (C)에서 'A flying camera?'라고 (A)의 내용을 묻고
    있으므로 (A) 다음에 (C)가 이어지고, (B)의 That이 (E)의 내
    용을 받고 있으므로 (E) 다음에 (B)가 이어지는 순서가 자연스
    럽다.

07 여자가 '이 냉장고는 냉장고 내부의 음식들을 감지해서 요리법
    을 제시해 줘.'라고 하자, 남자가 '유용하겠다.'라고 하고 있다.

08 상대방에게 설명을 요청 받을 때 Of course. / Yes. / Okay.

/ Sure. / All right. / No problem. 등으로 요청을 수락한다
는 의사를 먼저 표현할 수 있다.

09 'one of+복수 명사'로 '~ 중의 하나'라는 뜻이므로 arms로 복
수 형태가 되어야 한다.

10 '기계에 의해 빛, 소리, 전기 등의 형태로 전해지는 정보'를 가리
키는 말은 signal(신호)이다.

11 자신의 팔로 하고 싶은 것을 생각하고, 그 생각들이 전기 신호로
바뀌고, 그 신호들이 그의 뇌에서 로봇 팔로 이동해서 그 팔을
움직인다.

12 '과거 시제의 직설법 문장'을 가정법으로 고치면 '가정법 과거완
료'가 된다. If절에 'had+p.p.', 주절에 '조동사 과거+have+p.p.'
를 쓰되, 직설법과 반대되도록 not을 뺀다. ⑤는 수동태 문장이
라서 틀렸다.

13 'Sandy가 어제 Tommy에게 전화한 것은 발표를 준비시키도
록 하기 위해서였다.' 'in' 뒤에 절이 와야 하므로 'in order that
주어 might 동사' 형태가 적절하며, might 대신 would 또는
could도 가능하다.

14 가정법 과거에는 동사의 과거형이 온다. 이 경우 비인칭 주어 it
과 동사 rained를 쓴다는 것에 유의한다.

15 내용상 '가정법 과거완료' 문장이다. If절에 'had p.p.' 형태, 주
절에는 '조동사 과거형+have p.p.' 형태를 쓰기 때문에 주어진
can't를 'couldn't have p.p.'로 쓰고, 직설법으로 바꿀 때는
not이 없는 과거 시제 could로 고친다.

16 '~가 없다면'이라는 가정법 표현은 'If there were no ~'로 나
타내며, without 또는 'If it were not for ~'로 대체할 수 있
다. 'If it were not for'는 if를 생략해서 'were it not for ~'
로 표현 가능하다. 주절에는 조동사의 과거형을 쓴다. ①의
'should have done'은 '~했어야 했는데'라는 의미이다. ⑤
are → were가 적절하다.

17 ② this morning으로 봐서 내용상 가정법 과거완료 문장이다.
If절에 'had+p.p.', 주절에는 '조동사 과거+have+p.p.' 형태가
와야 한다. 'succeeded'를 'had succeeded'로 고치는 것이 적
절하다.

18 so that 뒤에는 절을 써야 한다. 'for her to get'을 'she
could[would/might] get'으로 고치는 것이 적절하다. 아니
면, 'so that'을 'in order'로 바꾸거나, 'so that for her'를 아
예 삭제해도 무방하다.

19 (1) 구조 로봇이 인간 소방관들의 위험을 줄이기 위해 불타는 건
물을 향해 다가가는 중이다. (2) 무리 로봇 안의 로봇들은 집단
으로서 일하기 위해 서로 소통한다.

20 가정법 과거의 주절이므로 조동사의 과거형 would가 적절하다.
가정법 과거: If+주어+동사의 과거형 ~, 주어+조동사의 과거형
[would/could/might]+동사원형 …

21 그들은 어디에서나 우리를 도울 수 있다. 우리의 집에서, 길에서
또는 재난 지역에서 말이다.

22 ⓑ와 ③: 앞에서 이미 언급했거나 상대방이 알고 있는 사람·사
물을 가리킬 때 명사의 반복을 피하기 위해 쓰는 부정대명사, ①
(강조의 의미로) 단 하나(의)(수사), ② 같은, 한(수사), ④ 하나

의(수사), ⑤ [총칭 인칭으로; 복수형 없음] (일반적으로) 사람(대명사)

23 이 글은 '로봇과 함께하는 우리의 미래'에 관한 글이므로, 제목으로는 ①번 '미래에 대한 전망'이 적절하다.

24 앞에 나오는 내용과 상반되는 내용이 뒤에 이어지므로 However가 가장 적절하다. ① 비슷하게, 마찬가지로, ③ 따라서, 그러므로, ④ 즉[말하자면], ⑤ 그 결과

25 주어진 문장의 Instead에 주목한다. ③번 앞 문장의 내용을 부연 설명하고 있으므로 ③번이 적절하다.

26 학생들은 학교에 갈 필요가 없고 집에서 다양한 앱을 사용하여 공부할 것이다.

27 미래의 학교 생활이 지금만큼 재미있고 의미 있기를 바란다고 했을 뿐이다.

단원별 예상문제
p.104~109

01 ②   02 ③   03 ⑤   04 ④
05 ①

06 줄을 서서 기다릴 필요가 없이 사고 싶은 것을 가지고 그냥 걸어나가면 스마트폰에 있는 앱이 물건 값을 지불한다.

07 ②, ④   08 ⑤   09 ④   10 ③
11 ①   12 ④   13 ②

14 If they learned the history of Korea, they could understand Dokdo more.

15 (1) not to forget   (2) so as not to forget
   (3) in order that

16 (1) so that he would not drive
   (2) in order that information could spread much faster

17 ④ / ④ If Sehee missed the school bus, she would be late for class. 또는 If Sehee had missed the school bus, she would have been late for class.

18 ⑤ / ⑤ The shopper didn't buy a thing so that she could save money.

19 (1) saw the show, would feel
   (2) knew your number, could contact
   (3) had been healthy, could have completed

20 ⑤   21 ③   22 ②   23 be used
24 a large group of robots / a robot swarm
25 as well as   26 ②   27 ④

28 학생들은 종이책을 더 이상 사용하지 않고 태블릿 피시나 클라우드에서 내려 받은 파일을 사용할 것이다.

29 (A) downloaded   (B) such   (C) worse
30 what school life will be like

01 '특히 유용한 어떤 것을 달거나 부착하다'는 equip(~에 (필요한 것을) 갖추다)이다.

02 주어진 문장, ③: 흔한 ① 공통의 ② 공공의 ④ 일반적인 ⑤ 공

원

03 task: 일, 과제, 과업, recognize: 인식하다, threat: 위협, 협박, destination: 목적지, 도착지, ensure: 보장하다, delivery: 배달, 전달

04 주어진 문장은 '그게 다야?'라고 묻는 것으로 ④번 앞에 나오는 내용에 대해 묻고 있으므로 ④번이 적절하다.

05 빈칸 다음에서 결재 방법에 대해 언급하고 있으므로 '어떻게 지불하는지' 묻는 것이 적절하다.

07 'It's likely that ~'은 가능성의 정도를 나타는 표현으로 'It is possible[probable] that ~' 등으로 나타낼 수도 있다.

08 B가 아니라 G가 느꼈다.

09 ① makes → made ② 가정법 과거완료이므로 would be → would have been ③ can → could ⑤ will → would

10 모든 빈칸에 들어갈 수 있는 단어는 so이다. 다만, ③은 '너무 ~ 해서 결국 …하다'라는 '결과'를 나타내는 접속사 'so ~ that'이다. 나머지는 모두 '목적'의 'so that'이다.

11 가정법 과거에 맞게 동사의 과거형을 쓰되, 이 예문의 경우 비인칭 주어 it과 부정문의 조동사 didn't rain을 활용하는 것에 유의한다.

12 ④ so that을 (al)though와 같은 '양보'의 접속사로 바꾸는 것이 적절하고, 그렇게 할 경우, 'Wendy는 더 열심히 공부했음에도 불구하고, 의사 자격증 획득에 실패했다.'라는 자연스런 문장이 된다.

13 ① so → so as 또는 in order 또는 so 삭제 ③ sadness → sad ④ not being → would not be ⑤ could → to 또는 for → that

14 내용상 가정법의 형태로 문장이 구성될 수밖에 없다. if절에 learn 동사의 과거형과, 주절에 조동사 can의 과거형을 사용하되, much의 비교급 more를 쓰는 것에 유의한다.

15 so that = in order that = so as to = in order to를 활용한다.

16 '목적'을 나타내는 부사절 'so that', 'in order that' 뒤의 문장 구조에 유의한다. (1) Mike는 직접 운전하지 않으려고 자율 주행차를 샀다. (2) Gutenberg는 정보가 더 빠르게, 더 넓게 퍼져나가도록 인쇄기를 발명했다.

17 ④ '세희가 스쿨 버스를 놓친다면, 수업에 지각하지 않을 텐데.'라는 문장은 어법과 의미에서 모두 어색하다. 가정법 과거 또는 가정법 과거 완료 둘 중 하나에 맞게 고치되, 내용상으로도 '버스를 놓치면 지각할 텐데' 또는 '버스를 놓쳤다면, 지각했을 텐데'와 같이 표현하는 것에 유의한다.

18 so as that은 '목적'을 나타내는 부사절을 이끌 수 없다. as를 삭제하고 so that을 쓴다.

19 (1), (2)는 가정법 과거, (3)은 가정법 과거완료이다. (4)의 경우, Yes라고 대답한 후에 but이 왔으므로, 뒤에 오는 문장은 '부정적 의미'가 필요하므로 가정법의 If절과 주절 모두에 not이 와야 하는 것에 유의한다.

20 이 글은 '이제 로봇은 '더 똑똑'해지고 있으며, 인공 지능(AI) 덕

19

분에 곧 인간처럼 생각할 수 있을지도 모른다.'는 내용의 글이므로, 제목으로는 ⑤번 '로봇이 똑똑해지고 있다'가 적절하다.

21 주어진 문장의 this에 주목한다. ③번 앞 문장의 내용을 받고 있으므로 ③번이 적절하다.

22 ⓑ와 ②: ~처럼(전치사), ① ~와 같은(무엇에 대해 남의 의견을 물을 때 씀, 전치사), 스페인에서 공부하는 건 어때요? ③ (~을) 좋아하다(동사), ④ ~하는 거처럼(접속사), ⑤ 비슷한(형용사)

23 다양한 장소에서 '사용될 수 있다'고 해야 하므로 수동태로 쓰는 것이 적절하다.

24 a large group of robots를 가리킨다. a group of+집합명사: 단수 취급, a group of+군집명사(구성원): 복수 취급

25 not only A but also B = B as well as A: A뿐만 아니라 B도

26 '누가 스마트폰을 발명했는지'는 알 수 없다. ① It was invented in 1992. ③ Yes, they can. ④ Yes, they can. ⑤ Yes, they can.

27 (C)의 However 다음에 주어진 글의 내용과 상반되는 내용이 뒤에 이어지므로 제일 먼저 오고 (A)의 this가 (C)의 내용을 가리키므로 (C) 다음에 (A)가 이어지고 (B)의 AI가 (A)의 마지막에 나오는 artificial intelligence (AI)를 가리키므로 (A) 다음에 (B)가 와야 한다. 그러므로 (C)-(A)-(B)의 순서가 적절하다.

29 (A) '다운로드된(내려 받은)' 파일이라고 해야 하므로 downloaded가 옳다. (B) 'such a+(형용사)+명사'의 순서이므로 such가 옳다. so+형용사/부사, 또는 so+형용사+a+명사, (C) 시력이 '나빠질 수 있다'고 해야 하므로 worse가 옳다.

30 know의 목적어이므로 간접의문문(의문사+주어+동사)의 순서로 쓰는 것이 적절하다.

서술형 실전문제   p.110~111

01 It is likely that cashiers will disappear at stores in the future.

02 The app on your smartphone will pay for the items you choose when you leave the store.

03 There are cameras and sensors in the store without cashiers.

04 (1) so that it would satisfy his thirst
   (2) in order to show them
   (3) order that I could raise

05 Jihun knew the actor's name, he would[could] search him online

06 wish I were[was] as smart as Bill

07 (A) that   (B) is   (C) make

08 robots are now getting "smarter," and soon they might be able to think like humans

09 (1) 인간이 로봇에게 실행하도록 프로그램을 설정한 단순 업무만을 수행했다.
   (2) 환경을 인식하고 의사 결정을 할 수 있고, 인간의 말을 인지하고, 농담을 건네며, 인간과 게임을 할 수 있다.

10 imperfect   11 becoming → to become

12 (A) disaster areas   (B) clear routes

01 계산원이 없는 매장에 관한 이야기를 하면서 마지막에 '미래에는 이런 종류의 매장이 더 흔해질 것 같아.'라고 하고 있다.

02 '네가 매장을 나갈 때 앱이 물건 값을 지불하는 거고?'라는 질문에 '바로 그거야.'라고 답하고 있다.

03 계산원이 없는 매장에는 매장 내에 카메라와 감지기가 있다.

04 '목적'의 의미를 표현할 때, 'so[in order] that' 부사절과 'in order to V' 부사구를 어디에 쓰는 것이 좋을지 결정하는 것에 유의한다. *satisfy thirst: 갈증을 채우다

05 직설법 문장을 해석해 보면, '지훈이가 그 배우의 이름을 모르는데, 인터넷으로 검색을 하고 싶어한다.'이므로, 가정법 과거 시제 '지훈이가 그 배우의 이름을 알면, 인터넷으로 검색할 텐데.'라고 표현하는 것이 적절하다.

06 직설법에서 'Bill과 같이 머리가 좋으면 좋겠다'고 했으므로, 가정법으로는 'Bill처럼 머리가 좋으면 좋을 텐데'를 표현하는 'I wish 가정법'이 적절하다.

07 (A) 선행사 easy tasks를 수식하는 '목적격 관계대명사'를 써야 하므로 that이 옳다. (B) What 다음의 동사가 makes여서 What이 'The thing which'임을 알 수 있으므로, 그에 맞춰 동사를 is로 하는 것이 적절하다. (C) 조동사 can 다음에 '동사원형'을 써야 하므로 make가 옳다.

08 앞 문장의 내용을 가리킨다.

09 과거에 로봇은 인간이 로봇에게 실행하도록 프로그램을 설정한 단순 업무만을 수행했지만, 이제 인공 지능을 가진 로봇은 '더 똑똑'해지고 있으며, 곧 인간처럼 생각할 수 있을지도 모른다고 하며 예로 든 것을 쓰는 것이 적절하다.

10 perfect의 반의어인 'imperfect'를 쓰는 것이 적절하다.

11 'expect+목적어+to부정사'로 쓰는 것이 적절하다.

12 수색 구조 로봇은 사람에게 위험한 '재난 지역'에서 사용될 수 있는데, 그곳에서 그들은 생존자를 찾고 위험한 상황을 처리하며, 사람들이 안전한 곳으로 대피할 수 있도록 '길을 확보한다.'

창의사고력 서술형 문제   p.112

|모범답안|

01 (1) It's likely that we can live under the sea in the near future.
   (2) It's possible for us to have a personal airplane in the near future.
   (3) It's probable that we will live in outer space in the near future.

02 (A) location　(B) using a variety of apps
　　(C) save time　(D) negative effects
　　(E) meet their friends

 단원별 모의고사 p.113~117

01 (1) survivor　(2) artificial　(3) (r)oute　(4) delivery
02 (1) resource　(2) safety　(3) signal　(4) sense
　　(5) likely
03 (1) (d)eal with, 처리하다, 다루다
　　(2) (s)olution, 해법, 해답　(3) (s)afety, 안전
　　(4) (s)warm, 떼, 군중
　　(5) (e)scape, 탈출하다, 달아나다, 벗어나다
　　(6) (p)erceive, 인지하다, 감지하다
04 ②
05 It is about a man who lost one of his arms in an accident.
06 ⑤　　　　　　　07 ④, ⑤
08 That's why I sometimes felt like they already knew my moves!
09 it is likely that we will have to change how we get our food
10 ①　　11 ④　　12 ⑤　　13 ⑤
14 ②　　15 ③　　16 ②
17 If robots sensed human emotions, we could play with them.
18 ②, ⑤　　19 flying　　20 various　　21 ④
22 a home helper robot　　23 ②
24 ⑤　　　　25 ④

01 survivor: 생존자, artificial flower: 조화, route: 경로, 길, delivery: 배달, 전달
02 likely: 있음직한, 가능하다고 생각되는, ~할 것 같은, resource: 자원, 재원, safety: 안전, 안전한 곳, sense: 감지하다, signal: 신호
03 (1) deal with: 처리하다, 다루다. 문제 같은 것을 다루거나 해결하다 (2) solution: 해법, 해답. 어떤 문제에 대한 답 (3) safety: 안전. 피해나 위험으로부터 안전한 상태 (4) swarm: 떼, 군중. 많은 살아 있는 것들 (5) escape: 탈출하다, 달아나다, 벗어나다. 자유롭게 되다 (6) perceive: 인지하다, 감지하다. 감각으로 어떤 것을 알아채다
04 '어떻게 작동하는 건지 더 구체적으로 설명해 줄 수 있니?'라는 질문에 '물론이지.'라고 하고서 설명을 하는 것이 아니라 '정말 멋지다.'라고 말하는 것은 어색하다.
06 전기 신호들이 그의 뇌에서 로봇 팔로 이동한다.
07 'It's likely that ~'은 가능성의 정도를 나타낼 때 사용하는 표현으로 'It is possible[probable] that ~' 등으로 가능성의 정도를 나타낼 수도 있다. appropriate: (~에) 적합한, 적절[적당]한

08 That's why ~.: 그것이 ~한 이유이다, feel like: ~처럼 느끼다
09 'It's likely that ~'은 자신이 생각하는 어떤 일에 대한 가능성의 정도를 나타낼 때 사용하는 표현이다.
10 (A) 앞에는 '동물을 죽이지 않게 될 것'이라는 내용이 나오고 뒤에는 '동물 세포를 이용하여 실험실에서 고기가 배양될 것'이라는 내용이 나오고 있으므로 Instead(대신에)가 적절하다. (B) 앞에 나온 내용에 추가하고 있으므로 Also(또한)가 적절하다.
11 ④를 제외한 모든 문장은 가정법 과거 시제이다. ④의 if는 의문사가 없는 간접의문문의 명사절을 이끄는 접속사이며, 나머지는 모두 가정법의 부사절을 이끄는 종속접속사이다.
12 ⑤를 제외한 나머지 so that은 '목적'을 나타내는 부사절을 이끈다. ⑤의 so that은 '결과'를 나타내며, 보통 앞에 콤마(,)가 온다.
13 <보기>의 would는 가정법의 주절에서 쓰이는 조동사이다. 'Lynn은 가족들이 떨어지는 것에 동의하지 않으면, 해외에서의 그 일자리를 포기할 텐데.' 보기와 같은 가정법의 조동사 would는 ⑤이다. '그 지원자가 타인을 설득하는 기술을 발전시키면, 그 직위를 얻을 텐데.' ① 공손한 질문 ② will의 과거시제 ③ 과거의 습관적 행위 ④ would like to = want to
14 ② '~하기 위해서'라는 목적의 부사절을 만들 때, so that 또는 in order that 절 뒤에 can 또는 could 등의 조동사를 쓴다. became을 could[would] become으로 고치는 것이 적절하다.
15 '인공지능이 없다면, 로봇들은 무엇을 해야 할지 결정할 수 없을 텐데.'라는 문장이다. '~가 없다면'은 'If it were not for = Were it not for = Without = But for' 등으로 표현하며, ③ 'Had it not been for'는 'If it had not been for'에서 if를 생략하고 도치된 표현으로 가정법 과거완료시제에 사용한다.
16 주어진 문장은 'Kobe가 상태가 좋으면, 다른 선수들보다 세 배의 클린슛을 성공시킬 텐데.'라는 가정법 과거 문장이다. 직설법으로는 반대의 현재시제이므로, As가 이끄는 종속절과 주절에 모두 현재시제가 있는 ②가 정답이다.
17 가정법 과거시제에 맞게 If절에 sense의 과거형을, 주절에 can의 과거형을 써서 알맞게 영작한다.
18 앞부분에 not이 있으므로 ① no longer와 ④ no more는 적절하지 않다.
19 앞의 명사 delivery robots를 수식하도록 현재분사 형태인 flying으로 쓰는 것이 적절하다.
20 a variety of = various: 다양한
21 이 글은 '로봇이 어디에서나 우리를 도울 수 있으며, 일을 더 빠르고 더 쉽게 해 주고 있다'는 내용의 글이므로, 제목으로는 ④번 '우리 주변의 로봇들 - 현재와 미래'가 적절하다.
22 '집안일 도우미 로봇'을 가리킨다.
23 '재난 지역 복구'는 '집안일 도우미 로봇'이 할 수 있는 일에 언급되어 있지 않다.
24 '어떤 사람들은 ~하고', '다른 사람들은 ~하다'라고 할 때는 'some people'과 'other people'을 사용하는 것이 적절하다. ① 둘 중 나머지 하나, ② 또 하나(셋 이상 중에서 두 번째 것을 언급할 때 사용, 항상 단수 취급), ③ 나머지 전체, ④ 서로
25 ⓑ와 ④: 명사적 용법, ①: 형용사적 용법, ②, ③, ⑤: 부사적 용법

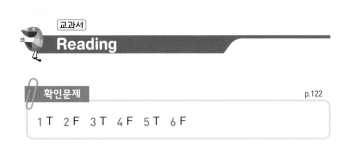

8

Which Is the Best Way?

확인문제   p.122

1 T   2 F   3 T   4 F   5 T   6 F

확인문제   p.123

1 T   2 F   3 T   4 F   5 T   6 F

확인문제   p.124

1 T   2 F   3 T   4 F   5 T

확인문제   p.125

1 T   2 F   3 T   4 F   5 T   6 F

교과서 확인학습 A   p.126~128

01 Wise	02 met
03 agreed	04 became lost
05 any further	06 for a while
07 correct	08 walk back
09 leave that way	10 walk around
11 keep walking	12 go on forever
13 new path	14 shook his head
15 could find	16 separate
17 reached, whole	18 shortest way out
19 hurried down	20 was gone
21 thought to himself, best way out	
22 wrong, the only wise	23 wrong
24 Everyone	25 created his future
26 walked deeper	27 was attacked, died of
28 protect himself	29 made his way out of

30 a group of	31 join them
32 great kindness	33 were moved
34 Later	35 a safe path
36 without getting lost	37 went straight
38 had been	39 Thanks to
40 who climbed	41 the quickest ways
42 This is how	43 one journey, another
44 your own path	45 act on it
46 have been living	

교과서 확인학습 B   p.129~131

1 The Five Wise Men

2 One day, five wise men met on the road.

3 They agreed to travel together

4 On the way, however, they became lost in a thick forest.

5 Before walking any further, they decided to stop and find the best way out.

6 After thinking for a while, the first man said, "I strongly feel that we should go left."

7 The second man said, "We should go right, because *right* also means 'correct.'"

8 Then the third man said, "Let's walk back.

9 We came that way, so we can leave that way.

10 Then we can walk around the forest."

11 The fourth man disagreed and said, "I think we should keep walking straight.

12 The forest cannot go on forever.

13 A new path will open."

14 Looking at them all, the fifth man shook his head and said, "I know how to solve this. Just wait."

15 He started to climb the tallest tree he could find.

16 As he climbed, everyone else decided to go their separate ways.

17 When the fifth man reached the top, he could see the whole forest.

18 Looking at all the paths, he found the shortest way out.

19 He hurried down to tell the others.

20 However, when he got to the bottom, everyone was gone.

21 He thought to himself, *Where did they go? I found the best way out.*

22 He thought they were all wrong and he was the only wise man.

23 However, he was wrong.

24 Everyone was wise.

25 Each man had chosen his path and created his future.

26 The man who went to the left walked deeper into the forest.

27 He was attacked by wild animals and almost died of hunger.

28 Soon he learned how to protect himself and find food.

29 In the end, he made his way out of the forest and taught others survival skills.

30 The man who went to the right met a group of thieves.

31 They took everything from him and made him join them.

32 While he was with them, he showed them great kindness.

33 The thieves were moved by his kindness and learned from his wisdom.

34 Later, they also became wise men.

35 The man who walked back created a safe path around the forest.

36 Using this path, people could get where they were going without getting lost, even though the trip took a little longer.

37 The man who went straight became a pioneer.

38 He left the forest and discovered places no one else had been before.

39 Thanks to him, people could enjoy these new beautiful lands.

40 The man who climbed the tree became a guide.

41 Since he had found many different paths, he was able to teach people how to find the quickest ways to their destinations.

42 This is how the five men found their own paths.

43 Like them, we are each on our own journey in life, and we cannot compare one journey to another.

44 You have to create your own path.

45 Listen to yourself, make a decision, and act on it.

46 Then, someday, you will realize that you have been living the life that is right for you.

서술형 실전문제
p.132~133

01 (1) Hunger (2) discover (3) wisdom (4) moved

02 ②

03 (1) Looking at them all, the fifth man shook his head.

(2) Listening to yourself, you will realize that your life is right.

(3) Moved by his kindness, the thieves learned from his wisdom.

04 has found → had found, 또는 he was able to → he is able to

05 was attacked by, how to protect himself

06 walking

07 While[As] he was looking at them all 또는 While[As] he looked at them all

08 '오른쪽'은 또한 '옳은'이라는 의미이기 때문이다.

09 a group of thieves

10 His kindness moved the thieves

11 the way how → the way나 how 또는 the way in which나 the way that

12 (A) your own journey (B) your own path

---

01 (1) hunger: 굶주림. 굶주림은 세상에 큰 고통을 야기한다. (2) discover: 발견하다, 찾다. 콜럼버스는 아메리카를 발견한 최초의 사람이 아니었다. (3) wisdom: 지혜, 슬기. 위대한 사람들의 지혜를 듣는 것은 좋은 일이다. (4) move: 감동시키다. 나는 그녀의 노래와 아름다운 목소리에 감동 받았다.

02 ②의 영영풀이는 protect(보호하다)의 영영풀이이다. ① agree: 동의하다, 찬성하다. 다른 사람이 제안한 아이디어를 받아들이다 ② attack: 공격하다. to try to hurt or damage(피해를 입히거나 다치게 하다) ③ survival: 생존. 어려운 상황에도 불구하고 이후에 계속 살아남는 상태. ④ pioneer: 선구자, 개척자. 어떤 일을 하거나 새로운 곳을 여행하는 최초의 사람들 중의 하나. ⑤ destination: 목적지, 도착지. 어떤 사람이나 사물이 가고 있는 혹은 보내지고 있는 장소

03 분사구문이 들어가는 다양한 문장들이다. (3)은 수동태에서 온 분사구문으로, move를 moved로 고치는 것에 유의한다.

04 내용상 '그가 여러 다양한 길을 발견했(었)기 때문에, 사람들에게 목적지에 이르는 가장 빠른 길을 찾는 법을 가르쳐줄 수 있(었)다.'는 내용이므로, 종속절과 주절의 시제가 일치해야 한다. has found를 had found로 과거완료시제로 고쳐서 주절의 was에 일치시키거나, he was able to를 he is able to로 고쳐서 종속절의 has found와 일치시키면 시제가 서로 맞게 된다.

05 야생동물들의 습격을 받은 것은 수동태로 표현한다. was

23

attacked by, 자신을 지키는 방법은 how to protect himself 이다.

06 keep ~ing: 계속해서 ~하다

07 'Looking at them all'은 동시동작을 나타내는 분사구문으로, 접속사 'while'이나 'as'를 사용하여 고치는 것이 적절하다.

08 'right'는 또한 'correct'라는 의미이기 때문이다.

09 '노둑 무리'를 가리킨다. a group of+집합명사: 단수 취급, a group of+군집명사(구성원): 복수 취급

10 His kindness를 주어로 하여 능동태로 고치는 것이 적절하다.

11 the way와 관계부사 how는 같이 쓸 수 없으므로 둘 중 하나만 쓰거나 the way in which 또는 the way that으로 쓰는 것이 적절하다.

12 여러분 각각은 인생에서 '자기 자신만의 여행'을 하고 있고, 한 여정을 다른 것과 비교할 수 없다. 당신은 자신의 목소리를 듣고, 결정하고, 그 결정에 따라 행동함으로써 '당신 자신만의 길'을 만들어가야 한다.

단원별 예상문제 p.134~138

01 on, on

02 (1) compare (2) disagrees (3) climb (4) realize

03 (1) (d)ivided (2) (u)nkindness (3) (t)hick

04 ⑤

05 (1) (s)olve (2) survival (3) (p)ioneer
   (4) (d)estination

06 (r)ealize   07 ④   08 ⑤   09 ④

10 ①   11 ④

12 realize that you have been living the life that is right

13 who climbed the tree, had found, how to find the quickest

14 who walked back created, Using, get where they were, without getting, even though

15 (A) forever   (B) a new path

16 nodded → shook   17 ④   18 ④

19 ③   20 the others   21 ②

22 him → himself   23 ⑤   24 ④

25 had been   26 they should

27 ①   28 ④

01 • on the way to ~: ~에 가는 길에. 너는 기차역으로 가는 길에 은행을 지나가게 된다. • act on: ~에 따라 행동하다. 단지 본능에 따라서만 행동한다면 당신은 동물입니다.

02 (1) compare: 비교하다, 견주다. 나는 인터넷으로 여러 디지털

카메라의 가격을 비교할 것이다. (2) disagree: 동의하지 않다, 의견이 다르다. Janet은 모든 것에 있어서 부모님과 의견이 다르다. (3) climb: 오르다, 올라가다. 그 산을 오르는 것은 쉽지 않다. (4) realize: 깨닫다, 자각하다. 그들은 자신들의 작품이 얼마나 창의적인지 자각하지 못했다.

03 (1) 동의어 관계이다. move: 감동시키다, touch: 감동시키다, separate: 분리된, divided: 분리된 (2) 반의어 관계이다. bottom: 밑, 바닥, top: 꼭대기, 정상, kindness: 친절, unkindness: 불친절 (3) 반의어 관계이다. agree: 동의하다, 찬성하다, disagree: 동의하지 않다, thick: 두꺼운, (나무가) 울창한, thin: 얇은, 가느다란

04 arrive at: 도착하다. 우리는 제시간에 공항에 도착하지 못한다. ① realize: 깨닫다, 자각하다 ② compare: 비교하다 ③ disagree: 동의하지 않다 ④ solve: (문제, 곤경을) 해결하다, 풀다 ⑤ reach: ~에 이르다, 도착하다

05 (1) solve: (문제, 곤경을) 해결하다 (2) survival: 생존 (3) pioneer: 선구자, 개척자 (4) destination: 목적지, 도착지

06 realize: 깨닫다, 자각하다. 어떤 것이 사실이거나 일어났다는 것을 알고 이해하다. 당신은 이것이 그녀에게 얼마나 중요한지 인식하지 못하고 있는 것 같다.

07 ④의 'to부정사'는 '부사적' 용법으로 쓰여서 '목적'(~하기 위해서)을 나타낸다. 나머지는 모두 '명사적' 용법으로, 동사의 '목적어'로 사용되었다.

08 보기의 'how to부정사'는 '명사구'로 '어떻게 ~할지'라는 뜻이다. 일반적으로 'how+주어+should+V' 형태로 바꿔 쓸 수 있으며, 내용상 주어는 they가 되어야 한다.

09 과거완료시제의 적절한 사용에 관한 질문이다. ④의 과거완료는 '다섯 번째 남자가 꼭대기에 노달했을 때, 그는 전체 숲을 (이미) 봤었다.'는 내용이 되어, 어법상 어색하다. had seen을 could see로 바꾸는 것이 자연스럽다.

10 분사구문은 '부사절'을 '부사구'로 전환한 것이다. 일반적으로 '부사절'은 '접속사+주어+동사'가 기본인데, 주절과 종속절의 주어가 같으면, 접속사와 주어를 생략하고, 동사를 분사로 전환하면 된다.

11 방법을 나타내는 선행사 the way가 있을 때, 두 문장을 관계부사 how로 연결할 수 있는데 the way와 how를 동시에 쓰는 것은 불가능하다. 그러므로 둘 중 하나만 쓰거나 선행사 뒤에 how 대신 관계부사 역할이 가능한 that 또는 '전치사+관계대명사 in which' 등을 쓸 수 있다. 관계대명사로 쓰인 that 앞에 전치사를 쓸 수 없으므로 in that은 부적절하다.

12 접속사 that과 관계대명사 that이 둘 다 나오고, 현재완료진행 시제가 나오는 문장이다. 주격 관계대명사 that의 선행사가 the life임에 유의하여, 적절히 영작한다.

13 중복 사용이 가능하므로 the는 자주 사용된다. '나무 위로 올라 간 남자'는 '관계대명사' who와 동사 climbed를 활용하고, '발 견했었기 때문'은 '과거완료시제 had found'를, '~를 찾는 법' 은 'how to부정사'를 이용한다. 형용사 quick의 '최상급' 'the quickest'를 쓰는 것에도 유의한다.

14 '분사구문' 표현 Using과, '가고자 하는 길에 다다르다'를 'get where they were going'으로 표현하는 것에 유의하여 알맞 게 빈칸을 채운다.

15 숲이 '영원히' 계속될 수는 없고 '새로운 길'이 열릴 것이라고 믿 었기 때문이다.

16 다섯 번째 남자가 "나는 이것을 해결하는 방법을 알아요. 잠깐 기다려 보세요."라고 말한 것은 앞의 말들에 동의한 것이 아니므 로 'nodded'를 'shook'으로 고치는 것이 적절하다. nod one's head: 고개를 끄덕이다; 찬성[승인, 인정]하다, shake one's head: 고개를 가로 젓다; 부정[거부]하다

17 세 번째 남자는 '뒤로 돌아가자'고 제안했고, 똑바로 계속 걸어 나가야 한다고 생각한 사람은 '네 번째 남자'이다.

18 앞에 나오는 내용과 상반되는 내용이 뒤에 이어지므로 However가 가장 적절하다. ② 즉[말하자면], ③ 게다가, 더욱 이, ⑤ 그러므로

19 주어진 문장의 'Looking at all the paths'에 주목한다. ③번 앞 문장의 결과에 해당하므로 ③번이 적절하다.

20 '다른 사람들'을 가리킨다. the others: 정해진 범위 안에서 일 부를 제외한 나머지 전부를 가리키는 부정대명사

21 ⓐ die of: ~으로 죽다, ⓑ take A from B: B에게서 A를 가 져가다

22 주어와 목적어가 같으므로 '재귀대명사'로 고치는 것이 적절하 다.

23 (B)와 ⑤: 감동시키다, ① (~의 길, 방향으로) 나아가다[진행되 다], ② 이사하다, ③ (몸 등을) 움직이다, (사물을) 옮기다, ④ <~할 것을> (동의로서) 제의[제안]하다

24 '오른쪽으로 간 남자가 도둑들과 얼마나 오래 살았는지'는 대답 할 수 없다. ① Wild animals attacked him. ② He taught others survival skills. ③ He met a group of thieves. ⑤ They were moved by the kindness of the man who went to the right, and they learned from his wisdom.

25 과거 시점을 기준으로 그 이전에 일어난 일이 과거의 한 시점까 지 영향을 미치는 상태를 나타내는 과거완료 had been으로 쓰 는 것이 적절하다.

26 '의문사+to부정사'는 '의문사+주어+should+동사원형'으로 바 꿔 쓸 수 있다.

27 ① 교훈적인, 이 글은 '우리는 각각 인생에서 자기 자신만의 여 행을 하고 있고, 우리는 한 여정을 다른 것과 비교할 수 없으며

당신은 당신 자신만의 길을 만들어가야 한다.'는 내용의 글이므 로, '교훈적인' 분위기라고 하는 것이 적절하다. ② 냉소적인, ③ 혼란스러운, ④ 의심 많은, 회의적인, ⑤ 축제 분위기의

28 이 글은 '우리는 각각 인생에서 자기 자신만의 여행을 하고 있 고, 우리는 한 여정을 다른 것과 비교할 수 없으며 당신은 당신 자신만의 길을 만들어가야 한다.'는 내용의 글이므로, 주제로는 ④번 '당신에게 맞는 삶을 살아가기'가 적절하다.

교과서 파헤치기

Lesson 6

1 broken, 고장 난   2 freely, 자유롭게   3 fix, 고치다
4 weakness, 약점   5 fee, 요금   6 concern, 우려, 근심
7 negative, 부정적인, 나쁜   8 choose, 선택하다, 고르다
9 download, 다운로드하다   10 discount, 할인
11 provide, 제공하다   12 reliable, 믿을 수 있는
13 return, 돌려주다, 반환하다
14 improve, 향상하나, 개선하다   15 economy, 성세
16 reasonable, 타당한, 합리적인, (값이) 적당한

01 환불	02 사용자	03 약점
04 문제(점), 쟁점	05 빌려주는 사람	06 부정적인, 나쁜
07 정기적으로	08 긍정적인	09 망가진, 고장 난
10 상태, 조건	11 제공하다	12 화난, 속상한
13 우려, 근심	14 타당한, 합리적인, (값이) 적당한	
15 업로드하다, 전송하다		16 정확한, 정밀한
17 어디든지	18 의사소통하다	19 할인
20 자원	21 균형 잡힌	22 경험하다
23 요금, 수수료	24 선택하다, 고르다	25 자유롭게
26 향상하다, 개선하다		27 돌려주다, 반납하다
28 주인, 소유주	29 개인의, 개인적인	30 다운로드하다
31 경제	32 목적	33 믿을 수 있는
34 빌리다	35 무료로	36 ~을 돌보다
37 ~을 알고 있다	38 도시를 떠나, 다른 곳으로 떠나	
39 ~을 돌보다	40 할인 중인	
41 ~보다 적은, ~ 미만의		
42 ~하면 어쩌지?, ~라면 어떻게 될까?	43 ~을 찾다	

01 choose	02 reliable	03 improve
04 exact	05 balanced	06 communicate
07 download	08 economy	09 concern
10 reasonable	11 borrow	12 weakness
13 discount	14 upload	15 freely
16 refund	17 broken	18 regularly
19 issue	20 condition	21 resource
22 positive	23 user	24 lender
25 experience	26 personal	27 wherever
28 fee	29 negative	30 owner
31 provide	32 purpose	33 share
34 return	35 less than	36 for free
37 on sale	38 search for	39 ask for
40 pick up	41 take care of = look after	
42 be aware of	43 out of town	

Listen & Talk 1 A

pairs, on sale, Which do you prefer / prefer, to, black ones / cheaper / design, white ones better

Listen & Talk 1 B

Which, prefer, or / healthier choice, made with, other, ingredients / much, expensive than / prefer, to / Eating healthy, to / cheaper, spend, on, instead / our spending habits, different

Listen & Talk 1 C

curly, straighten, recommend, good place / difference between, two / free treatment to keep, healthy / What about / provide, for free, student discounts / Which, prefer / prefer, to, for, to, regularly

Listen & Talk 2 A

get a refund, similar / Don't forget, receipt / get a refund / won't forget

Listen & Talk 2 B

flea market / to sell, market research / Market research, that / Because, find, what items are popular / decide what to sell / set reasonable prices / anything else / to register, by / reminding

Listen & Talk 2 C

review / How, review / focus on / don't forget to talk, bad points / won't, balanced review / it easier for, to choose better products / what, like to, useful information

Do It Yourself

speakers, pretty cool / Which do you prefer, black one / to, discount coupon / Although, right, better sound quality

Listen & Talk 1 A

G: These two pairs of shoes are on sale! Which do

you prefer?

B: Well, I prefer the white shoes to the black ones.

G: Why is that? The black ones are cheaper.

B: Yes, but I like the design of the white ones better.

G: Which do you prefer, the Special Sandwich or the Classic Sandwich?

B: Well, the Special Sandwich is the healthier choice. It's made with lots of fresh vegetables and other healthy ingredients.

G: But it's much more expensive than the Classic Sandwich.

B: I know, but I prefer the Special Sandwich to the Classic Sandwich. Eating healthy is important to me.

G: I prefer the cheaper one. I'll spend my money on books instead.

B: I guess our spending habits are different.

G1: I think my hair is too curly. I want to straighten my hair. Can you recommend a good place?

G2: Sure. I know two places, Styles Studio and Hair Castle.

G1: Is there any difference between the two?

G2: Well, Styles Studio provides free treatment to keep your hair healthy.

G1: That's great. What about Hair Castle?

G2: Hair Castle doesn't provide treatment for free, but they give student discounts.

G1: Okay. Which do you prefer?

G2: I prefer Styles Studio to Hair Castle. It's important for me to get hair treatment regularly.

B: I'm going to get a refund for these clothes this evening. I found I have similar ones.

W: Okay. Don't forget to bring your receipt. Last time you couldn't get a refund because you didn't bring it.

B: Okay, Mom. I won't forget it this time.

G: What should we sell at the flea market next month?

B: Before we choose anything to sell, I think we need to do some market research.

G: Market research? Why do we need that?

B: Because it helps us find out what items are popular these days.

G: I see. Then we can decide what to sell at the

market.

B: That's right. It will also help us set reasonable prices for our items.

G: Cool. Is there anything else we should do?

B: Oh, don't forget to register our names by this Friday.

G: Right. Thanks for reminding me.

G: I tried Spring Chips recently, and now I want to review them.

B: That sounds fun. How will you do your review?

G: I'll make a video. I want to focus on their delicious taste!

B: Okay, but don't forget to talk about their bad points too.

G: I won't. I want to give a balanced review.

B: Good. Your video will make it easier for people to choose better products.

G: That's exactly what I want. I'd like to give people more useful information about the product.

G: Jinho, look! These two speakers look pretty cool.

B: Yeah, they do. Which do you prefer, the red one or the black one?

G: I prefer the red one to the black one. It's only 20 dollars, and it comes with a discount coupon for music downloads.

B: Although the black one is 40 dollars, I think it's the right one for me. I heard it has better sound quality.

01 Life, Sharing Economy

02 What should we do

03 Why don't we

04 don't have, tent

05 Should, buy one

06 Also, take care of

07 Don't worry, apps, help

08 Borrow from, neighbors

09 helps, easily find, others

10 download, search, another, item

11 pick up, item, return

12 December 12, 2019

13 asked for, less than

14 saving, by borrowing, need

15 Also, environmentally friendly

16 fewer products, more resources

17 March 7, 2020

27

18 Seeing, positive reviews, borrow

19 got, however, was broken 20 so upset

21 March 9, 2020

22 such a negative experience

23 fix, lenders, update, regularly

24 let, know, exact, product 25 can look after

26 perfect app, lovers, owners

27 owners, reliable, look after

28 owner, looking, uploads, post

29 walkers, send messages, owner

30 checks, reviews, chooses, person

31 November 12, 2019

32 use, whenever, out of

33 concerns, personal information though

34 What if, other purposes 35 November 14, 2019

36 aware of, issue

37 allows, communicate, without showing

38 February 22, 2020

39 aren't allowed, have any

40 by using, experience, walking

41 What great apps   42 borrow, take care of

43 That's right

44 kinds, services, part, sharing

45 share, with, provide, fee

46 services, have, weaknesses

47 left negative reviews, services

48 more, use, services, improve

24 let, know, exact product 25 look after

26 the perfect app, lovers, owners

27 reliable people to look after

28 is looking for, a post   29 send messages to

30 checks, reviews, chooses 31 November

32 whenever, out of town

33 concerns, personal information

34 What if, for other purposes

35 November 14, 2019   36 aware of

37 allows, to communicate, without showing

38 February   39 aren't allowed, so

40 by using, can experience, walking

41 What

42 borrow, to take care of   43 right

44 kinds, sharing economy

45 share, with, provide, at a small fee, for free

46 do, weaknesses   47 left negative reviews

48 the more, the services, will improve

01 Life, Sharing Economy

02 What should we do   03 Why don't we

04 don't have   05 one

06 take care of

07 Don't worry, some apps 08 Borrow, neighbors

09 helps people easily find, borrow from

10 search for, the item they need

11 return it later   12 December 12

13 asked for, one, less than 14 by borrowing

15 Also, environmentally friendly

16 The fewer products, the more resources, save

17 March

18 Seeing, positive reviews, to borrow

19 however, was broken   20 so upset

21 March 9

22 such a negative experience

23 To fix, to update the pictures, regularly

1 공유 경제 속 삶

2 아들: 아빠, 우리 이번 주말에 뭐 할 거예요?

3 아빠: 캠핑 가는 건 어떠니?

4 아들: 그런데 우리 텐트가 없잖아요.

5 하나 사야 할까요?

6 게다가 우리 개는 누가 돌봐요?

7 아빠: 걱정하지 마. 내가 우리를 도와줄 수 있는 몇 개의 앱들을 알고 있지.

8 당신의 이웃들로부터 빌려라!

9 Ask Your Neighbors는 사람들이 다른 사람들로부터 빌릴 수 있는 물건을 쉽게 찾도록 돕는다.

10 우선, 사용자들은 그 앱을 내려받고 그들이 필요한 물건을 가지고 있는 또 다른 사용자를 찾는다.

11 그러고 나서 그들은 그 물건을 받아서 나중에 반납한다.

12 Jasmine / 2019년 12월 12일

13 저는 보드게임을 요청했고 30분도 안 되어 하나를 구했어요.

14 저는 제가 자주 필요하지 않은 것들을 빌림으로써 돈을 아낄 수 있다는 것이 마음에 들어요.

15 게다가 이것이 환경친화적이라고 생각해요.

16 우리가 제품들을 더 적게 구매할수록, 우리는 더 많은 자원들을 아끼는 거예요.

17 Cassandra / 2020년 3월 7일

18 많은 긍정적인 후기들을 보고 나서, 저는 자전거 헬멧을 빌리기로 결심했어요.

19 그러나 제가 그것을 얻었을 때, 그것은 망가져 있었어요.

20 저는 몹시 기분이 상했어요!

21 Ask Your Neighbors / 2020년 3월 9일

22 고객님이 그런 부정적인 경험을 겪게 해 드려 죄송합니다.

23 이 문제를 바로잡기 위해서, 저희는 빌려주는 사람들에게 그들의 물건 사진을 정기적으로 업데이트해 줄 것을 요구하고 있습니다.

24 이것이 다른 사용자들에게 그 제품의 정확한 상태를 알 수 있도록 해 줄 것입니다.

25 제가 당신의 반려동물을 돌볼 수 있어요!

26 Pet Sitter Finder는 반려동물을 좋아하는 사람들과 반려동물 주인들을 위한 완벽한 앱이다.

27 그것은 반려동물 주인들이 그들의 반려동물을 돌보는 데 신뢰할 만한 사람들을 찾도록 돕는다.

28 반려동물 주인이 반려동물을 돌보는 사람들을 찾을 때, 그 또는 그녀는 게시물을 올린다.

29 그러고 나서 반려동물을 돌보는 사람들이나 개를 산책시키는 사람들이 주인에게 메시지를 보낼 수 있다.

30 주인은 그들의 후기들을 확인하고 최고의 사람을 선택한다.

31 George / 2019년 11월 12일

32 저는 교외로 나갈 때마다 이 앱을 사용해요.

33 하지만 저의 개인 정보에 대한 몇 가지 걱정이 있어요.

34 만약 다른 사람들이 제 전화번호를 다른 목적으로 사용하면 어쩌죠?

35 Pet Sitter Finder / 2019년 11월 14일

36 저희는 이 문제를 알고 있습니다.

37 저희는 현재 사용자들이 자신의 개인 정보를 보여주지 않으면서 자유롭게 소통할 수 있는 시스템을 개발하는 중입니다.

38 Samantha / 2020년 2월 22일

39 동물들이 제 아파트에서는 허락되지 않아서, 저는 반려동물을 키울 수 없어요.

40 그런데 Pet Sitter Finder를 이용하면서, 저는 개를 산책시키는 즐거움을 경험할 수 있어요.

41 아들: 정말 좋은 앱들이네요!

42 우리는 텐트를 빌리고 우리 개를 돌볼 누군가를 찾을 수 있어요.

43 아빠: 그렇지.

44 이런 종류의 서비스가 '공유 경제'의 일부란다.

45 사람들은 자신의 물건을 다른 사람들과 공유할 수 있고 적은 비용이나 무료로 그들에게 서비스를 제공할 수 있어.

46 아들: 하지만 사실 이런 서비스들은 몇 가지 약점들을 가지고 있어요.

47 몇몇 사람들이 서비스에 대해 부정적인 후기들을 남겼잖아요.

48 아빠: 글쎄, 나는 사람들이 그 서비스들을 더 많이 사용할수록, 그것들이 더 개선될 것이라고 생각해.

1 Life in the Sharing Economy

2 Son: What should we do this weekend, Dad?

3 Dad: Why don't we go camping?

4 Son: But we don't have a tent.

6 Should we buy one?

6 Also, who will take care of our dog?

7 Dad: Don't worry. I know some apps that can help us.

8 Borrow from your neighbors!

9 Ask Your Neighbors helps people easily find items that they can borrow from others.

10 First, users download the app and search for another user that has the item they need.

11 Then they pick up the item and return it later.

12 Jasmine: December 12, 2019

13 I asked for a board game and got one in less than 30 minutes.

14 I love saving money by borrowing things that I don't often need.

15 Also, I think it's environmentally friendly.

16 The fewer products we buy, the more resources we save.

17 Cassandra: March 7, 2020

18 Seeing a lot of positive reviews, I decided to borrow a bike helmet.

19 When I got it, however, it was broken.

20 I was so upset!

21 Ask Your Neighbors: March 9, 2020

22 We're sorry that you had such a negative experience.

23 To fix this issue, we are asking lenders to update the pictures of their items regularly.

24 This will let other users know the exact condition of the product.

25 I can look after your pet!

26 Pet Sitter Finder is the perfect app for pet lovers and pet owners.

27 It helps pet owners find reliable people to look after their pets.

28 When a pet owner is looking for pet sitters, he or she uploads a post.

29 Pet sitters or dog walkers can then send messages to the owner.

30 The owner checks their reviews and chooses the best person.

31 George: November 12, 2019

32 I use this app whenever I'm going out of town.

33 I have some concerns about my personal information though.

34 What if people use my phone number for other purposes?

35 Pet Sitter Finder: November 14, 2019

36 We're aware of this issue.

37 We're now developing a system that allows users to communicate freely without showing their personal information.

38 Samantha: February 22, 2020

39 Animals aren't allowed in my apartment, so I don't have any pets.

40 However, by using Pet Sitter Finder, I can experience the joy of walking a dog.

41 Son: What great apps!

42 We can borrow a tent and find someone to take care of our dog.

43 Dad: That's right.

44 These kinds of services are part of the "sharing economy."

45 People can share their items with others and provide services to them at a small fee or for free.

46 Son: But these services do have some weaknesses.

47 Some people left negative reviews about the services.

48 Dad: Well, I think the more people use the services, the more they will improve.

3. get to, for a small fee

4. Ride sharing, reduces the number of, which, environmentally friendly

구석구석지문 TEST Step 2   p.25

Do It Yourself

1. Last Sunday, my family went to see a baseball game.

2. Cheering for our team, we had a really nice time together.

3. Happily, our team won the game.

4. Feeling happy about the win, we decided to celebrate.

5. Eating fried chicken together, we talked about the game.

After You Read C Get the BIG Picture

1. Sharing Economy

2. where people can share their items with or provide services to others

3. helps people find items to borrow from others

4. helps people save money and resources

5. needs regular updates on each item's condition

6. <⊕ benefit, ⊖ weakness>

Culture Link

1. Sharing Economies Around the World

2. I sometimes give other people a ride on my way to work.

3. They can get to their destinations for a small fee, and I can make some money.

4. Ride sharing also reduces the number of cars on the road, which is environmentally friendly.

구석구석지문 TEST Step 1   p.24

Do It Yourself

1. Last Sunday, went to see

2. Cheering for, had, nice time together

3. Happily, won the game

4. Feeling happy, decided to celebrate

5. Eating fried chicken together, talked about

After You Read C Get the BIG Picture

1. Sharing Economy

2. can share, with, provide, to others

3. helps, find, to borrow from others

4. helps people save, resources

5. regular updates, each item's condition

6 benefit, weakness

Culture Link

1. Sharing, Around

2. give, a ride on my way to work

단어 TEST Step 1　　　　　　　　　　　　　　p.26

01 일, 과제, 과업	02 위협, 협박	03 출납원
04 요리법	05 흔한	06 길을 찾다, 항해하다
07 예측, 예보	08 인지하다, 감지하다	
09 자원, 재원	10 배달, 전달	11 인공적인, 인위적인
12 굉장한, 아주 멋진	13 목적지, 도착지	14 인식하다
15 감지하다	16 밝은, 희망적인	17 차이, 차이점
18 자율 주행하는	19 공연하다, 실행하다	
20 영양소, 영양분	21 ~에 (필요한 것을) 갖추다	
22 떼, 군중, 벌 떼	23 칭찬	24 현실
25 지능, 정보	26 재해, 참사, 재난	
27 생존자, 살아남은 사람		28 보장하다
29 탈출하다, 달아나다, 벗어나다		30 해법, 해답, 해결책
31 현재의, 존재하는	32 길, 경로	33 안전, 안전한 곳
34 발명, 발명품	35 처리하다, 다루다	
36 ~에 노력을 들이다, 애쓰다		37 ~의 자국을 뒤밟다
38 ~와 같은	39 다양한	40 ~의 도움으로
41 ~하기 위하여	42 결정을 하다	43 앞날을 생각하다

단어 TEST Step 2　　　　　　　　　　　　　　p.27

01 intelligence	02 cashier	03 present
04 technology	05 praise	06 recipe
07 destination	08 swarm	09 artificial
10 perceive	11 threat	12 solution
13 difference	14 perform	15 safety
16 awesome	17 survivor	18 bright
19 disaster	20 navigate	21 escape
22 nutrient	23 self-driving	24 ensure
25 recognize	26 delivery	27 route
28 equip	29 resource	30 sense
31 common	32 forecast	33 convenient
34 invention	35 with the help of	
36 deal with	37 such as	38 a variety of
39 look toward	40 make decisions	
41 so that ~	42 throughout the day	
43 work on		

단어 TEST Step 3　　　　　　　　　　　　　　p.28

1 threat, 협박, 위협　　2 recognize, 인식하다

3 perform, 공연하다, 실행하다　　4 solution, 해법, 해답

5 survivor, 생존자　6 artificial, 인공적인, 인위적인

7 route, 경로　　8 sense, 감지하다　　9 task, 일, 과제, 과업

10 intelligence, 지능, 정보　　11 invention, 발명, 발명품

12 navigate, 길을 찾다, 항해하다

13 perceive, 인지하다, 감지하다

14 nutrient, 영양소, 영양분　　15 delivery, 배달, 전달

16 disaster, 참사, 재난, 재해

대화문 TEST Step 1　　　　　　　　　　　　　p.29~30

Listen & Talk 1 A

have, heard of / haven't, Could you explain what it is / that, weather forecast, is going to rain, makes, sound / convenient

Listen & Talk 1 B

inventions / great, invention / senses, it, suggests recipes / helpful / does, think of, flying / how it works / destination that, set, While it's flying / awesome, What, of / take pictures of flying

Listen & Talk 1 C

watching / who, one of, arms, Surprisingly, the drums / How, with / Actually, controlled, brain / awesome, explain in more detail / what, with, are turned into, travel from, to / technology

Listen & Talk 2 B

As, harder, may not be, resources, increasing, For this reason, it is likely that, how we get, Instead, will be grown, using, less land, other resources, such as, rich, nutrients

Listen & Talk 2 C

had to, in line, for almost twenty minutes / we'll never have to wait in line / do you mean / without cashiers, what, walk out / How, for / sensors, keep track of, send the information / them / It's likely that, kind of, common

Do It Yourself A

have, played, exciting / have, popular / it, are equipped with / explain in more detail / what human players do, develop their skills / why, felt like / It is likely that, get stronger and stronger

대화문 TEST Step 2　　　　　　　　　　　　　p.31~32

Listen & Talk 1 A

G: Hey, have you heard of a smart umbrella?

B: No, I haven't. Could you explain what it is?

G: Sure. It's an umbrella that gives you the weather

forecast for the day. If it is going to rain, the umbrella makes a sound.

B: That's very convenient.

Listen & Talk 1 B

G: Look at these. They are the new inventions of the month!

B: They all look great. What is the invention on the first page?

G: It's a new smart refrigerator. It senses the items inside it and suggests recipes.

B: That sounds helpful.

G: It does. What do you think of this flying camera? I want to buy it.

B: A flying camera? Could you explain how it works?

G: Of course. This machine flies to a destination that we have already set. While it's flying, it can take pictures from 500 meters above the location.

B: That sounds awesome. What do you want to take pictures of?

G: I want to take pictures of flying birds!

Listen & Talk 1 C

B: What are you watching?

G: It's a show about a man who lost one of his arms in an accident. Surprisingly, he can play the drums very well.

B: How can he play the drums with only one arm?

G: Actually he uses two arms. One is a robot arm controlled by his brain.

B: That's awesome. Could you explain in more detail?

G: Sure. First, he thinks what he wants to do with his arm. Then those thoughts are turned into electronic signals. The signals travel from his brain to his robot arm and move it.

B: That's amazing! I think this technology can help many people.

Listen & Talk 2 B

M: As climate change is going to make farming harder, there may not be enough resources for the increasing number of people on Earth. For this reason, it is likely that we will have to change how we get our food. For example, we won't kill animals for food. Instead, meat will be grown in a lab using animal cells. This will require less land, water, and other resources. Also, bugs such as ants will become part of our daily meals. You might not want to eat them, but they are actually very rich in nutrients!

Listen & Talk 2 C

G: I had to wait in line at the store for almost twenty minutes.

B: That's too bad. Maybe in the future we'll never have to wait in line.

G: What do you mean?

B: I read about a store without cashiers. You take what you want to buy and just walk out.

G: That's it? How do you pay for it?

B: There are cameras and sensors in the store. They keep track of the items you choose and send the information to an app on your smartphone.

G: Then the app pays for them when you leave the store?

B: Exactly. It's likely that these kinds of stores will be more common in the future.

Do It Yourself A

B: Hey, have you played this game? It's really exciting.

G: Yes, I have. That game is pretty popular these days.

B: The developers used AI technology in it. The game characters are equipped with AI.

G: Oh, really? Could you explain in more detail?

B: Sure. The AI characters in the game learn from what human players do and develop their skills.

G: Oh! That's why I sometimes felt like they already knew my moves!

B: They're very smart. It is likely that the AI in games will get stronger and stronger.

본문 TEST Step 1 p.33~34

01 Life with　　　　02 Where Do, See

03 not only, movies, anymore

04 Around, variety of tasks

05 delivery, flying, public places

06 delivery, in, sky　　　07 arms in, factory

08 service robot at　　　09 Are Becoming Smart

10 past, performed, tasks, programmed

11 getting, smarter, able, humans

12 What, possible, artificial intelligence

13 perceive environments, make decisions

14 recognize speech, jokes, humans

15 answer, questions, control machines

16 act just like real

17 walk, owners, recognize praise

18 around Us, Present, Future
19 things faster, easier
20 anywhere, in disaster areas
21 helps, throughout, day
22 cleaning would, easier, had
23 also, with, sense emotions
24 self-driving, doesn't need, driver
25 sensors, navitgate, relax, ride
26 swarm, large, another, like
27 used, variety, including, sites
28 work, tasks, solutions as
29 disaster areas, dangerous, humans
30 survivors, deal, routes, escape
31 Looking toward, Future
32 future, looks bright, perfect
33 expect, become, convenient, help
34 worry, cause, threats, safety
35 find, solutions, ensure, good

01 with Robots
02 Where Do, See
03 not only, anymore
04 a variety of tasks
05 flying, in public places
06 delivery
07 arms, factory
08 A service robot
09 Becoming Smart
10 performed, programmed them to do
11 getting, smarter, be able to
12 What makes this possible
13 perceive environments, decisions
14 recognize speech
15 control machines
16 act just like
17 owners, recognize praise
18 around Us, Present
19 faster, easier
20 anywhere, in disaster areas
21 helps, throughout the day
22 would be easier, had one
23 sense emotions
24 self-driving car, a driver
25 can navigate, so that, can
26 a group of robots, communicate with one another
27 can be used, including, building sites
28 work on, as a group
29 disaster areas, dangerous for humans
30 so that, can escape to safety
31 Looking toward
32 not perfect
33 to become, with the help of
34 they might cause, such as
35 to find, to ensure, good

1 로봇과 함께하는 삶

2 우리는 어디에서 로봇을 보는가?

3 로봇은 더는 영화와 책 속에만 있는 것은 아니다.

4 전 세계적으로 로봇은 다양한 임무를 수행하고 있다.

5 하늘에는 날아다니는 배달 로봇, 공장에는 로봇 팔, 그리고 공공장소에는 서비스 로봇이 있다.

6 하늘에서 날아다니는 배달 로봇

7 공장의 로봇 팔들

8 평창 올림픽의 서비스 로봇

9 로봇이 똑똑해지고 있다

10 과거에 로봇은 인간이 로봇에게 실행하도록 프로그램을 설정한 단순 업무만을 수행했다.

11 그러나 로봇은 이제 '더 똑똑'해지고 있으며, 곧 인간처럼 생각할 수 있을지도 모른다.

12 이러한 것을 가능하게 만드는 것은 인공 지능(AI)이다.

13 인공 지능을 가진 로봇은 환경을 인식하고 의사 결정을 할 수 있다.

14 그들은 또한 인간의 말을 인지하고, 농담을 건네며, 인간과 게임을 할 수 있다.

15 〈인공 지능 스피커〉 그들은 당신의 질문에 대답할 수 있고, 당신의 집에 있는 기계들을 조종할 수 있으며, 당신을 위해 음악을 재생할 수도 있다.

16 〈인공 지능 반려동물〉 그들은 마치 진짜 개처럼 행동한다.

17 그들은 그들의 주인과 함께 걷고 놀며 칭찬을 알아챈다.

18 우리 주변의 로봇들 – 현재와 미래

19 로봇은 일을 더 빠르고 더 쉽게 해 주고 있다.

20 그들은 어디에서나 우리를 도울 수 있다. 우리의 집에서, 길에서 또는 재난 지역에서 말이다.

21 〈집안일 도우미 로봇〉 이 로봇은 온종일 당신의 가족을 돕는다.

22 만약 당신이 이 로봇 하나를 가지고 있다면 요리와 청소가 더 쉬워질 것이다.

23 이 로봇은 또한 가족 모두와 이야기를 나누며 감정을 파악할 수 있다.

24 〈자율 주행 자동차〉 자율 주행 자동차는 운전자를 필요로 하지 않는다.

25 카메라, 감지기 그리고 소프트웨어를 갖춘 채, 이 자동차는 당신이 쉬면서 주행을 즐길 수 있도록 당신을 위해 길을 찾아갈 수 있다.

26 〈로봇 군집〉 로봇 군집은 개미나 벌처럼, 서로 의사소통할 수 있는 로봇의 대규모 집단을 말한다.

27 이 로봇들은 농장이나 건설 현장을 포함한 다양한 장소에서 사용될 수 있다.

28 그들은 하나의 집단으로서 임무를 완수하고 해결책을 찾는다.

29 〈수색 구조 로봇〉 수색 구조 로봇은 사람에게 위험한 재난 지역에 투입될 수 있다.

30 그들은 생존자를 찾고 위험한 상황을 처리하며, 사람들이 안전한 곳으로 대피할 수 있도록 길을 확보한다.

31 미래에 대한 전망

32 로봇과 함께하는 우리의 미래는 밝지만 완벽하지는 않다.

33 어떤 사람들은 로봇의 도움으로 삶이 더욱 편리해질 것을 기대한다.

34 그러나 다른 사람들은 우리의 일자리와 안전에 대한 위협과 같이, 로봇이 일으킬지 모르는 문제들에 대해 걱정한다.

35 중요한 것은 가능한 해결책을 찾아내는 것과 로봇이 오로지 좋은 일을 위해서만 쓰이게 됨을 확실히 하는 것이다.

본문 TEST Step 4~Step 5 p.39~42

1 Life with Robots

2 Where Do We See Robots?

3 Robots are not only in movies and books anymore.

4 Around the world, robots are doing a variety of tasks.

5 There are delivery robots flying in the sky, robot arms in factories, and service robots in public places.

6 A delivery robot in the sky

7 Robot arms in a factory

8 A service robot at the PyeongChang Olympics

9 Robots Are Becoming Smart

10 In the past, robots performed only easy tasks that humans programmed them to do.

11 However, robots are now getting "smarter," and soon they might be able to think like humans.

12 What makes this possible is artificial intelligence (AI).

13 Robots that have AI can perceive environments and make decisions.

14 They can also recognize speech, tell jokes, and play games with humans.

15 AI Speakers: They can answer your questions, control machines in your home, and play music for you.

16 AI Pets: They act just like real dogs.

17 They walk and play with their owners and recognize praise.

18 Robots around Us – Present and Future

19 Robots are making things faster and easier.

20 They can help us anywhere — in our homes, on roads, or in disaster areas

21 Home Helper Robot: This robot helps your family throughout the day.

22 Cooking and cleaning would be easier if you had one.

23 It also talks with family members and can sense emotions.

24 Self-Driving Car: A self-driving car doesn't need a driver.

25 With cameras, sensors, and software, it can navigate roads for you so that you can relax and enjoy the ride.

26 Robot Swarm: A robot swarm is a large group of robots that can communicate with one another, like ants or bees.

27 They can be used in a variety of places, including farms or building sites.

28 They work on tasks and find solutions as a group.

29 Search-and-Rescue Robot: Search-and-rescue robots can go into disaster areas that are dangerous for humans.

30 They find survivors, deal with dangers, and clear routes so that people can escape to safety.

31 Looking toward the Future

32 Our future with robots looks bright but not perfect.

33 Some people expect life to become more convenient with the help of robots.

34 However, other people worry about problems they might cause, such as threats to our jobs and safety.

35 The important thing is to find possible solutions and to ensure that robots are only used for good.

구석구석지문 TEST Step 1 p.43

Presentation Time Step 3

1. What do you think

2. helping people clean their houses

3. looks similar to, vacuum cleaners, have some differences

4. unlike today's robot vacuum cleaners, is controlled by

After You Read B

1. tried to cheer up, work for

2. because of, bad grades

3. hit, help a boy to escape

4. communicated with one another, by working together

Think and Write Step 3

1. in

2. will be, different from

3. It is likely that, a big change in location

4. won't have to

5. Instead, using a variety of apps

6. positive effect, would be, because, not have to go, come back

7. could be, negative effects

8. wouldn't be able to, as

9. what school life will be like, as, as it is now

구석구석지문 TEST Step 2   p.44

Presentation Time Step 3

1. What do you think this painting shows?

2. I think it shows a machine helping people clean their houses.

3. The machine looks similar to today's robot vacuum cleaners, but they have some differences.

4. For example, unlike today's robot vacuum cleaners, the machine in the painting is controlled by a human.

After You Read B

1. home helper robot: I tried to cheer up a child of the family I work for.

2. He felt sad because of his bad grades.

3. search-and-rescue robot: Last week, after a storm hit, I cleared a route to help a boy to escape.

4. robot swarm: We communicated with one another and built a tower by working together.

Think and Write Step 3

1. School Life in 30 Years

2. In 30 years, school life will be very different from now.

3. It is likely that there will be a big change in location.

4. Students won't have to go to school.

5. Instead, they will study at home using a variety of apps.

6. One positive effect of such a change would be that students could save time because they would not have to go to school and come back.

7. However, there could be some negative effects too.

8. For example, students wouldn't be able to meet their friends as often.

9. We don't know exactly what school life will be like in the future, but I hope it will be as fun and meaningful as it is now.

Lesson 8

단어 TEST Step 1   p.45

01 도둑	02 오르다, 올라가다	03 친절
04 길	05 생존	06 여행; 여행하다
07 전체의, 모든	08 비교하다	09 선구자, 개척자
10 강경히, 강하게	11 공격하다	12 밑, 바닥
13 분리된, 서로 다른	14 목적지, 도착지	15 옳은
16 지혜로운, 현명한	17 깨닫다, 자각하다	18 더 멀리; 더 먼
19 가버린, 떠난	20 창조하다	
21 서두르다, 서둘러 가다		
22 (미래의) 언젠가, 훗날		23 선구자, 개척자
24 굶주림	25 두꺼운, (나무가) 울창한	
26 지혜, 슬기	27 보호하다	
28 ~에 이르다[닿다], 도착하다		
29 동의하지 않다, 의견이 다르다		30 안내인, 가이드
31 똑바로	32 (시간이) 걸리다	
33 움직이다, 감동시키다		
34 (문제, 곤경을) 해결하다, 풀다		35 ~ 덕분에
36 마침내, 결국	37 ~에 따라 행동하다	
38 ~로 나아가다	39 길을 잃다	40 나가는 길, 출구
41 가는 길에	42 ~으로 죽다	43 ~하지 않고

단어 TEST Step 2   p.46

01 hunger	02 kindness	03 protect
04 agree	05 wise	06 hurry
07 survival	08 thick	09 compare
10 thief	11 wisdom	12 correct
13 realize	14 pioneer	15 separate
16 attack	17 solve	18 destination
19 straight	20 create	21 path
22 guide	23 strongly	24 disagree
25 further	26 whole	27 take
28 gone	29 move	30 bottom
31 climb	32 reach	33 someday
34 travel	35 the way out	36 act on
37 in the end	38 become lost	39 on the way
40 thanks to	41 die of	42 without ~ing
43 make one's way to ~		

단어 TEST Step 3   p.47

1 attack, 공격하다   2 climb, 오르다, 올라가다

3 hunger, 굶주림   4 separate, 분리된

5 move, 감동시키다

6 disagree, 동의하지 않다, 의견이 다르다

7 agree, 동의하다　8 survival, 생존　9 path, 길

10 destination, 목적지, 도착지　11 kindness, 친절

12 pioneer, 선구자, 개척자　13 realize, 깨닫다, 자각하다

14 compare, 비교하다　15 protect, 보호하다

16 wisdom, 지혜, 슬기

본문 TEST Step 1　p.48~50

01 Five Wise Men　02 One, wise, met on

03 agreed to travel together

04 way, became lost, thick　05 any further, way out

06 thinking, while, strongly, left

07 second, right, because, correct

08 third, walk back　09 way, so, leave that

10 walk around, forest

11 disagreed, keep walking straight

12 forest, go on forever　13 new path, open

14 Looking, fifth, shook, solve

15 climb, tallest, could find

16 climbed, decided, separate ways

17 reached, top, whole forest

18 paths, shortest way out　19 hurried down, others

20 got, bottom, was gone

21 thought, himself, found, out

22 thought, wrong, only wise　23 However, wrong

24 Everyone, wise

25 chosen, path, created, future

26 walked deeper into, forest

27 attacked, died of hunger

28 learned how, protect himself

29 end, forest, survival skills

30 right, group of thieves

31 took, from, made, join

32 While, with, great kindness

33 thieves, moved, kindness, wisdom

34 Later, become wise men

35 walked back, safe path

36 without getting lost, longer

37 went straight became, pioneer

38 forest, places, had been

39 Thanks to, enjoy, lands

40 who climbed, became, guide

41 Since, able, ways, destinations

42 how, found, own paths

43 Like, compare, journey, another

44 have, your own path

45 make, decision, act on

46 realize, been living, right

본문 TEST Step 2　p.51~53

01 Wise Men　02 One day, met

03 agreed to travel

04 became lost, thick forest　05 any further, way out

06 for a while, strongly feel　07 because, correct

08 Let's walk back　09 so, leave that way

10 walk around

11 disagreed, keep walking straight

12 go on forever　13 new path, open

14 shook his head, how to solve

15 to climb, could find　16 separate

17 reached, whole forest

18 Looking at, shortest way out

19 hurried down, the others　20 was gone

21 thought to himself, best way out

22 wrong, the only wise　23 However, wrong

24 Everyone, wise

25 had chosen, created his future

26 walked deeper into

27 was attacked, died of hunger

28 how to protect himself

29 made his way out of, survival skills

30 a group of thieves　31 join them

32 While, great kindness

33 were moved by, kindness

34 Later, become wise men

35 walked back, a safe path

36 without getting lost, even though

37 went straight, pioneer　38 had been

39 Thanks to　40 who climbed

41 different paths, the quickest ways, their destinations

42 This is how, their own paths

43 Like, one journey, another

44 have to, your own path

45 make, decision, act on it

46 have been living, right for

본문 TEST Step 3　p.54~56

1 5명의 지혜로운 사람들

2 어느 날 5명의 지혜로운 사람들이 길에서 만났다.

3 그들은 여행을 함께 하기로 했다.

4 그러나 도중에 그들은 울창한 숲속에서 길을 잃게 되었다.

5 더 멀리 가기 전에 그들은 멈추고 빠져나갈 최선의 방법을 찾기로 결정했다.

6 잠시 동안 생각한 후, 첫 번째 남자는 "우리가 왼쪽으로 가야 한다는 생각이 강하게 들어요."라고 말했다.

7 두 번째 남자가 "우리는 오른쪽으로 가야 해요. 왜냐하면 '오른쪽'은 또한 '옳은'이라는 의미이기 때문이죠."라고 말했다.

8 그러자 세 번째 남자가 "뒤로 돌아갑시다.

9 우리가 그 길로 왔으니 그 길로 나갈 수 있을 겁니다.

10 그러면 우리는 숲을 한 바퀴 돌 수 있고요."라고 말했다.

11 네 번째 남자가 이의를 제기하며 "나는 우리가 똑바로 계속 걸어 나가야 한다고 생각해요.

12 숲이 영원히 계속될 수는 없으니까요.

13 새로운 길이 열릴 것입니다."라고 말했다.

14 모두를 바라보면서 다섯 번째 남자가 고개를 저으며 "나는 이것을 해결하는 방법을 알아요. 잠깐 기다려 보세요."라고 말했다.

15 그는 그가 찾을 수 있는 가장 높은 나무를 오르기 시작했다.

16 그가 올라가자 다른 모든 사람들은 각자 서로 다른 길을 가기로 결정했다.

17 다섯 번째 남자가 꼭대기에 이르자 그는 전체 숲을 볼 수 있었다.

18 모든 길을 바라보며 그는 빠져나갈 가장 짧은 길을 찾았다.

19 그는 다른 사람들에게 알리기 위해 급히 내려갔다.

20 하지만 그가 밑으로 내려왔을 때, 모든 사람들은 이미 가 버리고 없었다.

21 그는 '다들 어디 간 거야? 내가 빠져나갈 최선의 길을 찾았는데.'라고 마음속으로 생각했다.

22 그는 그들이 모두 틀렸고 자신이 유일하게 현명한 사람이라고 생각했다.

23 그러나 그가 틀렸다.

24 모두가 지혜로웠다.

25 각자 자신의 길을 선택했고 자신의 미래를 만들었다.

26 왼쪽으로 간 남자는 숲속으로 더 깊이 걸어 들어갔다.

27 그는 야생 동물들의 습격을 받았고 거의 굶어 죽을 뻔했다.

28 머지않아 그는 자신을 지키고 먹을 것을 찾는 방법을 터득했다.

29 결국 그는 숲 밖으로 빠져나왔고 다른 사람들에게 생존 기술을 가르쳤다.

30 오른쪽으로 간 남자는 도둑 무리를 만났다.

31 그들은 그에게서 모든 것을 가져갔고 그를 그들과 합류시켰다.

32 그는 그들과 함께 있는 동안 그들에게 많은 친절을 베풀었다.

33 그 도둑들은 그의 친절에 감동을 받았고 그의 지혜에서 배우게 되었다.

34 나중에 그들 또한 지혜로운 사람들이 되었다.

35 뒤돌아 간 남자는 숲 주변에 안전한 길을 만들었다.

36 사람들은 이 길을 이용할 때 길을 잃지 않고 자신이 가고자 하는 길에 다다를 수 있었다. 비록 이동 시간이 약간 더 오래

걸려도 말이다.

37 똑바로 간 남자는 개척자가 되었다.

38 그는 숲을 벗어나 아무도 이전에 가 본 적이 없는 곳을 발견했다.

39 그 남자 덕분에, 사람들은 이 새롭고 아름다운 지역을 즐길 수 있었다.

40 나무 위로 올라간 남자는 가이드가 되었다.

41 그는 여러 다양한 길을 발견했었기 때문에, 사람들에게 자신의 목적지에 이르는 가장 빠른 길을 찾는 법을 가르쳐 줄 수 있었다.

42 이런 식으로 다섯 남자는 자신만의 길을 찾아냈다.

43 그들처럼 우리는 각각 인생에서 자기 자신만의 여행을 하고 있고, 우리는 한 여정을 다른 것과 비교할 수 없다.

44 당신은 당신 자신만의 길을 만들어가야 한다.

45 자신의 목소리를 듣고, 결정하고, 그 결정에 따라 행동하라.

46 그러면 언젠가 당신은 당신에게 맞는 삶을 살아가고 있다는 것을 깨닫게 될 것이다.

본문 TEST Step 4 - Step 5 p.57~62

1 The Five Wise Men

2 One day, five wise men met on the road.

3 They agreed to travel together.

4 On the way, however, they became lost in a thick forest.

5 Before walking any further, they decided to stop and find the best way out.

6 After thinking for a while, the first man said, "I strongly feel that we should go left."

7 The second man said, "We should go right, because *right* also means 'correct.'"

8 Then the third man said, "Let's walk back.

9 We came that way, so we can leave that way.

10 Then we can walk around the forest."

11 The fourth man disagreed and said, "I think we should keep walking straight.

12 The forest cannot go on forever.

13 A new path will open."

14 Looking at them all, the fifth man shook his head and said, "I know how to solve this. Just wait."

15 He started to climb the tallest tree he could find.

16 As he climbed, everyone else decided to go their separate ways.

17 When the fifth man reached the top, he could see the whole forest.

18 Looking at all the paths, he found the shortest way out.

19 He hurried down to tell the others.

20 However, when he got to the bottom, everyone was gone.

21 He thought to himself, *Where did they go? I found the best way out.*

22 He thought they were all wrong and he was the only wise man.

23 However, he was wrong.

24 Everyone was wise.

25 Each man had chosen his path and created his future.

26 The man who went to the left walked deeper into the forest.

27 He was attacked by wild animals and almost died of hunger.

28 Soon he learned how to protect himself and find food.

29 In the end, he made his way out of the forest and taught others survival skills.

30 The man who went to the right met a group of thieves.

31 They took everything from him and made him join them.

32 While he was with them, he showed them great kindness.

33 The thieves were moved by his kindness and learned from his wisdom.

34 Later, they also became wise men.

35 The man who walked back created a safe path around the forest.

36 Using this path, people could get where they were going without getting lost, even though the trip took a little longer.

37 The man who went straight became a pioneer.

38 He left the forest and discovered places no one else had been before.

39 Thanks to him, people could enjoy these new beautiful lands.

40 The man who climbed the tree became a guide.

41 Since he had found many different paths, he was able to teach people how to find the quickest ways to their destinations.

42 This is how the five men found their own paths.

43 Like them, we are each on our own journey in life, and we cannot compare one journey to another.

44 You have to create your own path.

45 Listen to yourself, make a decision, and act on it.

46 Then, someday, you will realize that you have been living the life that is right for you.

MEMO

적중100

영어 기출 문제집

정답 및 해설

능률 | 김성곤